To the Glory of God and the Service of Man

To Prusilla Squok

TO THE
GLORY OF GOD
AND THE
SERVICE OF MAN

The Life of James A. Campbell, M.D.

MALACHI J. FLANAGAN, M.D.

FHC PRESS
Winnetka, Illinois

Malachi J. Flanagan, M.D., is Emeritus Professor of Urology
at Rush University Medical Center. He is the author of
*Roots of Faith: A History of Catholicism in New Trier Township and
the Founding of Saints Faith, Hope, and Charity Parish, Winnetka, Illinois*
and numerous scientific articles dealing with urology.

FHC Press, Winnetka 60093
© 2005 by Malachi J. Flanagan

All rights reserved. Published 2005
Printed in the United States of America

ISBN: 0-9764956-0-0

∞ The paper used in this publication meets the minimum requirements
of the American National Standard for Information Sciences–
Permanence of Paper for Printed Library Materials, ANSI Z39.48-1992.

Contents

Foreword

I am pleased to have an opportunity to contribute in a small way to this book, which pays tribute to Dr. James Allan Campbell, a distinguished physician, medical educator, and institutional builder. Campbell devoted much of his professional career to the impressive development of a major academic medical center in one of the great cities in the United States. The author of this work, Dr. Malachi J. Flanagan, himself an outstanding physician and senior member of the professional staff, devoted enormous time and energy to documenting the exciting evolution of the Rush–Presbyterian–St. Luke's Medical Center and the seminal role played by Dr. Campbell in first defining the ultimate goal and then providing the leadership that resulted in achieving it. He deserves the commendation of all who read this chronicle.

Jim Campbell and I were classmates at the Harvard Medical School where we became fast friends; we both pursued training in internal medicine and maintained a very close association thereafter. I therefore had the privilege of seeing Jim's growth in the several leading academic centers where he honed his skills and gained his well-deserved reputation as an excellent clinician, inspiring teacher, and productive investigator. Part of his early training was at Johns

Hopkins, where he worked with Richard Bing and participated in pioneering studies in cardiac catheterization. In 1949, shortly after a number of full-time departments were established in the Presbyterian Hospital in Chicago, Campbell accepted a position in the Department of Medicine to establish a cardiac catheterization facility, and in the ensuing years, he was appointed head of the department. He showed his vision and dedication to quality in the way he recruited an excellent group of colleagues with expertise in important areas of medicine. Despite his administrative responsibilities, he took an active role in working with interns and residents and establishing conferences and other teaching exercises that were modeled on those he had experienced in training on the Harvard Medical Services of the Boston City Hospital and Johns Hopkins.

During this period, I was pursuing my own academic career at Washington University Medical School and was in close touch with Campbell as we both attended the annual meetings of societies focusing on new and exciting research that was emerging at a rapid rate, in large part by virtue of support from the National Institutes of Health.

One of Campbell's important attributes was his ability to work well with the Trustees of the Presbyterian Hospital. He was extremely effective in conveying his vision of how a great medical center could be created, and his board supported him with enthusiasm. I had the privilege of serving as a consultant to Campbell and his board and thus saw first hand how Jim's leadership was manifested.

Not surprisingly, Jim had a key role in the complex negotiations that led to the merger of the Presbyterian and St. Luke's Hospitals, a critical step in the development of the medical center. Similarly, he was a powerful and effective advocate of the reactivation of the charter of the Rush Medical College, which at an earlier time was the locus of the clinical programs of the University of Chicago. Here again, with the strong support of the trustees, an outstanding group of leading Chicago citizens, Campbell's effort resulted in the creation of the Rush–Presbyterian–St. Luke's Medical Center and ultimately Rush University.

As Dr. Flanagan delineates in detail, Campbell was in many ways the driving force in expanding programs and facilities, continuing attraction of outstanding faculty members, and organizing a smooth and effective administrative infrastructure so that the entity became a model of educational, clinical and investigative excellence. Obviously, in so doing, Campbell and his team of senior colleagues were well prepared to face the never-ending challenges in the broad field of health care related to the advances in technology and the need to exploit in the best sense of the word the rapid enhancement of knowledge flowing from research.

Sadly, Jim Campbell developed cardiovascular disease and succumbed to its ravages at the age of 66. Fortunately, he did live to see the fruits of his dedicated labor, and he leaves as his legacy the Rush–Presbyterian–St. Luke's Medical Center, which will be an enduring tribute to his remarkable career. All of those who knew Jim Campbell, not only his professional colleagues but those who contributed to the institution at all levels, will remember him with admiration and respect.

ROBERT J. GLASER, M.D.

Preface and Acknowledgments

The account that follows takes place for the most part in a time frame often referred to as American Medicine's Golden Era, the period from the beginning of World War II in 1939 until 1983, the year that Dr. James Campbell died. A beneficent federal government was providing generously for medical research. Physicians and others responsible for the health of the American people had been placed on a pedestal by the public and were held in higher regard than they are today. Campbell seized that opportunity to lead the way in maintaining a singular and vigilant focus on the patient and patient care when other powerful forces, good in themselves, began to compete and take away from that emphasis. And at the same time, Campbell was able to oversee the development of an outstanding medical center in professional, technical, educational, investigational, social, and financial terms, always maintaining the focus on the patient, and to add many visionary ideas of his own along the way in this extraordinary period of growth in American medicine. For those of us who followed, his leadership conferred a legacy that has served as an enduring example and an ongoing reminder of the high purpose and privilege that is ours as professionals.

Much of the information presented here is based on 275 interviews carried out between the years 1998 and 2002 with individuals who lived through that period and were familiar with the life and times of Jim Campbell. Some were formal scheduled encounters; others came through casual conversation. A great deal of material was obtained from telephone calls with individuals in almost every part of the United States, and a number of people provided written narratives of their recollections of Jim Campbell and the Medical Center. More than one interview was held with a number of individuals. Some of these people have since passed on. Had this work commenced earlier, a number of people important to the story, such as Dr. Mark Lepper and Dr. Ormond Julian, could have contributed more detail to this history.

But many people of the Campbell era were available, some going back to Campbell's very early years at Knox College, the University of Chicago Medical School, and Harvard Medical School. Jim Campbell was such a forceful individual that it wasn't difficult to recall the many stories, anecdotes, and reflections regarding his life and career. Dr. Robert Glaser, Jim's best friend, was just such an individual who generously gave of his time in relating many keen insights into the story. Dr. Louis Selverstone, a long-time colleague from both Boston and Chicago who spent several years in close professional association with Campbell, was another.

Campbell's life had an enormous impact on individuals of the generation that followed his, individuals such as Mr. Donald Oder, and this group was an extremely important resource for this undertaking. However, in a few settings with other individuals, there were situations and stories related that clearly did not match with other accounts, and these were not used unless they could be corroborated by others. Many of Campbell's contemporaries are now in their eighties, and Mark Twain's aphorism, "When I was younger, I could remember everything whether it happened or not, but now I am getting old, and soon I shall remember only the latter," should be kept in mind.[1]

1. John Lauber, *The Making of Mark Twain* (New York: American Heritage Press, 1985), p. 18.

All of the individual interviews for this work are listed in a separate acknowledgment at the end of the work. Without them, the work could not have been carried out, and I am very grateful to each and every individual for their help.

In 1986, Rush–Presbyterian–St. Luke's Medical Center engaged the professional writing services of Mr. Jim Bowman to record the history of Rush in observance of its sesquicentennial or 150 year anniversary in 1987. All the notes that Mr. Bowman made in preparation for that book have been preserved by the Rush–Presbyterian–St. Luke's Medical Center Archives, and all were made available for this work. The notes, ranging from two to four pages in length, of 40 individuals who were considered significant resources for the history of Rush at the time have provided an additional useful source of information. And in recording the story of Rush, the role that Campbell played was mentioned or discussed at some length in almost all of the notes, such was his prominence at the time. Many portions of Bowman's interviews never appeared in the final book, but still were important to the Campbell story. And many of the individuals interviewed have since passed on. For example, the only written recollections available from Mrs. Elda Campbell and from Dr. Joseph Muenster, Dr. Campbell's personal physician and friend, are found in Bowman's notes. The individuals interviewed in Bowman's work are so listed in a separate acknowledgment section at the end of this book. It wasn't always possible to differentiate direct quotes, paraphrases, and other types of information in Bowman's notes; so the text rendered may not be totally accurate in this regard.

Much of the history of Rush Medical College came from the work of the late Dr. Roger Bone. Dr. Bone came to Rush–Presbyterian–St. Luke's Medical Center as Chairman of the Department of Internal Medicine not long after Jim Campbell died. Campbell had interviewed him for the position in August 1983. Dr. Bone's great career was prematurely terminated in 1994 by illness; but beginning in 1992, he and a colleague, Mr. James Breeling, had started to compile information about Rush Medical College's history, with the plan of preparing at least two works about Rush and connecting it to the history of the new Rush. Mr. Breeling and Dr. Bone's wife, Rosemary, graciously provided all the notes that had been compiled in this undertaking, which sadly was never completed. I am very grateful indeed for this treasure of information.

The cooperation of the Rush University Medical Center Archives, under the overall direction first of Mr. Jack Bohlen and more recently Ms. Diane McKeever, with the permission of the president of the medical center, Dr. Leo Henikoff, has made this work immeasurably easier. Archivists Stuart Campbell and Ken Hernden made themselves available for consultation and advice on innumerable occasions and generously provided invaluable assistance and information about correct protocol and procedure. The extensive Campbell Presidential papers, the Oral History Collection, and many other documents form an indispensable base of information, without which this work could not have been carried out.

Harvard University Medical School, with the cooperation of Registrar Carole Duffy, released all the records in their possession on medical student James Campbell from the time period of 1941 to 1944, and in addition Campbell's grades and evaluations from his time at the University of Chicago from 1939 to 1942. The availability of this material opened up countless leads for other sources that greatly enriched this work. The Archives Division of the Francis Countway Library of Harvard Medical School made available several documents relating to the activities of Campbell's class after graduation. And the Alumni Office at Harvard under the direction of Dr. David Feddermann has provided information and help on an ongoing basis.

Columbia University's Oral History Research Office Collection of the Reminiscences of Robert Maynard Hutchins, 1968, provided unique information about the University of Chicago president, as Hutchins had never prepared his own biography. Much insight was gained about the Rush–University of Chicago stormy relationship in the 1930s, and Hutchins's role in the dissolution of this affiliation.

The Knox College Office of Development, under the direction Mr. John Mohr, was most cooperative in providing all the informa-

tion they could find about both Campbell's years as a student at Knox, and later the many years he served as a trustee of Knox. And Knox librarian Carley Robison provided copies of all of Campbell's many activities as a student recorded in its yearbook and other publications.

The cooperation of several individuals and departments within the University of Chicago was essential for the completion of this story. The Special Collections Department of the Regenstein Library made available on numerous occasions the files of the Presidential Papers from 1925 to 1945, which illuminate the story of the relationship of Rush and the University. It would have been impossible to sort out this complex narrative without the many notes and letters that passed between President Robert Maynard Hutchins and representatives of Rush. Associate Director of the Special Collections Research Center of the Regenstein Library Daniel Meyer and Mr. Jay Satterfield were particularly helpful in this regard. Dean of Students of the University of Chicago School of Medicine, Dr. Norma Waggoner, graciously contributed the application of James Campbell to the University in 1939, which included all his grades at Knox College, and Rochelle High School. World-renowned gastroenterologist Dr. Joseph Kirsner has provided ongoing interest and encouragement for this work from the beginning. His distinguished medical career of over seventy years continues, even now, at the turn of the century. Dr. Kirsner was a legendary figure in medicine in Chicago when my brothers Dr. Charles Flanagan and Dr. George Flanagan attended the University of Chicago from 1947 to 1955.

A special word of thanks goes to the many individuals who provided editorial assistance to this presentation. Overall review of the work was contributed by: Dr. Joseph Kirsner, Dr. Robert Carton, Dr. Pastora San Juan Caferty, Dr. Ruth Rothstein, Mr. Jack Bohlen, Dr. Leo Henikoff, Dr. Arnold Widen, Dr. Whitney Addington, Dr. L. Penfield Faber, Mr. Donald Oder, Mrs. Linda Nolan, Ms. Mary Anne Dzuback, Mr. Marshall Field V, Dr. Bruce Campbell, and Mr. Harold Byron Smith. Review of the early years of Dr. Campbell and the Medical Center was provided by: Dr. Bernard Blaauw, Dr. Randall

McNally, Dr. Frank Kelly, Jr., Mrs. Betty Graettinger, Dr. Richard Sassetti, Dr. Janet Wolter, Dr. Donald Fisher, Mr. Jamie Campbell, and Dr. Stuart Levin. Mr. Donald Oder provided analysis of the Campbell management years along with Dr. Wayne Lerner, Mrs. Jean Lopota, and Ms. Marie Sinoris. Dr. Diane Crocker, Dr. Louis Selverstone, and Dr. Joseph Messer gave extremely important and detailed review in regard to the background of Boston medicine when Campbell was in training; and Dr. L. Penfield Faber and Mrs. Evelyn Coogan Hubbard reviewed many of the significant events involved in the merger of Presbyterian and St. Luke's Hospitals. Senior Rush–Presbyterian–St. Luke's Medical Center medical staff members Dr. Frank Malloy and Dr. Frederick Kittle provided, throughout this work, ongoing information about the history of Chicago medicine, both past and present.

A special acknowledgment is due Mrs. Jean Eckenfels, who served as my editor throughout the time it took to put this story together, a period of more than five years. I shall always be grateful for the countless ways she contributed to this endeavor.

From as far back as I can remember, medicine and most everything related to medicine have been a significant part of my life. In addition to my two older brothers, Dr. Charles Larkin and Dr. George, three of my cousins were also physicians in Chicago: Drs. James Brierton Flanagan, Cornelius Hagerty, and Robert Ranquist. Larkin and George were primarily University of Chicago–oriented, as they received most of their training and spent a good portion of their professional careers there. Larkin eventually moved on to Northwestern University Medical Center, and George, after spending some time as an endocrine fellow at the Cleveland Clinic, moved to Presbyterian Hospital and worked with Dr. Campbell; eventually George became Associate Dean of Curriculum in the reactivated Rush Medical College. Two of my cousins, Dr. Hagerty and Dr. Ranquist, were graduates of Rush Medical College in the 1930s. My other cousin Dr. James Flanagan was a graduate of the University of Illinois Medical School in 1941, and I myself graduated from the Loyola University Stritch School of Medicine in 1957. The attitudes and beliefs about Chicago medicine that I developed were all influenced by these family relationships. My experiences and struggles in "pre-med," medical school, clerkships, externships, internships, call rotations, residencies, fellowships, and then later in the many facets of private medical practice, teaching hospitals, the challenges of the operating room, a single standard of medical care for all, and research were shared with these good people.

After I completed my formal training in urology in 1962, I spent my entire career at what was eventually to become Rush University Medical Center and served as president of its Medical Staff from 1985 to 1987. Along the way, I also served on the Examination Committee of the American Board of Urology for several years and was the principal investigator for Rush in its participation in the National Bladder Cancer Program for the National Institutes of Health from 1973 to 1984. I have also been active in a number of professional organizations and have served as president of both the Chicago Urological Society and the Institute of Medicine of Chicago.

I knew Dr. Campbell personally and admired him very much. There was no one quite like him: he was perhaps the most influential leader in Chicago medicine in the second half of the twentieth century. His story needs to be retold, as it has important messages today for those charged with the awesome responsibility of participating directly in, as well as supervising and planning, the care of the patient.

1

The Beginnings

Like so many accounts of American lives of noteworthy achievement, the Jim Campbell story starts out in humble and modest circumstances.

Rochelle is a town of about 9000 in North Central Illinois located 75 miles west of Chicago in a fertile agricultural valley. It was founded in the middle of the nineteenth century and served as a railroad stop for two of the transcontinental railroads that were being put together at that time. Before that, the Black Hawk War had been fought in the general area and was ended after Native American Chief Black Hawk was defeated by Illinois militia troops that included a future president, Zachary Taylor, a future Confederate president, Jefferson Davis, and a young grocery clerk and future president, Abraham Lincoln.

Rochelle developed into a food processing center and the California Packing Corporation, later known as the Del Monte Company, was a major employer for the entire region. In the 1930s processing corn, peas, lima beans, asparagus, and several other foods provided summer employment for people living in the area. Jim Campbell worked there, as did his brother John and a later associate of Campbell's from nearby Mendota, Penfield Faber.

1

During the Great Depression, Rochelle was relatively immune to the harsh unemployment realities that the rest of the country experienced. The work was hard, sometimes 15 to 18 hours each day. Detasseling corn, picking peas, and working inside as both a timekeeper and canning processor kept Jim Campbell busy and tired in the summer months. But students going to college could earn most if not all of their expenses for school by working in the cannery or picking vegetables in the field.

Food processing remains a major industry of the community even today. But the labor intensive field work is now carried out largely by migrant workers. Unlike many other small "downstate" towns in Illinois, Rochelle has maintained its population and even grown, and some of its residents commute to Chicago to work. The massive twin cooling towers of the Commonwealth Nuclear Facility in nearby Byron are visible for miles and serve to point one in the general direction of Rochelle.

Rochelle was the home of the Frank and Gertrude Campbell family from 1924 to 1943. Jim attended Rochelle High School, where he excelled scholastically, gaining a four-year average of 93. Jim, at 125 pounds also played center on the senior football team. Jim was offered a scholarship to Harvard but apparently did not pursue it because of the expenses involved with travel and the like. Coach Forrest Hitchcock, a Knox College graduate, encouraged Jim to consider Knox, located in Galesburg, Illinois, about 100 miles west and south of Rochelle, for his college choice.

During his senior year at Rochelle High, a recruiting representative from the U.S. Naval Academy visited the school and interviewed Campbell. Jim was very anxious to receive an appointment and set his heart on going to Annapolis. But his application was turned down, and he was told that he would never be accepted because of his facial scarring, the result of severe acne. Jim often mentioned this experience to his friends over the years. The blunt and cruel way in which this message had been delivered was a traumatizing event that Jim never forgot. This incident hurt his pride, but it may have actually enhanced his drive, his determination, and his ambition. And the course of his life would have been very different had he become a naval officer.

In the mid-eighteenth century, the Campbell family had emigrated from Scotland and, according to family legend, brought their whisky, a rifle, and a Bible to the small farming community of New Florence, Pennsylvania, in the Allegheny Mountains. In his teens, Jim's father Frank Campbell, moved on to the mountainous sparsely populated region of eastern Tennessee, where he taught school before attending college at Merryville College in the Tennessee Highlands. Frank then decided to enter the ministry and studied at the Lane Theological Seminary in Cincinnati. During that time he married Gertrude Dowling, a graduate of the University of Cincinnati. After Frank was ordained in 1912, he served in a number of missionary Presbyterian churches in Tennessee and Illinois. Among those communities was Moweaqua, Illinois, where James Allan was born on November 29, 1917. Jim had a younger brother and sister, John and Eleanor. The Frank Campbell family then settled in Lexington, Illinois, from 1920 to 1924.

During all this time, the Reverend Frank Campbell also engaged in local theatre as a stand-up vaudeville comedian. Impersonations were his favorite presentations. The "1000 Faces of Frank Campbell" played in several communities in both Tennessee and Illinois. Readings, monologues, and character sketches were featured. He was described as a "high-class entertainer." The posters read, "Frank Campbell, Preacher, Lecturer, and Entertainer, A man with a Message. Born in Pennsylvania, reared in east Tennessee, and worked his way through College and the Seminary, Combines native ability with scholastic attainments and a pleasing personality." Those who attended Jim Campbell's Medical Grand Rounds many years later would understand without any difficulty where Jim acquired many of his theatrical talents. Frank Campbell solicited for presentations to several types of groups: Masonic meetings, commencement celebrations, patriotic holidays, and religious meetings for special occasions.

The Campbells then moved on from Lexington to Rochelle, Illinois, where Frank served the First United Presbyterian Church as its pastor for longer than any other minister in the history of this 125-year-old congregation. Frank received many new members into the church, raised money to pay off the debt, and refurbished the

buildings. Upon his departure in 1943, he was praised by his congregation for shepherding the group through the Roaring Twenties,
the Great Depression, and the beginning of World War II. No one
could have guided the congregation through a more critical period.
Nothing, they said, could stop Rev. Campbell from teaching and
preaching the love of God. He was praised for his openness on all
issues. He walked the streets, soliciting ads for his church newspaper,
The Rochelle Messenger, and made friends to support the work of the
church. The *Messenger* was produced in Frank's print shop in the
basement of his home, and it made money for the church. Frank was
also a carpenter, and he personally remodeled many parts of the
sixty-year-old church and the manse.

Gertrude was highly regarded and well liked by the congregation and also quite active in church and civic affairs. But there were
hard times for the family of five who lived in the manse next to the
church at 420 North Sixth Street. (The church was later moved, and
the Rochelle Police station is now at that location.) There was simply no money, Jim would later recall. The three children had to use
the same water for bathing: hot water cost money. The manse was a
bit shabby and run down. Frank prided himself on the garden he
tended in his backyard, but in truth, on some days all the food they
had was spinach and root vegetables, such as carrots, potatoes, and
radishes. And Gertrude preserved fruits and vegetables in the basement to hold them over during the winter.

John and Jim's fruit and vegetable wagon was a small but useful part of the family income. But late one day after trying to "ped-
dle" spinach to their neighbors, John came into the house exasperated: No one wanted to buy because they were all "spinached out."
Jim, however, prided himself on his entrepreneurial skills, saying
that, properly presented, cleaned, and washed, spinach would
always sell. Yet later in life he refused to eat spinach, claiming the
vegetable's nutritional value in iron "could be exceeded by sucking
on a nail."

Many years later when he lived in Lake Forest and drove a
Mercedes, Jim still liked to talk about the old days and those lean
years in Rochelle. "My coat was worn and threadbare, and it was the

only one I had," he would say. But Jim's friends were thinking to themselves that he was still wearing the same coat, for he was not by any standard a sharp dresser. With the perseverance of these frugal ways, some thought Jim simply didn't like to spend a lot of money on personal amenities, while others would say that he was a bit on the cheap side.

But the family was a happy one. Gertrude was an excellent mother. When Jim came home from Knox with scarlet fever, the other children had to move out while Gertrude nursed Jim back to health. The dog was an unexpected victim, however, succumbing to the disinfectant that the doctors had ordered for Jim's treatment program.

According to his brother and sister, Jim was bright but not especially disciplined. He had a lot of nervous energy and did most everything, scouting, editing the school yearbook, athletics, and the like. Jim's brightness may have come from his mother but he was also very close to his father, although they had many disagreements.

In 1943, Frank moved on to another assignment and then another, until he retired in 1969. The family dispersed and separated when the children went off to school, and the war intervened. John first attended Knox College and eventually went to Harvard, where he earned a Ph.D. in psychology, and later served the government in the Department of Health, Education, and Welfare. John wrote a book about his combat experiences in World War II entitled *The Men of Company K*. Eleanor went to Monmouth College, earned a master's degree in education from the University of Illinois, and later did social work and taught school in Bethesda, Maryland. Her husband, Dr. Frank Scharletzki, became head of the Department of Philosophy at the University of Maryland.

When Jim's son Bruce visited his grandparents in Rochelle, there were no more than a handful of older members of the congregation in attendance at Sunday service. There were near poverty conditions everywhere in the home. It was both remarkable and a tribute to the Campbell family that all the children were able not only to receive a college education, but to go on to graduate school as well. Both Frank and Gertrude were very proud of this.

Jim kept in touch with his parents. Gertrude died in 1953, but Frank lived on until 1974. Jim, now Dr. James Campbell, attended to Frank as a patient. During a long period of convalescence at Presbyterian Hospital, Frank wrote his book *Sermon Outlines for a Country Preacher.* Jim promised that he would have these sermons published. And indeed, they were. Several of Jim's associates in the medical center were given copies of Frank's book and remembered many of the sayings and quotations. To many, the stories and homilies were really an expression of Jim's thoughts and personal philosophy of leadership. There was a certainty of conviction and a religious zeal in Jim's style that came from his father's form of oratorical delivery, leading his congregation to the highest moral ground and enthusiastically engaging his "Christian soldiers" to follow. His father's book in reality represented many of Jim's own personal beliefs and ideals.

In the foreword of the book, Frank acknowledges that he "freely borrowed from other sermons in adapting from them in ministering to his people. If any of the brethren find here a thought or sentence that sounds like one of his own, before he accuses me of stealing, that he would make sure that we both have not borrowed from the same source."[1]

The Reverend Campbell would exhort his people to be "steadfast and unmovable."[2] "Being steadfast is stronger than being confident. Steadfast means you could falter, but you are not going to. You have this victory of Christ in your soul. You are not to die and perish. Because you are an immortal being, and hence not a beast, therefore you have a mission in life." No one, later on, could deny that his son Jim indeed did have a mission in life.

And Reverend Campbell quotes a quaternion of sentences on the subject of knowledge, many of which have been in the lexicon of physician maxims for peer assessment for many generations.

1. Rev. Frank Campbell, *Sermon Outlines of a Country Preacher* (1958), p. v.
2. Ibid., pp. 53–57.

The man who knows not and knows not that he knows not,
is a fool. Shun him.

The man who knows not and knows that he knows not,
is hungry. Teach him.

The man who knows and knows not that he knows, is a scholar.
Put him to work.

But the man who knows and knows that he knows, is a
wise man. Follow him.[3]

When Jim left Rochelle for Knox College in Galesburg in 1935, he
was in a sense repeating the itinerary that his father, the Reverend
Frank Campbell, would take, when Frank performed on the vaudeville stage. Galesburg was the site of a vaudeville theater, the
Orpheum, one of several enterprises that Galesburg supported, bely-
ing its modest small town population of 34,000 people. The
Orpheum was recently restored and is again a major component of
the theatre tradition in Galesburg. In addition to Knox College, the
town had the Galesburg Symphony and the Galesburg *Register Mail*
newspaper and it was a major center for two transcontinental railroads, the Burlington and the Santa Fe.

Galesburg and Knox College shared a common founder,
George Washington Gale, who came to this remote area in the 1830s
to found a community and a school to proselytize the frontier for the
religious beliefs of the Congregational and Presbyterian Churches of
Upstate New York. Here a school for combined training in farming
and religious beliefs was established. Knox was named after General
Henry Knox, a Revolutionary War hero and a member of President
George Washington's first cabinet. Very early on, Knox was established
as a top quality school, and attracted young men of promise for their
education. The most important tradition for both Knox and Galesburg

3. Ibid., pp. 79–84.

occurred in October 1858, when the fifth of the seven famous Abraham Lincoln–Stephen Douglas debates over the issue of slavery took place on a platform erected in front of the Old Main Building on the campus.[4]

Jim supported himself in several ways during his time at Knox. In the first year, in addition to the income he had from his summer work in Rochelle, Jim and his roommate, lifelong friend Merrill Minks, helped pay for their room and board by doing various household chores for two ladies in whose basement apartment they lived. After that year, Jim lived in the fraternity house of Beta Theta Pi, waited on tables, and washed dishes. Jim earned some money for editing both the student newspaper and the yearbook and received a monthly stipend for service in the Reserve Officers Training Corps.

Whether or not Jim considered choosing a career in the ministry is unclear. Being the son of a minister and going to a school with strong Protestant traditions would suggest Jim could have been leaning in that direction. Although he initially enrolled in the premedical program, his final decision to enter medicine did not evolve until his fourth year. Jim did well in his courses in the first year of premedical studies including chemistry.

But then Jim got involved in what many would claim was the love of his life, the theater. He started out in his freshman year in the drama club and before long was playing the lead role in the popular serious play of that time, Maxwell Anderson's *Winterset*. In his highly praised role as Mio, Jim worked to establish the innocence of his father who was unjustly accused of murder. Jim's poise on stage was described as miraculous, and he could also ad lib Shakespeare if necessary. Among Jim's favorite Shakespearean roles was Brutus in *Julius Caesar*. He took six hours of drama and four hours of Shakespeare in his third year of premed, somewhat unusual for the traditional premed grind.

4. On October 7, 1994, C-Span produced a reenactment of the debates for a national audience, and thus extended in a very special way the folklore of this fascinating historical event. Galesburg has been, right from the beginning, a very close-knit community. For the reenactment, five hundred people volunteered to participate in the TV production in costumes of the times.

Jim joined the theater group headed by Professor Paul (Doc) Foley, who had spent some time on Broadway before coming to Knox. The group was a serious organization and the campus's most lively and closely followed enterprise. These students put in long hours in all phases of theater production: building their own sets, designing their own costumes, selling tickets, and stage-managing. And in all of this, Campbell was ever present. Everybody, both students and faculty, came to know who Jim Campbell was.

Foley took his group to New England on a barnstorming tour. The Knox Drama Program was becoming well known in sophisticated Eastern circles. Jim's talents did not go unnoticed: he was offered a scholarship to the Yale School of Drama. The sort of opportunity presented to Jim was indeed a far cry from the vaudeville stage where his father Frank had performed in tiny communities such as Lexington, Illinois.

But the stage alone was not enough for this energetic young man. Jim became editor of the student newspaper, *The Knox Student*, and started a column called the "Knocks Student," which was followed closely for inside stories, humor, gossip, rumors, and the like. Then Campbell moved on to be the editor of the college magazine, called the *Siwasher*. (Knox was known in collegiate circles as "Old Siwash," the name given to a fictitious small Midwestern college by author and Knox alumnus George Fitch.) His work there relied more heavily on humor than any serious literary worth. Soon everyone on campus came to know where Jim came from, something about his canning factory experiences, and that his home town carried a French name.

But by the end of his third year, Campbell had to make a decision about what he was going to do. There was the tempting offer from Yale that could become the springboard to a big career on Broadway. Jim was taking some of the required premedical courses, but had done poorly in his third year in organic chemistry. This course required a lot of time in the laboratory, and what with acting, theater barnstorming, editing the school paper, and staying active in the ROTC, his scholastic performance suffered. Jim's father had always been a bit skeptical about Jim studying medicine. He was concerned about the difficult scholastic grind required and, of course, the very long time to get through it all. Even then, the premedical program required at least three and sometimes four years, medical school four years, internship one year, and then the possibility of further training in residency programs after that. There was also Jim's involvement in the ROTC that would entail some period of obligation at some future time. And, of course, there was the cost of all this. Where would the money come from?

Jim's roommate, Merrill Minks, remembers just how difficult it was for Jim as he struggled to decide whether to go into theater or to continue in premed. Jim loved acting but knew that he would have to put it aside completely if he wanted to stay in premed. His grades had suffered, and he was woefully behind in the courses required for entrance into medical school. There was a tough road ahead for him if he chose medicine.

Campbell was considered a brilliant student in spite of his poor grades in organic chemistry. In a small school of just under a thousand, it is easy for people to take notice of such an individual. He and classmate J. Alan Linquist were the "brains" of the class. Linquist later helped Jim financially while he was attending medical school. And Campbell's record at Knox was such that he was listed in *Who's Who in American Colleges and Universities.*

Dr. Carter Davidson, a noted member of the faculty, took a personal interest in Jim. Davidson later became president of Knox College and eventually moved on to become president of Union College in Albany, New York. Davidson thought Jim had the potential to become an outstanding physician and encouraged him to stay on and try to get into medical school. Knox sometimes had a way of helping financially in achieving such goals and his ROTC commitment could be put off until his education was completed.

Knox premedical advisor Dr. Charles Furrow knew Jim could do the work if he gave it his full time and attention even though he had done poorly in organic chemistry. Dr. Furrow also admired the well-liked Campbell and was pulling for this intense, bright, and very clever young man from a quite modest background to succeed. He outlined a crash program for Jim, heavily science-weighted, for the first semester of his fourth year and said that if Jim did well, he would guarantee that Jim would get into medical school. Dr. Furrow and others of the Knox faculty family had strong ties with a number of universities with medical schools, one of which was the University of Chicago. Many of the Knox faculty had studied there.

After Jim decided on medicine rather than acting, it was full speed ahead as he became highly focused and very single-minded in pursuing this career choice. He stayed on the Knox campus to study right through the Thanksgiving and Christmas holidays of 1938, and in the spring of 1939, he was accepted for entrance to the University of Chicago Medical School.

Jim never made much of this period of intense study in his last few months at Knox. He could read a page from a book and remember it word for word. Later on, his Harvard Medical School roommate Dr. Jack Taylor related that Jim never studied very much at Harvard either, but he graduated cum laude and was elected to the prestigious national medical honor society, Alpha Omega Alpha.

Jim's scholastic achievements for that short time in his last year of premed became legendary. Dr. Bill Holmes, a Knox student in the 1940s and also a good friend of Jim's, was being advised by Dr. Furrow about what courses to take in the premedical curriculum. A number of different programs and schedules were discussed, including the "Campbell crash course," that is, taking all but two of the required premedical courses in six months. Jim had been the only one who had ever done that. Holmes was interested. So Dr. Furrow told him, "Go talk to Jimmy, and see what he says." Jimmy by that time was the youngest medical school dean in the country at Albany Medical College, just a little more than ten years later. Holmes eventually decided on the more traditional premedical programs.

Campbell's relationship with Knox College was not to end at graduation. He had made a great impression on many of the faculty and also the student body. Jim became an active alumnus and in 1950 was appointed a member of the Board of Trustees, on which he served for many years. He was awarded an honorary degree from his alma mater in 1965. Jim visited the campus often, and two of his sons, Jamie and Douglas, attended college there as well. Many of the faculty of the Rush–Presbyterian–St. Luke's Medical Center and their children also attended Knox. In the process of reactivating Rush Medical School, Jim developed a scheme for relationships with feeder colleges and universities with premedical programs by integrating them into the actual medical school curriculum. Knox College was one of the schools that Rush was to become affiliated with.

2

Rush Medical College and the University of Chicago

As Jim Campbell was about to enter medical school at the University of Chicago, the school itself was in the process of upheaval and major reorganization. The president of the university, Robert Maynard Hutchins, had made a startling announcement on September 15, 1939, that beginning with the entering class, that is, Jim's class, students would be admitted only in numbers that could be accommodated at the medical campus on the Midway, and no students destined for Rush Medical College would enter. Hence, after two years, undergraduate work at Rush would end.[1]

Within three years of Campbell's entrance to the university as a medical student, the venerable union of 44 years bonding the university with Rush would terminate completely. Just what did the hundred-year-old Rush Medical College tradition consist of, how did it all come about, why did it terminate, and, more important, how could this have any bearing on Jim Campbell, whose career was just starting out?

1. Robert M. Hutchins, "The State of the University, September Fifteenth, Nineteen Hundred Thirty Nine: A Report to the Alumni and Friends of the University of Chicago," p. 12, Special Collections Research Center, Regenstein Library, University of Chicago.

There were immediate implications for Campbell to consider. There were in Jim's freshman class at the university students who had planned to go to Rush for their last two years, known as the clinical years. Campbell may have been one of them. Now the option of selecting Rush for the third and fourth years of medical school was no longer available. A pathway for medical education quite different from those of other schools had been determined by the university. Now in the third and fourth years, students would be drilled in the fundamentals of research and steered away from the "clinical disciplines" that were the rule for most schools in the country, and particularly so for Rush.

Campbell was not one usually taken by surprise. His decision to enter medicine was clearly directed and focused. He was always thinking ahead and his thoughts were well organized. He now would have to consider incorporating the implications of these curricular changes into his career planning. Would a full-time university research-oriented career be in his future, as was being espoused at the Midway? Would his choice be the more traditional private practice of medicine? Or would it turn out to be something quite different indeed?

Feedback from the upper classmen was that there was another way out there, the Rush way, and some thought that way was very good indeed. Campbell would not have the opportunity to go in this direction. He had no choice. But he was aware that there was another way that most individuals in training in medicine were taking.

One of his teachers at the university, pathologist Dr. Paul Cannon, who had an important influence on Jim and his career, was a graduate of Rush Medical College in 1925. Campbell would spend more than a year and a half under the special instruction of Dr. Cannon in 1941 and 1942. Was the story of the Rush–University of Chicago breakup something that Campbell and Dr. Cannon talked about while Jim was being trained to do post mortem examinations and other techniques in Dr. Cannon's department? Very likely it was.

So Jim Campbell as a student came to know something about Rush Medical College even though he was not there on the West

Side as it was carrying on in its last three years of undergraduate education from 1939 to 1942.

Rush is important to the Campbell story because it was he, James Campbell, who, some thirty years later, would lead the way to its rebirth from the heap of idleness and stagnation and restore its prestige as a first-rate medical school and furthermore to establish Rush–Presbyterian–St. Luke's Medical Center as a major American academic university medical center.

The story of Rush Medical College goes back to 1836, when a twenty-four-year-old graduate of Jefferson Medical College in Philadelphia, Dr. Daniel Brainard, arrived in Chicago with high hopes of serving what was envisioned to be the center of population of the new and great West. In the beginning as a young surgeon he struggled, but after he successfully performed a difficult amputation of a canal worker's leg in the presence of most of the town's physicians, his reputation was established. News of this feat spread rapidly and brought him high regard among his peers and, eventually, the patronage of the prairie aristocracy. Brainard then went on to become the most notable of all Chicago's pioneer physicians.

On 2 March 1837, Brainard and another colleague, Dr. Josiah Goodhue, the son of a medical school president in Massachusetts, petitioned the Illinois State Legislature, then located in Vandalia, to issue a charter for the founding of the first educational institution in Illinois, Rush Medical College. Two days later, a Charter for Incorporation of the City of Chicago was granted. The financial reverses of the times prevented Brainard from opening Rush Medical College until 1843, when twenty-two students were accepted for instruction.[2]

2. In 1855 he recalled this delayed opening: "The application had been made in good faith, and with the full expectation of immediately organizing an institution under it, but the revulsion [severe economic depression] which took place in business in 1837, fell with blistering influence upon private and public enterprises alike; and some of those, who, the year before, had the means and the disposition to aid and handsomely endow the institution, here found themselves without the means of supporting their own families"; *Proceedings of the Institute of Medicine of Chicago* (1925) 5(3): 199.

The original faculty of fourteen professional men were remarkable for their youth and ability. Among this original group were Dr. Nathan Davis Smith, a founding member of the American Medical Association, and Dr. John Evans, who later founded Northwestern University and had the village of Evanston named after him. The original building site for the school is where the current Chicago Medical Society Building is located at 515 North Dearborn. Chicago's population when the school opened was 7500. The building was financed by a number of prominent founding fathers, including William Ogden and Walter Newberry, and was hailed as bona fide evidence of Chicago's capabilities for holding a commanding rank among her sisters of the West from an intellectual and moral, as well as commercial point of view.[3]

In his inaugural address, Brainard declared, "The health, the happiness and the life of your dearest friends, and your own, may and will some day depend on the skill of some of the members of the profession. To elevate the standards of skill and knowledge in the profession, to excite an honorable emulation among its members, to disseminate for their successors in this new region the principles of medical science, are the objects held in view by the founders of this institution."[4]

Brainard was a serious and dedicated professional; in contrast, several of his contemporaries divided their time between farming, real estate, and medicine. Brainard did, however, digress from his professional activities when he ran for mayor of Chicago in 1858 and was defeated. He studied for several years in Paris, then considered a center of medicine for the world. His work won him fame throughout the nation,[5] and his paper on the healing of un-

3. Thomas Neville Bonner, *Medicine in Chicago, 1850–1950: A Chapter in the Social and Scientific Development of a City* (Urbana and Chicago: University of Illinois Press, 1991), p. 48.

4. Index card quotations, James A. Campbell, M.D., Box 35, File 4, C97-052, James A. Campbell, M.D., Papers 1924–1983, Record Group 002000, Office of the President, Rush–Presbyterian–St. Luke's Medical Center/Rush University Medical Center Archives, Chicago, Ill.

5. Diane Shannon, "The Golden Age of German Medicine and Its Impact upon American Medicine," Poster, Rush Research Days, April 1999.

united fractures brought him the vice presidency of the American Medical Association in 1853, when that organization was just six years old.

Daniel Brainard died in 1866 of cholera as he was preparing a scientific paper for presentation on that disease. His death was widely mourned in the city. He had been an active combatant in the front line against many diseases; he had personally participated in the founding of the first medical school, in the founding of the first hospital, and had been the author of the first original research to come out of Chicago.[6]

The selection of the name Rush for the medical college Brainard and his associates founded would be the obvious and logical choice for what was envisioned to be a leading medical school for the new American West. Brainard had trained in Philadelphia, where the name of Dr. Benjamin Rush was by that time legendary and revered. Physician, patriot, philosopher, intellectual, educator, and advocate of the rights of the disadvantaged were descriptions that could all be used to depict Dr. Rush as one of our nation's leading citizens.

Rush was considered the Father of American Medicine in the same sense that Thomas Syndenham was regarded as the Father of Medicine in Great Britain. Rush was not only the foremost medical man of his time, but he was one of the colonies' most eminent citizens. He was one of the signers of the Declaration of Independence and took an active part in the Revolutionary War and in the life of the United States after this country had won its independence. He utilized his chemistry training from Europe in assisting and advising the colonials on the manufacture of gunpowder.[7] He was treasurer of the U.S. Mint from 1799 to 1813. Rush produced a military manual for hygiene, *Directions for Preserving Health of Soldiers*, which remained in use until 1908.[8] He financed the publication and gave the title to the book *Common Sense*, by his friend Thomas Paine.

6. Bonner, *Medicine in Chicago*, p. 17.

7. Sarah R. Reidman and Clarence C. Green, *Benjamin Rush: Physician, Patriot, and Founding Father* (New York: Abelhard Schumann, 1964).

8. Dr. Frederick Kittle, "Benjamin Rush: Heritage and Hope," *Magazine*, Rush–Presbyterian–St. Luke's Medical Center, Winter 1976–77, pp. 46–51.

The expected need for educated leaders for the young country led Rush to publish an essay in 1787 proposing the creation of a national university in which the following arts and sciences be taught by a series of lectures: government, history, agriculture, manufacturing, commerce, mathematics, natural philosophy, natural history, philology, German, and French. Rush's idea was strongly supported at the Constitutional Convention in 1787 by James Madison. Although it was not officially endorsed, the idea of a national university was favored by the first six presidents of the United States. President George Washington personally granted land for this purpose.[9]

Benjamin Rush had graduated from Princeton in 1760 and Edinburgh in 1768 and then became professor of medicine at the University of Pennsylvania, whose medical school had its origins in the nation's first medical school, the College of Philadelphia.[10] He was an extremely active member of the American Philosophical Society, was a close friend of Benjamin Franklin, and attended Franklin at his death in 1790.[11]

Thomas Jefferson and Rush corresponded with each other over a period of 11 years beginning in 1800.[12] They did not always agree. In one instance, Jefferson, while lamenting the devastation of the yellow fever epidemics, noted that in this case, as with most evils, they become the means of producing good things. He was referring to the effect that the epidemic would have on discouraging the growth of great cities, which he viewed as pestilential to the morals, the health, and the liberties of man. Rush had taken an active part in the fight against the great yellow fever epidemic in 1793 and wrote a vivid description of it.[13]

9. *Princeton University Annual Alumni Report* (Princeton, N.J.: Princeton University, 1982–83).

10. Rosemary Stevens, *American Medicine and the Public Interest* (New Haven and London: Yale University Press, 1971), p. 19.

11. Carl Van Doren, *Benjamin Franklin: A Biography* (New York: Bramall House, 1938), p. 779.

12. Thomas Jefferson, *Writings: Letters*, Library Classics of the United States (New York: Library of America, 1984), pp. 1080–82, 1122–26, and 1234–39.

13. In another letter, Jefferson discussed at some length with Dr. Rush his somewhat complicated relationship with fellow former American president, John Adams. Later a

Rush was a man of resolute opinions, strongly opposed to war, slavery, alcoholism, and the death penalty, and a strong advocate of education for women. He was particularly concerned about care of the indigent and treated thousands of them. He opened the first free clinic in America, the Philadelphia Dispensary, in 1776. In due time, Rush Medical College would open its Charity Dispensary in Chicago, in 1843.

Rush's last work was an elaborate one, *Diseases of the Mind,* and because of it he is regarded as the Father of American Psychiatry. At the time people were thought to be mad because they were possessed by the devil or were suffering for their sins. Rush was the first American to proclaim that mental illness was a disease.

It was Benjamin Rush who said, "The physician has lived to little purpose who does not leave his profession in a more improved state than he found it." These would be powerful words for Brainard and Campbell and the others who would follow later. The American Medical Association erected a monument to Rush in Washington in 1904 in recognition of his great eminence.

Rush Medical College grew with the emerging sprawling giant city of the Midwest but suffered a severe setback from the Chicago Fire, which destroyed the entire facility. Rush eventually settled in its current location on the West Side at the corner of Harrison and Wood in 1876. Then, in 1883, as a result of a ban on teaching in the wards of Cook County Hospital by the County Commissioners, the Rush Trustees in conjunction with the Presbyterian Churches of Chicago built the Presbyterian Hospital, which was to become the first hospital in the United States dedicated to teaching as well as patient care for a faculty of medicine.[14] The

---

restitution of the Adams-Jefferson friendship occurred, which Rush is credited with repairing. In the recent observation of the 200th anniversary of America's greatest adventure story, the Lewis and Clark exploration of the Great Northwest, Rush's involvement is joyfully celebrated in Stephen Ambrose's *Undaunted Courage: The Story of Lewis and Clark and the Exploration of the American West* and again in another history of that period, David McCullough's *John Adams.*

14. John S. Graettinger, An Autobiographic History: Section of Cardio-Respiratory Diseases and the Department of Medicine, Presbyterian St. Luke's Hospital, 1953–1970 (March 1, 1996), p. 3.

Central Free Dispensary was also organized so that by the last decade of the nineteenth century, Rush had become the largest medical school in the United States. Thus, because of its insistence on teaching, the Rush-Presbyterian organization was one of the national forerunners in raising the professional standards of medicine. Distinguished medical educator and physician Dr. Francis Peabody said that the term "teaching hospital" was almost synonymous with the term "good hospital."[15]

But all was not well with medical education in the United States. Those who were able flocked for their training to Europe, to Germany and Austria, where major advances in scientific and laboratory medicine were taking place, often within a university-sponsored setting. Christine Fenger, Ludwig Hekteon, William Belfield, Nickolas Senn, Bertram Sippy, and James Herrick were among the Rush faculty who established Rush's position as a preeminent school for the time by passing on to their students the knowledge they gained from their training in Europe. Dr. Senn, a gifted surgeon, conducted the largest surgical clinic in the world in the Rush Medical College Amphitheater, located at the corner of Harrison and Wood streets in Chicago (later to be replaced by the Rawson Building).

Almost all of the medical schools in the United States were of the "proprietary" type. They were profit-oriented and owned by physicians who looked upon them exclusively as a means of supplementing their income from private practice. Because most medical schools relied solely upon tuition fees for income, they could not afford modern equipment. These schools tended to languish in the dark ages of medicine. Prerequisite educational requirements for entrance into medical school were very irregular, and in some cases nonexistent. In 1904 in a survey conducted by the newly formed Council on Medical Education of the American Medical Association, chaired by Dr. Arthur Dean Bevan, a Rush professor, the group found only 5 out of 158 U.S. medical schools that required two or

15. Kenneth M. Ludmerer, *Time to Heal: American Medical Education from the Turn of the Century to the Era of Managed Care* (Oxford and New York: Oxford University Press, 1999), p. 20.

more years of college training as a condition for admission.[16] Rush was one of those five. A survey in 1910, known as the Flexner Report, again confirmed these findings.[17]

The Rush faculty donated much of its time for the advancement of education and science, but Rush was the exception rather than the rule in American medical education. As pathologist H. Gideon Wells described its educational and professional environment, "Regardless of proprietary or not, Rush men were dedicated and idealistic."[18]

In the last part of the nineteenth century medical schools were beginning to seek affiliation with universities. Rush had entered into an affiliation with the University of Chicago that lasted about 10 years before the university went bankrupt.[19] At about the same time, a fortuitous association of William Rainey Harper and a Baptist and former minister Frederick Gates was to bring about a revival of the University of Chicago, thanks to funding from John D. Rockefeller. Harper, Rockefeller, and Gates got together to organize the new University of Chicago. Gates was particularly persuasive in directing the interest of Rockefeller to Chicago, rather than the initially preferred site, New York City.

A child prodigy, the popular and energetic William Rainey Harper (1856–1906) came from the small town of Concord, Ohio. He had obtained his Ph.D. at the age of eighteen. His special field of

16. Arthur Dean Bevan, "Cooperation in Medical Education and Medical Services," *Journal of the American Medical Association* 90 (April 14, 1928): 1173–75.

17. Abraham Flexner, *Medical Education in the United States and Canada: A Report to the Carnegie Foundation for the Advancement of Teaching* (New York, 1910), pp. 216–20.

18. H. Gideon Wells, "Investigative Work at Rush," *Bulletin of Alumni Association of Rush Medical College*, August 1922, pp. 15–19.

19. The original site for this Baptist-sponsored university was at 35th Street and Lake Michigan, a site donated by Senator Stephen A. Douglas. Rush then turned to Presbyterian-sponsored Lake Forest University and established an affiliation that continued into the last decade of the nineteenth century. Rush's activities were not exclusively confined to the clinic or the hospital wards: it sponsored a football team whose schedule in 1894 included West Division High School, Prairie Club, Oak Park, University of Chicago, the Chicago Athletic Association, Lake Forest University, all at home; and Beloit College, Notre Dame University, Grinnell College, and Monmouth College, away. Rush played Notre Dame to a 6–6 tie on November 22, 1894, at South Bend.

interest was Hebrew language, which he taught through correspondence schools throughout the country.[20] His academic career, before he became the founding president of the restructured University of Chicago in 1891, included appointments as instructor at the Baptist Union Theological Seminary (Morgan Park) in Chicago and professor of semantics at Yale.

John D. Rockefeller (1840–1937) amassed vast wealth before the age of thirty, when he established a near monopoly in the oil business. For many during his lifetime, he was the devil personified because of his ruthless business practices. But in addition to being the richest man in the world, he was also a devout Baptist and taught Sunday school. Most of the last half of his long life was devoted to philanthropic, not business concerns. Three quarters (73%) of all philanthropic money (estimated at $500 million) for higher education in the country in the first third of the twentieth century came from Rockefeller.[21] In a recent biography, Rockefeller is depicted as having a good side that was every bit as good as his bad side was bad. "Seldom has history produced such a contradictory figure."[22]

Rockefeller admired Harper and enthusiastically approved his appointment as the university's first president. Rockefeller had come to know Harper as their paths crossed frequently in the academic world in the 1880s. Harper often visited Vassar when he was at Yale and came to know Rockefeller, who visited his daughter while she attended school there.[23] Harper had seriously considered staying at Yale and not accepting the offer to head the renewed university. He had difficulty persuading Rockefeller to establish a university rather than to begin modestly as a college. So the modern University of Chicago thus came into being.

Although Rockefeller was delighted with his investment in the university, he and Harper had ongoing disagreements about the

20. Thomas Wakefield Goodspeed, *William Rainey Harper, First President of the University of Chicago* (Chicago: University of Chicago Press, 1928), p. 47.

21. Howard S. Berliner, *System of Scientific Medicine: Philanthropic Foundations in the Flexner Era* (New York and London: Tavistock Publications, 1985), p. 36.

22. Ron Chernow, *Titan: The Life of John D. Rockefeller, Sr.* (New York: Random House, 1998), p. 467.

23. Ibid., p. 308.

deficits that Harper ran up while developing the new school. Gates had become Rockefeller's watchdog on expenditures and subsequently Gates's relationship with Harper became strained.[24]

Hoping to further expand and extend the professional standing of Rush Medical College, Dr. E. Fletcher Ingalls and Dr. Frank Billings of the Rush faculty approached Harper to propose an affiliation or union with the new university. Harper was well aware of the deficiencies of American medical education and envisioned the development of a top flight school so that Americans would no longer have to go to Europe to get the best training. Rush was established and considered Chicago's leading school: it had a distinguished faculty and had access to the teaching material of Presbyterian Hospital. However, Rush was a proprietary school, a fact that made it unacceptable to the university.

Eventually an agreement was worked out for an affiliation that required the Rush faculty to give up their appointments to the Rush board; Harper would appoint a replacement board of lay trustees with no pecuniary interest in Rush earnings. The Rush faculty was held in very high regard by the university, in part because it commanded the loyalty of several extremely able doctors who combined practice and teaching with an interest in the science of medicine.[25] Two other important points in this agreement called for Rush to retire its debt (which it did) and to raise its entrance requirements to two years of college by the year 1902. This was a revolutionary concept, and other schools followed suit. Subsequently Rush freshmen and sophomores would move to the South Side university campus for their basic science courses and move on to the Rush campus on the West Side for the last two years. Rush voluntarily agreed in effect to become a two-year school, forfeiting its status as a four-year school. Incoming Rush freshmen enrolled as students of both Rush and the university.[26]

24. Ibid., p. 327.

25. Richard J. Storr, *Harper's University: A History of the University of Chicago* (Chicago and London: University of Chicago Press, 1966), p. 142.

26. Jim Bowman, *Good Medicine: The First 150 Years of Rush–Presbyterian–St. Luke's Medical Center* (Chicago: Chicago Review Press, 1987), pp. 69–70.

In 1897, when Harper and the university trustees presented this plan to Rockefeller and Gates, it was not enthusiastically received. Gates wanted to see the development of a medical school entirely devoted to research and not committed to patient care and teaching. Such a school did not exist in the United States. Gates, after reading Osler's *Textbook of Medicine,* was struck by how little scientific method and discipline had been integrated in medical education and practice. The concept of medical research as we understand it today was not well accepted in this country in those times. It seemed rash to spend time in a laboratory even if it produced some useful discoveries.[27]

Rockefeller's reservations about the Harper proposal were on an entirely different basis. And although the founder never gave his unconditional blessing to the idea, he made a number of proposals to support the Harper-Rush plan. Gates, however, would not concur and Rockefeller's real reasons for some of his financial decisions were never entirely clear. As his attorney Joseph Choate pointed out, "Rockefeller's partners seldom knew what he was thinking but he always knew what they were thinking."[28]

All during this time the deficits that Harper was generating to develop the school were becoming a source of increasing concern to sometimes generous and sometimes parsimonious Rockefeller and put a strain on their near father-son relationship. At one point, Rockefeller was on the verge of nervous exhaustion over the shortfalls.

Moreover, Rockefeller believed strongly in homeopathic medicine. He did not believe in allopathy, the method that Rush, Harvard, Columbia, and most other American schools followed.[29] This was

27. Chernow, *Titan,* p. 471.
28. Ibid., p. 296.
29. At the turn of the century, there were many different sects of medical belief in America, but homeopathy and allopathy were the principal schools. Homeopathy was based on the theory that the symptoms that a body exhibits during an illness were an expression of its attempt to cure itself. Therapy was based on expanding or increasing the symptoms of the disease. Also drug use was very minimal. Homeopathy enjoyed a following among some Americans, including some in the leadership community. Allopathy, on the other hand, was based on the belief that the purpose of medicine was to try to eliminate the symptoms of the disease. There was heavy use of drugs, chemicals, bleed-

another reason, possibly the principal reason, for his not giving his blessing to Harper's proposal.

Harper and the University of Chicago Board of Trustees went ahead with the Rush affiliation in spite of these objections. A school had been all but arranged.[30] The university administration felt that the Gates model would be an isolated project without a teaching function and was contrary to Harper's idea of the organization of all departments in a university. University officials felt it would be unwise for the university to depart from its general policy in this particular division of its work. In every other department of the university provision was made for instruction. Only in this way could the university secure men well prepared for other higher work of instruction; furthermore, in the work of instruction investigators most frequently find their greatest inspiration. The instruction of students – the preparation of medical practitioners of the best type, such as the Rush model was – was quite as much a function of a university as the promotion of research.[31] Here the University Trustees strongly supported the idea of union with Rush. Harper believed in this arrangement very strongly and called it a very significant step in the history of medical education. Rush would then go on to become the University of Chicago Medical School for the next 44 years.

Because of the lack of support from New York, Harper threatened at one time to resign, but never did.[32] In order to downplay the objections of Gates and Rockefeller, Harper stressed affiliation rather than a permanent union. And Harper was going ahead with the affiliation without committing to another expensive program, which would not have been seen favorably at that particular time.

When the university went ahead with the affiliation, Gates was furious and never had a good thing to say about Chicago medicine again.[33] In 1902, Rockefeller proposed the idea of a $2 million

ing, and purging. The two sects were economic competitors. Rockefeller persisted in his beliefs for decades, well into the twentieth century.

30. Storr, *Harper's University*, p. 286.

31. Ibid., p. 289.

32. Bowman, *Good Medicine*, p. 71.

33. Berliner, *System of Scientific Medicine*, p. 50.

gift to Rush, but Gates convinced him that it would be better placed in an institution devoted exclusively to research.[34]

Not long after Harper traveled to New York to present some new proposals to Gates and Rockefeller, and with it another large deficit, Harper became ill. He had been chastised by Mr. Rockefeller and his advisors and was sternly told he must stay within budget in the future.[35] Harper underwent an appendectomy at Presbyterian Hospital in 1904, and for a while recovered to resume his full schedule. His friend, Dr. Frank Billings, was his personal physician. An abdominal exploration subsequently disclosed extensive cancer, and eventually Harper was told of this. He knew the implications, as did his associates. When the news of Harper's fatal illness became known to Mr. Rockefeller, he was quite distressed. The two spent many hours together repairing their strained relationship.[36] True to his convictions, the founder tried to persuade President Harper to seek homeopathic remedies.[37] Upon Harper's death Mr. Rockfeller said, "I am personally conscious of having met with an irreparable loss." The deficit of the university was again covered and a gift was made to build a library in honor of Harper.

In looking back over the mournful turn of events, the legendary Dr. James Herrick thought that "had Harper lived, the result might have been different."[38] Perhaps the sense that Harper had enjoyed a special trust with Mr. Rockefeller would have resulted eventually in winning him over. And there is some evidence that Harper had given private assurances to the Rush people that things would work out. And although the New York interests insisted that Rush was never to become the permanent U. of C. medical school, the Trustees of the University never agreed to that stipulation.[39]

The joining of forces of the city's oldest educational institution and the city's rising new star in academia was an outstanding success.

34. Ibid.
35. Chernow, Titan, p. 494.
36. Ibid., p. 495.
37. Berliner, *System of Scientific Medicine*, p. 45.
38. Herrick, *Memories of Eighty Years* (Chicago: University of Chicago Press, 1949), p. 253.
39. Storr, *Harper's University*, p. 144.

The newly reorganized Rush Medical College of the University of Chicago developed into the best medical school in the Midwest and one of the best in the nation.[40]

Leading the list of Rush contributors in the advancement of medical science was Dr. James Herrick. In 1912, Herrick presented his monumental research on acute obstruction of the coronary arteries, known as an acute heart attack or coronary thrombosis. He was the first to describe the clinical features of this disabling and sometimes fatal disease, including its different types of presentation and conditions to be considered in the differential diagnosis. He was also, in conjunction with his young colleague Dr. Earnest Irons, the first to recognize the condition that was to become known as sickle cell anemia. Herrick developed several cardiac measuring devices in his laboratory at Presbyterian Hospital, one of which was to be the forerunner of the modern electrocardiograph (EKG).

Dr. Herrick was the embodiment of the Rush volunteer tradition. He had graduated from Rush in 1888 and studied extensively in Europe. In spite of his renown, he continued to carry out a general practice of medicine. He felt that the time he spent in general medicine added to his experience in diagnosing and treating other more complicated illnesses. His commitment to his profession is exemplified in his statement on the occasion of the dedication of the Murdock Building at Presbyterian Hospital in 1912:

> The Presbyterian Hospital was founded with two high purposes, caring for the sick and aiding in medical education. The hospital that confines itself solely to the treatment of the sick is somewhat dwarfed. To keep alive and progressive it should have the stimulus of necessity of instructing young active wide-awake undergraduates, interns, and nurses. Unless the spirit of research is in a hospital, unless it pervades the various branches of the medical institution, the

40. C. W. Vermeulen, M.D., "For the Greatest Good to the Largest Number: A History of the Medical Center, the University of Chicago, 1927–1977" (Vice-President for Public Affairs, the University of Chicago, 1977), p. 2, Special Collections, Regenstein Library, University of Chicago.

educational function of the hospital languishes and the
atmosphere becomes stale: things fail to progress and the
patients suffer. And yet no matter what view we may take
the central figure in the hospital to be, it should be the
patient. The concern for the patient is the unifying force
which will bind your humanity to your science, your service
to education, and yourselves to one another. It makes each
specialty more special as it becomes part of the whole. [41]

In the early part of the twentieth century, Dr. Frank Billings
was among the most forceful personalities in Chicago medicine. He
was dean of Rush Medical College and encouraged strengthening
the relationship of the Rush–University of Chicago affiliation to
complete union. He was also a remarkable fundraiser. He carried on
an active private practice at Presbyterian Hospital and was Rush's
second physician to be elected president of the American Medical
Association in 1903, following Nicholas Senn, Rush's first physician
to be so honored in 1898.[42]
     Many components in the Rush–U. of C. affiliation excelled in
the first three to four decades of the twentieth century. Morris
Fishbein was a graduate of that era. He became one of medicine's
most widely known and highly respected spokesmen. In recounting
his days as a student at Rush,[43] Fishbein was lavish in his praise of
its distinguished faculty, which he cited as totally dedicated to the
ideal of the great contribution a physician can make in training

41. Index card quotations, James A. Campbell, M.D., Box 35, File 4, C97-052, James
A. Campbell, M.D., Papers, 1924–1983, Record Group 002000, Office of the President,
Rush–Presbyterian–St. Luke's Medical Center/Rush University Medical Center
Archives, Chicago, Ill.
42. Subsequently, the honor was conferred on eight others who were either Rush students or faculty: John B. Murphy (1911), Arthur Dean Bevan (1918), Malcolm Harris
(1929), Dean Lewis (1934), Herman Kretschmer (1944), R. L. Sensenich (1948), Earnest
R. Irons (1949), and George Fister (1962). In the 1940s and 1950s only Harvard could
claim more AMA presidents than Rush.
43. Morris Fishbein, *Morris Fishbein, M.D., An Autobiography* (Garden City, N.Y.:
Doubleday, 1969), p. 18.

young men who will follow him and extend his work. On the faculty were three of the most learned pathologists in the United States, Ludwig Hektoen, H. Gideon Wells, and E. R. LeCount, and at least five distinguished surgeons, Arthur Dean Bevan, Dean Lewis, Vernon David, Evarts Graham, and his father, D. W. Graham. There were many distinguished subspecialists as well.

But the pride of the entire faculty was in the Department of Internal Medicine: Billings, Sippy, and Herrick. The second string included Joseph Capps, Leon Bloch, Sidney Portis, Wilbur Post, Earnest Irons, Samuel Slaymaker, and Theodore Tieken. Some went on to other centers; for example, Evarts Graham performed the first lobectomy (removal of a lung) for lung cancer in the world, at Barnes Hospital of Washington University, St. Louis. Lewis succeeded Dr. William Halsted as Chief of Surgery at Johns Hopkins. In the same group as Billings and Herrick was Bertram Sippy, whose name will forever be identified with the diagnosis and treatment of peptic ulcer. These individuals, in addition to being original contributors to the basic knowledge of medicine, were all outstanding teachers. For example, Sippy's trainees included the well-known Walter L. Palmer, Sara Jordan, Edward Emery, and Ralph Brown.

In leading medical centers such as Rush and the University of Chicago, the dedication, work habits, and values that many pre-clinical and clinical faculty members brought to their teaching in that era left an indelible imprint on their students. Many professors were larger than life. It was a time of heroes who often shaped the values and aspirations of these young people entering the profession over their entire lifetime.[44]

Chicagoan Dr. Julius Richmond, later in life a Harvard professor and a recognized leader in medical education, emphasized the importance of these Rush greats by citing them as leaders in American medicine in the era of great clinical insights and great descriptive ideas, "and they did this all without a lab."[45] Richard Richter, another great physician of that time went even further to say that between 1880 and

44. Kenneth M. Ludmerer, *Time to Heal: American Medical Education from the Turn of the Century to the Era of Managed Care* (Oxford and New York: Oxford University Press, 1999), p. 29.
45. Julius Richmond, M.D., personal interview, December 22, 1999.

1920 Rush Medical College reached its peak as the strongest medical school in the West. For every illustrious faculty name claimed by other schools, Rush had half a dozen in every department.[46]

The Rush McCormick Institute for Infectious Diseases was established. Here Dr. George and Gladys Dick studied scarlet fever, determined its cause, devised a test for susceptibility to it, and an antitoxin for treatment. Dr. Howard Taylor Ricketts became a medical martyr while discovering the cure for typhus. There was the world renowned Dr. Ludwig Hektoen, who, among his other accomplishments, was the first to recognize that it mattered who gave blood to whom in the new field of blood transfusion. Dr. Arthur Dean Bevan, a Rush teacher, surgeon, and Presbyterian Hospital staff member, in addition to pioneering the use of ethylene oxide as an anesthetic with the University of Chicago physiologist Arno Luckhardt, became a major national figure because of his contributions to the American Medical Association study of medical education, which later evolved into the Flexner report.[47]

The names of notable men who claimed Rush as their school were endless. Roland Woodyatt, a pioneer in metabolism and diabetes; Waltman Walters, chairman of Surgery at Mayo Clinic and author of Lewis and Walter's *Practice of Surgery;* Frederick Christopher, author and editor of *Surgery;* Willis Potts, the pediatric cardiac surgeon; and on an artistic note, Dr. Jules Stein.[48] Stein had been an ophthalmologist by training.[49]

46. Richard Richter, M.D., "A Short History of the Medical School at the University of Chicago," *Chicago Medical Alumni Bulletin* 1966, p. 3.

47. Bevan was second only to Halsted at Johns Hopkins in training surgical department chairmen: Lewis, Graham, Charles Rowan, David, Henry Harkins, Waltman Walters, Lester Dragstedt, and Dallas Phemister.

48. Stein (theatrical name for Styne), became a well-known musical composer ("Everything's Coming Up Roses," "Just in Time," "The Party's Over," "I'll Walk Alone," "Time after Time," "Make Someone Happy," and many more). He was a Rush graduate of 1922, and as a student organized and played in jazz bands. He not only generated a handsome income for himself, but provided employment for many of his Rush schoolmates as well. In the 1920s, the speakeasy business expanded and Stein in 1924 founded the Music Corporation of America (MCA). He was awarded an Oscar in 1975.

49. Campbell, "Some Persons at Rush," *Transactions of the American Clinical and Climatological Association* 89 (1977): 169.

The Rush name became known all over the United States. Consequently upwards of 40 percent of the incoming Rush third-year class came from medical schools other than the University of Chicago. Rush accepted transferees from feeder schools that provided only the first two years of training.[50] These transferees often came from the western half of the United States, where Rush was considered the best school for training to become a practicing physician.

The Rush educational program evolved well beyond the borders of Presbyterian Hospital and its Central Free Dispensary. The affiliation of Cook County Hospital with the Rush training program added to its attractiveness for the third and fourth years of medical school. County Hospital had emerged from a scandal-ridden time when physicians paid money for appointments. A civil service examination was a requirement for staff appointment, and County began to go in the direction of reaching its enormous potential as a great medical institution. The examination had to be taken every six years and these positions were highly competitive. There was considerable prestige associated with this position, and no pay. Many of the teachers in Rush Medical College were attending physicians in various capacities at County. A great deal of education of Rush students at that time was carried out on the services there as well as on the Presbyterian services.[51]

Rush also encouraged original investigational programs. Between 25 and 30 students at any given time in the first two years of medical school were engaged in original work in the biological sciences, and many more in the last two years. Several students had taken their Ph.D. degree.[52] The exposure of the students in the first two years to the science courses at the university in the Ogden

50. Jim Bowman, *Good Medicine: The First 150 Years of Rush–Presbyterian–St. Luke's Medical Center* (Chicago: Chicago Review Press, 1987), p. 78.

51. Stanton A. Freidberg (interview), Some Medical Reminiscences [of] Francis H. Straus, M.D., March 29, April 1–2, 1980 (094-038), Oral History Collection, Rush–Presbyterian–St. Luke's Medical Center Archives.

52. H. Gideon Wells, "Investigative Work at Rush Medical College," *Bulletin of Rush Medical College*, January 1917, pp. 18–20.

Graduate School of Science encouraged this activity, but the stimulus to clinical research was provided by the Rush clinical staff.

Presbyterian Hospital grew to a capacity of four hundred beds and was the best-endowed general hospital in Chicago.[53] In 1930, only one out of every 65 applicants for internship was selected.[54] The internship was then 16 to 18 months long. Advanced diagnostic and treatment programs for patients were available. Patient care and teaching were stressed, as well as research. Presbyterian was, in fact, the university hospital gaining in experience and knowledge in the demanding and ever increasing task of providing care for the sick, teaching students in preparation for the practice of medicine, and carrying out a credible research program. Rush, in affiliation with the University of Chicago and Presbyterian Hospital, was considered the best that Chicago medicine had to offer.

For the country, the transformation of the standards from the proprietary hospital to the modern sophisticated teaching hospital starting in the 1870s up through the 1920s was not accidental. The new university teaching hospital bore no more resemblance to the proprietary hospital than a twentieth-century factory to a craftsman's workshop. This effort was difficult, and the frustrations, failures, and mistakes along the way only barely suggest the complexity of the movement. But it was the visionary determination of the medical leaders for the time that finally resulted in the development of this new system of medical education, which led to the emergence of an implicit social contract between the medical profession and the nation. Medical schools and hospitals would provide the type of doctor that society needed and in return society would provide these schools and hospitals the resources they needed to conduct research and teaching on a high plane.[55]

53. Edwin F. Hirsch, *Frank Billings, A Leader in Chicago Medicine* (Chicago: Printing Department, University of Chicago, 1966), p. 119.
54. Summary transcript of interview with R. K. Gilchrist, M.D., by Jim Bowman, July 14, 1986, in preparation for *Good Medicine: The First 150 Years of Rush–Presbyterian–St. Luke's Medical Center.*
55. Ludmerer, *Time to Heal,* p. 22.

Following the death of President Harper, the University of Chicago changed course to some extent and went through an extended period of consolidation through its three succeeding presidents: Professors Earnest Burton, Harry Judson, and Max Mason. Rockefeller's support for some university programs dropped off.

The issue of whether Rush was to be forever an affiliate of the university or would eventually join into permanent union had been tabled. In 1911, Rush trustees approached University Board Chairman Martin Ryerson about this matter, asking whether Rush should go its own way and affiliate with another institution. Ryerson said "No" to the Rush officials; they should wait and let things evolve for a while until something stronger developed. Rush was discouraging other schools in Chicago interested in merger, affiliation, or union, preferring to further its relationship with the school that was rapidly evolving into a very highly respected educational enterprise. However, Rush was not getting its full recognition for doing the university's hospital training and its fundraising capacity was hampered by lack of a program for a more defined grander plan.[56]

Rush graduates were found in every part of the United States. To be a Rush graduate meant something. There weren't that many reputable medical schools around. Their diplomas read, "Degree of Doctor of Medicine conferred by Rush Medical College in affiliation with the University of Chicago." The graduation exercises were held in the upper amphitheater of the Rush Medical College on Harrison Street, and the early diplomas were signed by Harper.[57] In 1925, the location of graduation exercises was changed to the University of Chicago Midway campus, first at Hutchinson Court and later moved to Rockefeller Memorial Chapel.

The serious deficiencies in medical education in a high percentage of the existing schools that was first pointed out by the Bevan AMA report in 1904, and later by the highly influential

56. Bowman, *Good Medicine*, pp. 72–73.
57. "The Old Structure Passes," *Bulletin of the Alumni Association of Rush Medical College* (1923) 17 (no. 3): 5.

Flexner Report, resulted eventually in more than a hundred U.S. medical schools either dissolving or being absorbed by universities. Many medical schools in the United States were woefully lacking in quality of instruction and scientific facilities. Rush was among the few that was considered acceptable.

Dr. Abraham Flexner, the report's author, was an associate of Frederick Gates and both were identified with the Rockefeller General Education Board philanthropic interests. The Flexner Report, in addition to exposing abuses, made constructive criticisms and recommendations. It urged the development of a full-time salaried faculty for medical schools, at least for the major departments. The response to this report, issued in 1910, was slow. Only Johns Hopkins by 1915 had a semblance of such a program in operation.

The Rockefeller Foundation through Flexner, Dr. Frank Billings, and other Rush and university representatives eventually got together in 1916 to work out an agreement for further development of the medical school. Flexner had been given many millions by the Rockefeller group for the improvement and reform of medical education, and eventually a great deal of that money would come to the university.[58]

Gates and Flexner wanted the University of Chicago and other schools such as Vanderbilt to become totally full time in their faculty organization. The newly proposed organization was to be an endowed school without any element of commercial medical practice. It was to be strictly scientific and controlled by a staff with no duties to perform but to teach, do research, and research-related clinical work. Flexner was fearful that if the entire medical program as developed at Rush were to prevail, a full-time plan would not develop. Yet, as Dr. James Campbell pointed out many years later, Ingalls and his Rush faculty associates had effectively achieved in a secular way recognition of sciences and medicine in the university significantly different from the Gates Baptist approach.[59]

58. Vermeulen, "For the Greatest Good to the Largest Number," pp. 5–8.
59. "Some Persons at Rush," speech by James A. Campbell, M.D., presented to the Clinical and Climatological Association, October 25, 1977, folder 14, Box 7, C97-052,

Flexner and those who followed at the University of Chicago Medical School were very critical of Harper's original affiliation with Rush. He was a "young man in a hurry, so it was said."[60]

Their plan called for a new medical school facility on the South Side Midway campus to replace Rush and be staffed only by full-time physicians. Rush's role in this new scheme was to develop a postgraduate medical school to train licensed physicians on the most advanced new initiatives in medicine and to further refine their existing skills. Such schools existed in Europe at the time but disappeared after World War I. Postgraduate training in the form of hospital-sponsored specialty programs requiring longer periods of study, evolved as the standard in the United States to provide for education after medical school. So the proposed 1916 scheme was out of date almost from the beginning.

The plan also called for trustees of the university and Rush to commingle, with degrees to be conferred by the university. All Rush students and faculty would then be University of Chicago faculty and students. Rush would also surrender all of its property to the university.

The announcement in 1916 of this plan was heralded as big news throughout the entire country.[61] Dr. John Milton Dodson, the dean of students at Rush, cited Rush's willingness to agree to this as another remarkable example of its farsightedness. He then referred back to an earlier time at the beginning of the century recalling the words of Harper that the action of the faculty of Rush Medical College in surrendering the control of its authority to the university (for that is what the act of affiliation really meant) was one of the most remarkable and significant events in the history of education in America. He had reference in this declaration to the generous spirit that originally moved the faculty members to take such a step. A

James A. Campbell, M.D., Papers 1924–1983, Record Group 002000, Office of the President, Rush–Presbyterian–St. Luke's Medical Center/Rush University Medical Center Archives, Chicago, Ill.

60. Walter Lincoln Palmer, M.D., Remarks, Commencement Banquet of the Alumni Association of Rush Medical College, *Record*, pp. 13–15.

61. *Bulletin of the Alumni Association of Rush Medical College*, January 1917, pp. 13–18

small group of men in possession of a thriving institution at the apparent height of its prosperity with a valuable physical property, a long and honorable history, and a loyal body of alumni, and with every promise of continued success gave the institution into the hands of the university because they believed they could insure more certainly the future development and usefulness of the school and advance the interest of medical education.[62]

However, eleven years passed before this plan became operational in 1927. The permanent union of Rush and the university did not take place until 1924. This long delay indicated to many that the 1916 agreement between Rush and the university would not work and could not be fulfilled. Rush's position within the university structure had become more powerful and dominant as time went on. Over 25 percent of all the university's graduates, some 4000 in number, came from Rush.[63] Many of these physicians identified more closely with the college and were not interested in the diminution of Rush in any way.

World War I added to the delay, as did a steep rise in building costs. Rush and its educational components on the West Side were moving forward. Having an operational program that was working well may have diminished the urgency within the university for all this to take place.

After 1924, regular notices of the activities of the medical school both at the Rush West Side facility as well as the South Side campus were chronicled in the *University of Chicago Magazine*. Photographs of the new buildings under construction on the Midway appeared regularly. Perhaps the most striking historically was one that appeared on the March 1930 inside cover showing the twin seals of Rush and the University of Chicago, which had been engraved in stone on the entrance to the new Medical School Court on East Fifty-eighth Street.[64] This monument is still there today.

62. John Milton Dodson, ibid., p. 23.
63. Ralph Webster, "What the University Has Done for Rush, and What Rush Can Do for the University," *University of Chicago Magazine*, November 1925, pp. 13–14.
64. *University of Chicago Magazine*, Jan.1930, p. 131.

A parallel but much more modest program for Rush was undertaken with the construction of the Rawson Building to replace the original Rush Medical College Building at the corner of Harrison and Wood. It was also to house the Rush Postgraduate program. The 1916 Flexner-Rockefeller plan had also called for a million dollar separate West Side school endowment.[65]

The pressure to back off from some of the harsh demands that the university had made on Rush were evident when University President Burton commented that representatives of the university welcomed the new arrangement for several reasons. They believed that, by developing medical education at two centers in the city, one in close contact with the great hospitals of the West Side and the other on the university quadrangle in close contact with the graduate departments of science of the university, more could be accomplished for medical science than by concentrating work at either point.[66]

65. Vermeulen, "For the Greatest Good to the Largest Number," p. 6.

66. Earnest D. Burton, "Rush Medical College and the University of Chicago," *Bulletin of the Alumni Association of Rush Medical College* (1924) 18(no. 2):4–5.

3

Robert M. Hutchins and the Breakup of Rush

The Rush operational organization on the West Side changed very little when the new school and the new Billings Hospital on the South Side opened in 1927. Rush's Dr. Earnest Irons was the appointed dean for both schools. After the first two years, students were given the choice for their third and fourth years of staying on the South Side at the new school or going to the Rush complex on the West Side. In the first few years, the vast majority of students chose Rush because that program had established a proven curriculum and an excellent reputation. Rush attracted young men and women for training as future practitioners utilizing the large patient base and clinical facilities of the West Side medical center complex, while the new university school program for the third and fourth years was just getting started. The idea of training individual students primarily for research was quite new. "There were a few patients but we had an earnest and dedicated staff," an early graduate recalls.[1] The first group from the four-year program on the Midway in 1929 consisted

1. Paul Jeremiah Patchen, M.D., Records and Reminiscences of the Graduating Class of 1929 of Rush Medical College of the University of Chicago (1979), Medical Alumni Office, University of Chicago, p. 18.

of three graduates, but things began to change and the number of graduates had grown to a total of 34 over the first five years.[2]

In 1933, election to Alpha Omega Alpha, the national medical honor society, was awarded to 42 students for both schools, 8 of whom had elected to stay at the Midway for their last two years and the remaining 34 on the West Side at Rush.[3] Rush was one of the largest schools in the country. Flexner and his associates saw no advantage in this. The new school, "the School of Medicine of the Division of Biological Sciences," was to have a reduced number of students, along with heavy emphasis on training in research and affiliation with the basic sciences.

Many appointed to the new school faculty, such as Drs. Franklin McLean, Dean Lewis, and Paul Cannon, came from Rush. So in a sense, while Rush was still one school, it was also two schools under one umbrella. As time went on, rivalries developed between those who moved to the South Side and those who remained on the West Side. The South Side group was heavily research-oriented and salaried, whereas those on the West Side were clinically oriented, almost all nonsalaried, and derived their incomes from private practice.

In 1926, Flexner, the Rockefeller Foundation watchdog on development of the new school, approved the plan to continue undergraduate work at Rush without bringing forward any objections.[4] The university's Board of Trustees supported an increase in teaching facilities and a reorganization of the Presbyterian Hospital in its number of clinics and beds toward the end of developing the Rush postgraduate school and in participation by the College in undergraduate training, which the board felt must continue for some

2. Ilza Veith and Franklin McLean, *The University of Chicago Clinics and Clinical Departments, 1927-1952* (Chicago: University of Chicago, 1952), p. 81.

3. In 1960 James Campbell became the national secretary-treasurer of AOA, and its national office was relocated to Rush–Presbyterian–St. Luke's Medical Center on the West Side and remained there for almost two decades.

4. Franklin McLean to Max Mason, Chicago, 1 October 1926, President's Papers 1925–1945, Box 70, Folder 3, Regenstein Library, Department of Special Collections, University of Chicago, Chicago, Illinois.

years at least.[5] Flexner later was very critical of this start, saying that the two schools should not have been considered equal. In his view Rush should pursue its agreed-upon commitment of 1916 to develop postgraduate education. By not doing so, and by continuing to actively educate students in their third and fourth years, Rush was partially defeating the purpose for which Flexner's reorganization plan had been conceived.[6]

The new school and Billings Hospital on the Midway would take time to organize not only as a teaching and research facility, but also to develop an experienced staff for care of patients. In the beginning, the new South Side facility could not accept a full class of students moving on from their second year in medical school to the third year because there were not enough patients in the new hospital to support such an operation. The original intended mission for Billings Hospital was to provide care only for patients with illnesses of teaching and research value. No fees were to be rendered for such care. There were no financial criteria and deficits were to be made up by the university.

However in early 1929, even before Robert Maynard Hutchins, the central figure in the eventual Rush–University of Chicago dissolution story had arrived on the Midway, Professor Frederick Woodward, the acting president of the university, made a proposal that Presbyterian Hospital, the center of the Rush complex on the West Side, move its entire operation to the Midway.[7] There was nothing in the original agreement of 1916 or the union of 1924 that called for such a move. The university pointed out that by so doing, both schools could be combined into one. The Board of Trustees of Presbyterian Hospital politely but firmly declined, and thereafter the relationship between Rush Medical College and the

5. Minutes, Faculty Meeting, Rush Medical College, 28 October 1926, President's Papers 1925–1945, Box 70, Folder 3, Regenstein Library, Department of Special Collections, University of Chicago, Chicago, Illinois.

6. Abraham Flexner, *I Remember* (New York: Simon & Schuster, 1940), p. 271.

7. Frederick Woodward to Robert McDougal, January 14, 1929, President's Papers 1925–1945, Box 70, Folder 3, Regenstein Library, Department of Special Collections, University of Chicago, Chicago, Illinois.

university became strained and gradually deteriorated. Subsequently, Presbyterian Hospital's Board of Trustee's requests for the university to support Presbyterian Hospital fundraising were denied, and the atmosphere became even less cordial between the two boards. After he arrived, Hutchins restated the proposal for the relocation of Presbyterian Hospital again and again over the next several years and the hospital's refusal to move south was given as the reason that Hutchins closed the medical school for any further Rush students ten years later.[8]

The Great Depression beginning in 1929 then intervened. Income at Billings Hospital did not meet expenses even with gifts, endowment, and other philanthropy. Large deficits were being sustained even after the full-time staff gave up the idea of not charging patients and started rendering fees. Faculty salaries had to be cut, even for doctors who had started on a full-time career at some financial loss. Expenses were cut drastically everywhere. In 1932, the financial situation became desperate. An outside management consultant firm was called in.[9] The Rockefeller General Education Board also found itself short of funds and unable to renew its subsidy to meet its subscriptions.[10] Recruitment of physicians for the hospital was not easy. Many came and went, without achieving distinction as teachers or researchers. They had little time except for patient care. Serving patients became an end in itself and the hospital could not forgo that as long as hospital finances depended upon keeping its beds full.[11]

The leadership of Dr. Dallas Phemister was largely instrumental in keeping morale high among the newly appointed full-time

8. Robert M. Hutchins, The State of the University, September Fifteenth, Nineteen Hundred Thirty Nine: A Report to the Alumni and Friends of the University of Chicago, p. 12.

9. C. W. Vermeulen, M.D., "For the Greatest Good to the Largest Number: A History of the Medical Center, the University of Chicago, 1927–1977" (Vice President for Public Affairs, the University of Chicago, 1977), p. 41.

10. Walter Lincoln Palmer, M.D., Remarks, Commencement Banquet of the Alumni Association of Rush Medical College, Record, pp. 13–15.

11. William McNeil, *Hutchins' University: A Memoir of the University of Chicago, 1929–1950* (Chicago and London: University of Chicago Press, 1991), p. 85.

medical staff at the university. Phemister, a Rush graduate, had been trained in the highly regarded Bevan surgical program at Presbyterian Hospital.[12] Dr. Bevan had set up his own Surgical Pathology Section, which he personally funded and staffed with two technicians. All surgical specimens were reviewed there by all members of the department, and trainees such as Phemister and a contemporary Rush–Presbyterian–St. Luke's notable, Dr. Francis Straus, would spend six months on this rotation. This training was considered unequaled in the city, and possibly even in the entire nation.[13] Phemister later gave up a lucrative career in private practice to become Chairman of Surgery at the new school after Dr. Dean Lewis, the original choice and another Bevan trainee, moved on to Hopkins. Phemister combined special interests in bone pathology and outstanding skills as a surgeon.

One of the original full-time faculty, Dr. Charles Huggins, was awarded the Nobel Prize for Medicine and Physiology in 1966 for his prostate cancer research carried out in 1943. The university could point with pride to a Department of Health, Education, and Welfare study done in 1967, which showed that the U. of C. had among the highest percentage of graduates going on to occupy full-time faculty positions in American medical schools.[14] The beloved and world-renowned gastroenterologist, Dr. Joseph Kirsner started his career in the 1930s at Billings Hospital. Reflecting back on those days sixty years later, he described some of the stern academic realities of those times. "There was a modest salary. You were expected to take your place to teach and take care of patients. You had to do credible research or you would never be promoted, and, by the way here is a hundred dollars a month to do research." Kirsner added that many physicians with outstanding clinical skills

12. C. Frederick Kittle, M.D., "The Development of Academic Surgery in Chicago," *Surgery* 62 (no. 1, July 1967): 1–11.

13. Stanton A. Freidberg (interview), Some Medical Reminiscences [of] Francis H. Straus, M.D., March 29, April 1–2, 1980 (094-038), Oral History Collection, Rush–Presbyterian–St. Luke's Medical Center Archives.

14. Vermeulen, "For the Greatest Good to the Largest Number," p. 119.

left because only those engaged in research were adequately rewarded with promotion.[15]

Another member of the faculty who excelled in the academic world was Pathology Chairman Dr. Paul Cannon. He was selected for membership in the prestigious National Academy of Sciences. Jim Campbell studied extensively under Dr. Cannon.

Dean Earnest Irons was one of Rush's brightest stars. He had attended college at the University of Chicago before going to Rush. *The University of Chicago Magazine* called him "highly esteemed, one of the good old boys we point to with pride."[16] Eventually he became identified with the Rush faction as the struggle between the Rush and U. of C. faculties intensified. At the insistence of Hutchins, Irons agreed to reduce the number of Rush students if Hutchins could make up this financial shortfall. All of Rush's income was derived from tuition. But he was given no money for this or the other programs that Rush needed. There were many long and bitter conferences between Irons and Hutchins over Hutchins's refusal to divert any funds from the university to support Rush.[17]

The proposal to create a postgraduate school was again revisited. And a study commissioned by Hutchins under Dr. Dean Scammon of the Biological Science Division in 1931 advised against such type of work as being unworthy of the University of Chicago. The study reported that the quality of work done in existing postgraduate schools was not high.

Enrollment for the third and fourth years at the Midway school increased to about 50 per class by the mid thirties. But Rush continued with its enrollment of 140 to 150 students per class for the last two years, because, although more University of Chicago students chose the Midway rather than Rush, Rush continued to attract large numbers of students recruited from other two-year medical schools throughout the country. Beginning in 1937, however, Rush

15. Dr. Joseph Kirsner, personal interview, May 28, 1998.
16. *University of Chicago Magazine*, November 1929, pp. 13–17.
17. Palmer, Remarks, p. 14.

class size began to decline as the number of qualified students applying from two-year medical schools started to drop.

The economics of the two schools were entirely different. The Midway school could look for philanthropic money to cover part of the cost of educating students, whereas all support for the West Side school came from tuition: it had no other source of support.

There were disagreements between the full-time salaried researchers on the Midway and the volunteer teacher-practitioners of Rush about the best way to train students. For the Rush faculty, the tried and true way based on large clinical experience at Presbyterian, the Central Free Dispensary, and Cook County Hospital was the best. A medical school was necessary for Rush to continue to infuse new blood into its programs. And there were Rush graduates all over the country conducting honorable practices from that experience.[18] The compensation for the faculty was the prestige of identifying with excellent medicine. Several Rush faculty were not enthusiastic about the U. of C. model, which emphasized research and science heavily and deemphasized clinical experience. Acting President Woodward acknowledged that there were differences in organization, method, and emphasis, but he hoped experience would show the way to reconcile these differences. The two schools should complement each other with valuable results.[19]

In 1936 Dr. Emmett Bay, the first physician employed by the university hospital when it opened in 1927, replaced Irons as dean and the office was moved from the West Side to the South Side. However, Woodward emphasized that it had definitely been decided that teaching and research would continue on the West Side. Rush was training more doctors than any other university in the United States. It may be, he said, that in the end undergraduate instruction would disappear entirely from the West Side, but he went

18. Arthur Dean Bevan, M.D., "Rush Medical College, Pioneer Professional School of the West," *University of Chicago Magazine*, June 1934, pp. 271–74.
19. Frederick Woodward, "Vice President Woodward Broaches the Subject," *University of Chicago Magazine*, Midsummer 1936, p. 9.

on to emphasize that no precipitous action would be taken. Rush was an institution that had a magnificent history and promised to have an even greater history in the future.[20]

Bay also discussed the future of Rush, but in a rather more guarded fashion. He pointed out that the West Side, with 159 seniors and 140 juniors, was hampered by overcrowded physical plants, minimal personal attention for students, and excessive teaching responsibility for the faculty. As a result of the Depression, the Central Free Dispensary caseload had doubled or tripled. He talked about various ideas that Rush might undertake in the postgraduate area although he later did a study for Hutchins and found the prospects for such development rather dim.[21] And finally Bay mentioned very briefly that there was lack of money for the College.[22]

In 1929, the world of education was startled when twenty-nine-year-old Robert Maynard Hutchins was selected to be the fifth president of the university. Hutchins, who had been the dean of Yale Law School, was brilliant, outspoken and filled the bill for those on the selection committee who hoped to have a vitality reinfused into the university to bring it back to its earlier preeminence under Harper.[23]

Educational reform was the central aspect of his tenure at the university, which lasted until 1951. His impact on American education was to be indelible, thanks to his magnetism and daring. He made education an exciting adventure. The purpose of education was to unsettle the minds of young men and women and to inflame their intellect. He warned students against the ideas of practical men.

20. Woodward, "Vice President Woodward Broaches the Subject," p. 9.

21. Emmett Bay, M.D., "Rush Medical College: The First 100 Years," *University of Chicago Magazine*, November 1936, pp. 8–10.

22. E. E. Irons, M.D., to Emmett Bay, M.D., October 7, 1939, Presidential Papers 1925–1945, Box 70, Folder b6, Regenstein Library, Department of Special Collections, University of Chicago, Chicago, Illinois.

23. Milton Mayer, *Robert Maynard Hutchins, A Memoir* (Berkeley: University of California Press, 1993), p. 209.

The Hutchins tenure was often a national story. Among his many noted faculty members were Mortimer Adler and sociologist Beardsley Rummel, who devised the "pay as you go" method for tax collection to augment revenue for the federal government. Hutchins's outspokenness went well for the times as serious rethinking of the American way of life during and following the Great Depression was high on many people's agenda. He was frequently identified with Franklin Roosevelt and the New Deal and was mentioned as his possible running mate in 1940.[24]

Hutchins had very little use for physical conditioning and the like. Whenever he got the urge to exercise, so the story goes, he would lie down until the urge passed. And his abolishment of football in 1940 is still considered a significant event in the history of American sports.[25] It was stated that at the university particular interests and conditions are such that its students derive no special benefit from football. So it could not be said, as the story goes, that at the Midway one could win twelve letters without knowing how to write one.[26]

Robert Hutchins was very much a public figure, whether he was conducting the University of Chicago Round Table discussions aired nationally over the radio or exploring potential mergers with other institutions such as Northwestern. A term from later times, media person, would have suited him nicely. Hutchins was also a staunch defender of academic freedom and, in spite of his liberal leanings, he was an effective fundraiser for the university.

There was another side to Hutchins, however. Described as being out of joint, with stiff-necked pride and a tendency to be very overbearing, he was always going against the grain. The search com-

---

24. Harry Ashmore, *Unseasonable Truths: The Life of Robert Maynard Hutchins* (Boston: Little, Brown, 1989), p. 129.

25. David Maraniss, *When Pride Still Mattered: A Life of Vince Lombardi* (New York: Simon & Schuster, 1999), p. 43.

26. The Maroon football team had been in the decline since the 1920s, although Jay Berwanger of the 1935 Maroons received the first Heisman Trophy ever awarded as college football's outstanding player. Berwanger was also the first choice of the first NFL draft in 1936 (*New York Times*, June 28, 2002, Obituaries, Section C, p. 15).

mittee was told by his Yale associates that Hutchins was ruthless and impatient and needed five to ten years to temper his impatience in dealing with some of his colleagues at Yale. A recent view of Hutchins concludes that, once he made a decision, his notorious obduracy and the conditions over which he had no control (the Depression and the war) impaired his ability to act and burdened the institution as a whole for want of flexibility. Departments lost many faculty members and a decline in enrolment was also attributed in part to Hutchins. Some of these losses occurred because of the tensions Hutchins's administrative policies created and because of the choices he made as a leader of the institution. He chose to focus narrowly on the intellectual life of the university, going against its progressive empirically oriented tradition, thus arousing extensive faculty opposition.[27] After his departure, the university abandoned most of his reforms and returned to the educational practices of other major American universities.[28]

When Hutchins arrived in November 1929, one of his early pronouncements was to acclaim Rush Medical College a "jewel in the crown of the university," but only a year and a half later, in June 1931, the "boy wonder" president told Rush constituents that the university still did not know what to do with Rush. The university must have either one school or two on a different basis. Costs prohibited development of two first-class institutions.[29] In 1931, Harvard Dean David Edsell advised Hutchins that Rush was the best school in the region and enjoyed a dignified position. Moving Presbyterian Hospital out to the South Side to the university campus would mean a significant loss of clinical material.[30]

27. Mary Ann Dzuback, *Robert M. Hutchins: Portrait of an Educator* (Chicago and London: University of Chicago Press, 1991), pp. 69–70, 76.

28. *Encyclopedia Britannica* CD Rom 1994–1998. Hutchins served on the board of Encyclopedia Britannica.

29. Jim Bowman, *Good Medicine: The First 150 Years of Rush–Presbyterian–St. Luke's Medical Center* (Chicago: Chicago Review Press, 1987), p. 81.

30. David Edsell, Boston, to Robert Hutchins, Chicago, 23 October 1931, Presidential Papers 1925–1945, Box 70, Folder 4, Regenstein Library, Department of Special Collections, University of Chicago, Chicago, Illinois.

There were stories handed down from generation to generation that Hutchins had a real aversion for doctors. Even physicians at the Midway felt his sting: they were not up to the standards he set for the university. He thought of doctors as tradesmen, and so they were treated like stepchildren. In 1968, when Hutchins referred back to this period of the 1930s he said one school was enough and he often thought that was too much.[31]

Hutchins continued to push for the Presbyterian board to relocate the hospital to the South Side. The response from the West Side was for more permanent support of its teaching facilities. The Presbyterian board had a rather dim view of the full-time philosophy at the Midway and suggested that the university might consider a program similar to one at Harvard Medical School, which had tried and abandoned full-time medicine as unworkable.[32] The response from the Midway was that Harvard had succeeded in spite of itself.

These strained relations at the top filtered down to the faculty and students. The Rush student body protested about a story, all rumor, that they would have to move to the South Side.[33] And the faculty at the university wrote a letter of protest to Hutchins, balking at a rumored story that the new hospital and school would carry the name of Rush ahead of the University of Chicago.[34]

A number of Rush faculty had moved to the South Side, and this loss was significant to the Rush educational program. The preoccupation with survival probably took a toll, but up to the end, the clinical programs at Rush remained outstanding. There was simply no comparison between the clinical experience of students at Rush and those at the University.

31. Columbia Oral History Project, The Reminiscences of Robert M. Hutchins, 1968, Oral History Collection of Columbia University, p. 96.

32. Alfred Carton, Chicago, to Harold Swift, Chicago, July 19, 1934, Presidential Papers 1925–1945, Box 70, Folder 4, Regenstein Library, Department of Special Collections, University of Chicago, Chicago, Illinois.

33. Bowman, *Good Medicine*, p. 81.

34. Faculty of the School of Medicine of the University of Chicago to Robert Hutchins (undated), Presidential Papers 1925–1945, Box 70, Folder 5, Regenstein Library, Department of Special Collections, University of Chicago, Chicago, Illinois.

The Depression wore on, and after another failed attempt by Hutchins to persuade Presbyterian to move south, an announcement was made that the university, beginning in the fall of 1939, would accept students for the upcoming freshman class in numbers only to be accommodated on the South Side campus, and no further classes would be conducted by the university at Rush after the spring of 1942. Hutchins was aware that Rush could not remain open without an affiliation since it was severely depleted of funds. So Rush either had to close, make an immediate arrangement with Hutchins to move the hospital to the South Side, or find another university with which to affiliate.

In the course of a routinely scheduled conference Hutchins casually mentioned to Dr. Irons that the university would no longer receive Rush students. Prior to that time, Irons had been assured that everything was moving along reasonably satisfactorily.[35] Even the U. of C. faculty contingent was upset by the abruptness of the decision. It had been assumed that in time Rush would get smaller and be absorbed by the university. The university catalogue, "Announcements for the Medical Schools for the Session of 1938–1939," made no mention of the change, listing the separate faculties of both schools.[36]

Although polarization of the faculties on a number of issues emerged after the Midway school was started in 1927, there existed a camaraderie and loyalty that in many ways transcended all these conflicts. Many of the university faculty were Rush graduates and proud of that tradition. And many of the Rush people had strong ties with the university. Many thousands of Rush alumni were also very upset by this matter. For them the Rush affiliation meant a great deal more than a college tie. Being associated with a highly regarded medical school in an era when there had been so many substandard schools reassured both medical colleagues and patients of one's credentials. A college or university affiliation would ordinarily be for four years, but for its many graduates the Rush affiliation might be

35. Mary Irons, personal interview, May 14, 1999.
36. Catalogue Announcements, The University of Chicago, The Medical Schools for the Sessions of 1938–1939, vol. 38, no. 15, June 10, 1938.

for most of one's entire professional career. Presbyterian Hospital would later affiliate with the University of Illinois for several clinical programs, but this was not, for many of those involved, a similar or satisfactory substitute arrangement.

So much bitterness and bad feelings remained on both sides for years. Many Rush physicians had actively participated in fundraising for the construction of Billings Hospital, and now they were being dismissed.[37] The Rush faculty felt that they were betrayed after having given up their independent identity to form a complete union with the university. The U. of C. faculty thought the total full-time approach was the better one and in some ways the wave of the future, and the Rush approach was perhaps inferior. It took almost two generations and the reopening of Rush almost thirty years later for these sentiments to begin to heal.

Political polarization of the leadership might have added to the conflict. Hutchins had been closely identified with the New Deal and all the ramifications for social change that this implied at the time. Irons, on the other hand, espoused the traditional views of medicine and would continue to do so when he became president of the AMA in 1949. More enlightened and creative leadership might well have made a very significant difference. Perhaps the Rush faculty might have been a little more sympathetic to some elements of a full-time plan. As it would happen, the Presbyterian board, beginning in 1946, recruited several leading eastern physician-scholars to head some of its major departments on a full-time basis. But the traditional private practice, fee-for-service system, and emphasis on clinical traditions were preserved at Presbyterian. The university, on the other hand, became and remained the only undergraduate medical school in the country, perhaps in the world, that had a complete full-time clinical faculty.[38] Recently several modifications of that arrange-

37. Rush Medical College of the University of Chicago in 1926, Exhibition Gallery in the Department of Special Collections at the Regenstein Library of the University of Chicago, Spring–Summer 2001.

38. Henry Ricketts, M.D., "Forty Years of Full-time Medicine at the University of Chicago," *Journal of the American Medical Association* 208 (no. 11, June 16, 1969): 2069–73.

ment have occurred and some university physicians are no longer completely full-time salaried.

Hutchins, in his formal announcement of the termination of the 44-year Rush affiliation, expressed regret and recognized the great contribution Rush had made to American medicine. University of Chicago history professor William McNeil lamented the dissolution of the Rush–U. of C. bond, particularly because of the strong ties between the two. Over half of the Rush graduates did their undergraduate work at the U. of C. He pointed out that Rush had a proud tradition of its own that predated its affiliation with the U. of C. Thus, Rush faculty and alumni rebelled against such a sharply diminished role, especially since it was being dictated from the South Side. Rush assumed independent status and became a rival rather than an ally of the school on the Midway.[39]

Many years later, in 1968, Hutchins reflected back on this era.[40] The deliberations with Rush had occupied more than half of his time during the first ten years of his administration. He had wanted all along to "get rid of Rush," even though it enjoyed a national reputation for excellence.[41] He did not think Rush was the proper medical school for the university and the university could not afford two. He again pointed out that Rush was the alma mater of a high proportion of physicians in the Middle West. The Board of Trustees of Presbyterian Hospital were among Chicago's most eminent citizens. Located at some distance from the university, it was affiliated with Presbyterian Hospital, the most important one in the city, and it was staffed by the most prominent physicians. A large student body had kept students' costs relatively low, and the faculty was paid little by the university. Their compensation was received from private practice.

In light of this, it remains a puzzle why the university continued to make several attempts to persuade Presbyterian Hospital to

39. McNeil, *Hutchins' University*, pp. 44–45, 85.

40. Columbia Oral History Project: The Reminiscences of Robert M. Hutchins, 1968, Oral History Collection of Columbia University, pp. 20–21.

41. Ibid., pp. 86–90.

move to the South Side. Hutchins does not touch on this matter in his reminiscences. Coupled with these offers was the stipulation that the university would pay for the cost of construction of a new hospital. Quite possibly the severe economic deficits of the new Billings Hospital, which opened in 1927 with new admission policies, could have been a factor. If the well-established Presbyterian Hospital was in place, this might have been reversed. The harsh economic realities of the Great Depression clearly influenced this whole story as it did almost everything that happened in America in the thirties. For a hospital to move or branch out as Presbyterian would have to do to comply with Hutchins's demands would not be a minor or risk-free undertaking. Presbyterian held its own economically in the thirties. The University of Chicago Hospital and Clinics did not emerge from their financial crisis until 1935.

Conceivably efforts of the university to persuade Presbyterian to move might have been framed in such a way that Presbyterian had to refuse. Hutchins and the university could then break the affiliation with Rush with impunity. In this way, also, the university could gain some time to develop their own medical center before dismissing Rush. All the university's pronouncements of filial loyalty to Rush in retrospect seem to be empty rhetoric.

It is easy to make judgments in hindsight. Hutchins's views on the matter were quite rigid. One simply could not justify two theories of medical education and medical research as far apart as these two were in one institution. One of them had to be wrong. Of course, in retrospect, neither was entirely right or wrong.

One cannot help but wonder if a little more time and patience might have made a difference. The medical staff votes not to move Presbyterian Hospital to the South Side were close and an accommodation of some sort might have been made over time. The Rush staff was getting rather senior, and the university would have had a great deal of influence over all future appointments. The entire West Side medical facility cost to the university was minimal. Some financial support for Rush while it was reducing the number of students could have kept things going for a while. Having a university medical center in two locations has worked well in other cities, and the

combination of a strong clinical program and the emerging strong
academically oriented university medical school could have provided the medical world with an almost incomparable facility. The university went on to fulfill its destiny, and Rush was to be reopened 30
years later and rapidly evolve from a college into a health systems
university, with graduate schools in medicine, nursing, health sciences, and the graduate college. But in the process something was
lost. Clearly lost for the 10,976 physicians who had received the
Rush degree was the identification of having been trained at one of
the best medical schools anywhere, which is something one cannot
replace.[42]

    Perhaps Jim Campbell, even at an early stage in his profession,
might have learned from all this conflict, as he was able to engineer
the merger of two very strong medical institutions in Chicago,
Presbyterian and St. Luke's hospitals, some 15 years later.
Distinguished Rush surgeon Dr. Francis Straus's view was that
Hutchins simply could not visualize two medical schools competing
with each other in one institution. Ricketts would take strong exception to this competition, saying that two medical faculties, one part-
time and volunteer and one full-time and salaried would be incom-
patible. Later James Campbell would express the thought that two
separate schools did not make sense but it was unfortunate that more
than one hospital serving a single school could not be adequately
envisioned.

    Commenting on the Rush Medical College separation, Dr.
Ivan Sippy, a Rush graduate and faculty member, lamented the complete abandonment of Rush by the university. The University of
Chicago was bitterly denounced by many for having rejected Rush
and Presbyterian Hospital. The subsequent rebirth of Rush 30 years
later has modified this resentment to some extent.[43]

    42. James A. Campbell, M.D., "Some Persons at Rush," *Transactions of the American
Clinical and Climatological Association* 89 (1977): 162–71.

    43. Ivan Sippy, M.D., Comments on the University of Chicago and Rush Medical
College Separation, Record and Reminiscences of the Graduating Class of 1929 of the
University of Chicago, Medical Alumni Office, University of Chicago, 1979, pp. 115–16.

When the first Directory of Medical Specialists was published in 1939, 318 of the 1008 medical specialists listed for the State of Illinois were graduates of Rush. For the time, medical specialization could be considered to be on the very cutting edge of advances in medicine. This, in a way, was a concrete example of the Rush legacy.

And so the exciting years at Rush ended, and at that time it might have seemed forever. Rush had played an extremely valuable role in the history of this country. A great many of the good doctors for the time trained there. Rush Medical College enjoyed a century of eminence and was a leading center for training physicians, a record not many could claim. With its closure, Chicago and the nation suffered a significant and almost complete loss of the traditions of a unique and outstanding institution for almost two generations.

The mechanics of separation proceeded when the university returned to Rush all the property it acquired. A friendly suit was required by law to effect this. The parting was now complete. Lack of funds forced Rush to close its doors to undergraduate medical education for almost another 30 years.[44]

44. Wilbur Post, M.D., "Rush Medical College," *University of Chicago Magazine*, June 1941, pp. 13–14.

4

Building the Foundation

Whatever way the future of medical education at Rush and the University of Chicago might have turned out, it was of little immediate importance to Jim Campbell as he started his formal medical training in early September 1939. He had been accepted to the University of Chicago Medical School and that was that.

The train that brought him to Chicago stopped at the Englewood Station on the South Side, not far from the university campus. Jim would see Chicago for the first time as he went along Garfield Boulevard east toward the Midway campus. This neighborhood was undergoing a dramatic change in racial and ethnic character. Within the previous twenty years, a modest, white, lower-middle class of second-generation immigrants, including many of Irish extraction, was almost totally replaced by blacks, many of whom were impoverished. The migration of blacks from the South had occurred as a result of the labor shortages of World War I. Adjacent areas were experiencing the same changes, and as Jim traveled through Washington Park to the Midway and Hyde Park, he went through what was being called "a changing neighborhood." Eventually almost all of the South Side and much of the West Side of Chicago experienced similar disruptive changes that continued throughout the remainder of the twentieth century. The contrast of Chicago's South Side with the small towns of Rochelle and Galesburg must have been startling to Jim as he was preparing to start his first year of medical school. And the needs of poverty-stricken blacks for health care in Chicago would be an important concern for Campbell later in his career.

The world of 1939 is best remembered as the year Adolf Hitler invaded Poland, on September 1. Since Jim was active in the military reserve officers training program, the events in Europe were important to him. World War II significantly influenced countless millions of people over the next decade, and he would be no exception to this reality. However, his actual participation on active duty would not occur until 1947, when he was assigned as a medical officer at the Edgewood Arsenal in Maryland. And yet, during much of this time, Campbell would be wearing military khaki.

The country was struggling to emerge from the devastation of the Great Depression. Things were hardly any better in 1939 than they were in the early thirties. It took a prolonged jumpstart resulting from a wartime economy for prosperity to return.

The University of Chicago, too, was gravely affected by the Depression and the war. The endowment-rich institution's financial assets were severely reduced, by as much as one-third, from the Crash. The medical education program was particularly hard hit. A new medical school with new buildings was just being completed when financial disaster struck. The original intent of the admission policy to the new Billings Hospital had to be discarded. As the hospital struggled to attract paying patients, the utopian arrangement of determining hospital admission strictly on the basis of the teaching and research value of a patient's medical condition had to be put aside.

At the same time, however, World War II and the world's future were significantly affected by what occurred there on the Midway. In 1942, the first sustained chain nuclear reaction was generated in the double squash courts under the west stands of Stagg Field, located right in the middle of the university campus. The reaction was observed apprehensively by many of the world's leading scientists, including Nobel Prize winners Harold Clayton Urey and

Enrico Fermi. There was concern that a major explosion could occur. And, of course, all of this was going on in a top secret environment.[1]

Now a fully grown young man, Jim Campbell's intensity of expression was evident in his steely blue eyes. He was thin, but not quite wiry, with broad shoulders. Of medium height and brown hair with a brush cut, he walked with a somewhat military bearing. He smiled and seemed intent on pleasing people, but more often he was very serious. Yet the tension in this solemn young man's demeanor was offset by his keen sense of humor.

Campbell started his freshman year with the traditional courses: anatomy (dissection), histology, physiology, and biochemistry. The basic science curriculum in the first two years of medical school had been established in 1902, when Rush and the university first became affiliated.[2] Among the university's notable basic science faculty were physiologist Dr. Anton J. (Ajax) Carlson and bacteriologist Dr. Edward O. Jordan.

Jim's grade performance for the first year was about average for the students of this class.[3] He started his second year with courses in neuroanatomy, physiology, and general pathology, then continued to take the required pathology for the next quarter, and thereafter enrolled in the elective series, Research in Pathology, for three additional quarters in the spring, summer, and fall of 1941.

Pathology is a critical science for medical training because it provides the basis of knowledge to form a link between preclinical or basic science and clinical subjects. The Department of Pathology at the university enjoyed an outstanding professional reputation. It had been formed by Dr. Ludwig Hektoen in 1904 and included Drs. H. E. Lecount and H. Gideon Wells. In the early forties Dr. Paul R. Cannon, himself a Rush graduate of 1925, became the successor to

1. Both Urey and Fermi, as premedical student Charles Larkin Flanagan and many others would later recall, taught basic science at the university with great enthusiasm.

2. The courses had been conducted in the ancient Hull Biological Laboratory Building, located where the sharp-clawed gargoyles glare menacingly from the Cobb Gate on 57th Street.

3. Application of James Campbell to Harvard Medical School, November 12, 1941, courtesy, Registrar's Office, Harvard Medical School, Boston.

Wells to head the department. Cannon's field of expertise was protein nutrition and protein metabolism. Cannon's scientific renown was such that he and four other members of the university medical school faculty were elected to the highly prestigious National Academy of Sciences, an honor generally reserved only for those engaged in basic abstract research.

About the time that Jim was completing his second year, the Pathology Department was suddenly depleted of manpower when many of its resident staff were taken into the armed services. Jim, along with four others students, was asked to stay on in the department for the summer to help out with the workload. Jim agreed and remained in the department for an entire year. It was not unusual at that time for a student to drop out of school for a while to do some special project. Jim did not reenter his class then, which was in its third year, but stayed on in the Pathology Department, where he did the work of an advanced graduate physician resident 3 to 4 years his senior. This work included the performance of several post-mortem examinations. Jim also continued in several additional advanced pathology research courses. Fellow student Robert Wissler was also in that small group; he and Jim became good friends. Wissler eventually succeeded Cannon as chairman of the department.

Jim found in all this the fire to engage his very considerable energy and talent. He was quite highly thought of for his ability in research and research methods and for original thinking. He could well have become a proficient researcher, had he continued in this as his career choice. His enthusiasm for basic research was expressed in the following essay:[4]

> The introduction to Needhams's *Clinical Embryology*, read originally as philosophy, not science, was perhaps the greatest pique to my intellectual curiosity and the initial stimulus to my thinking in a scientific manner. Contacts with various personalities in undergraduate training were extremely important in opening new fields of thought to me, and the

4. Ibid.

advice and guidance obtained from some of the teachers. I have done much toward developing my interest from an observation to an active working plan. In my first year's medical work, I have become interested in experimental pathology and have become more interested in investigation as I have developed some experience in attacking the problems encountered in experimental studies. Due both to reading and to stimulation from my association with Dr. Paul Cannon, I have worked on problems in various phases of immunology and have found that such work creates more knowledge developing not only the field investigated but the investigator as well; and in addition I enjoy it.

All this enthusiasm along with his disarming sense of delight caught the attention of the faculty. Being very bright, Jim impressed the faculty with his high level of confidence, his drive and enthusiasm, his organizational skills and his obvious "ego strengths." While he was not overly argumentative, he could seem contrary when he was testing people.

These evaluations of Campbell were written by an intensely critical full-time faculty committed to developing future leaders and thinkers for medicine; such was the evident mission of the university at that time. They found Campbell to be exceedingly interesting.

These characterizations of Jim would be repeated over and over again throughout the years. What was unusual about his years at the university was his great interest in research because, although he would always stress the importance of research, he became clearly identified with the clinical side of medicine later. However, through this early research experience Jim was always able to discern good research methods and identify poor ones, important but uncommon skills for a medical leader. He had learned this from Dr. Cannon.

Once Jim had started his elective year in pathology in the fall of 1941, he looked into transferring to Harvard Medical School. Just why Jim considered moving is not exactly clear. It is true that the U. of C. in many ways was just getting started as a school although it was now twelve years old. Much faculty energy had to be expended in establishing a totally new curriculum incorporating the university's basic science departments, while at the same time comparisons of quality of instruction were being made between this new approach and the tried and true methods of Rush Medical College, the university's former medical school sibling. The Rush clinical approach was very important even to many of the old guard who remained with the university.

Back in 1935 Campbell had been unable to avail himself of the opportunity to attend Harvard after he graduated from high school. The Knox College faculty family was keeping a close watch on Jim. A few of Knox's brightest students had gone to Harvard, and the Honnold Fellowship for exceptional Knox students to attend either Harvard or Yale was available. Jim's younger brother John had attended Harvard. Knox President Carter Davidson encouraged Jim to work in the direction of transferring to Harvard. Plans of all Americans of Jim's generation were in a state of flux and were being more severely influenced each day by the deterioration of the war in Europe and the initiation of the Selective Service military draft. Once the United States entered the war in 1941, many medical schools required students to attend classes throughout the entire year by eliminating summer vacations.

Campbell and Dr. Cannon got along well together. When Jim told Dr. Cannon about the Honnold Fellowship, Cannon promised to help him, fully realizing that if Jim left it would be a loss because he was doing a very good job as a substitute resident in the department, already severely depleted in manpower. But Cannon was very high on Campbell as a young man of very lofty ideals. He had become a good teacher in Cannon's department, nor did he hesitate to take the initiative or assume responsibility.

Transfer of medical students at the end of the second year to other schools was an established pattern for the time. Western schools, such as those in the Dakotas, Utah, and Nebraska, traditionally provided students for the last two years at Rush. These two-year schools had no organized clinical training facilities to provide for the third and fourth years. Dartmouth, West Virginia, Alabama, and North

Carolina were similarly organized. Harvard took about 25 transferees into their third-year class each year from these and other schools.

Jim applied to Harvard in November 1941 for the third-year class, which was scheduled to start in July 1942. That class had already been going to school without any summer breaks and would finish in December 1943. While continuing his work in pathology as a resident, Campbell took additional special research courses in pathology. He also found time to make rounds with his upperclassmen and faculty in the school, things strictly speaking he was not required to do. He made night rounds on medical floors and gained clinical experience in physical diagnosis and case presentation. He attached himself to the senior medical resident Dr. Charles Spurr, a top-notch physician who went into hematology later at Bowman Gray School of Medicine. Campbell also spent some time on the surgical floors and made a good impression. Dr. J. Garrett Allen, then a junior member of the U. of C. faculty wrote, "Since my arrival here, James Campbell is one of my most able students. He has a pleasing personality, very good judgment and seems emotionally quite stable." Allen eventually rose to become chairman of the Department of Surgery at Stanford. Markle Scholar, upperclassman, and senior medical student Robert Ebert became a role model and lifelong friend for Jim. Ebert went on to Harvard and Boston City Hospital and then returned to the University of Chicago as a faculty member before finally returning to Harvard to become dean.

Because of all his time and study in pathology as a medical student, Jim became board certified in pathology in 1946. Such an achievement was no small thing. Dr. Cannon had given Jim a certificate verifying that he had completed training as a pathology resident, but he was not to show it until after he graduated from medical school.[5]

At the time when Harvard Associate Dean Worth Hale received Jim's application, there was no position open for 1942.

5. Jack Starr interview and Bruce Rattenbury commentary, fall 1973 and 1991; folder 22, Box 4, C97-052, James A. Campbell, M.D., Papers 1924–1983, Record Group 002000, Office of the President, Rush–Presbyterian–St. Luke's Medical Center/Rush University Medical Center Archives, Chicago,

Harvard had already committed to their third-year class. Campbell would have to hope that someone would cancel. Then Dr. Cannon went to bat again and sent a second very strong letter of recommendation and later made additional personal contacts with the associate dean. Hale wrote, "in comparison with Cannon's many other students James Campbell stands out above most in terms of industry, energy, imagination, independence and originality. His strong sense of duty and excellent character show the effects of a sound family background. Campbell also gets along well with people and has many friends."

Finally, on April 21, 1942, Jim heard from Boston and was accepted for the third-year medical school class at Harvard to start on July 1. He was one of the first, possibly the first, from the University of Chicago to make this sort of move. For the time such a change in course would have been considered an upward move. Harvard had taken transfer students mostly from Dartmouth and a very few from other schools, so in this respect his acceptance was unusual. Jim's records would have had to be checked scrupulously, and this change in course during medical school in itself would have stamped him clearly as an unusual person.

Had Jim stayed at the U. of C., he very likely would have pursued a career in research. The school on the Midway was gaining in strength. Its Faculty in Medicine included Drs. George Dick, Walter Lincoln Palmer, C. Philip Miller, Richard Richter, Wright Adams, Henry Ricketts, as well as many bright research-oriented trainees. Had Jim decided to go into surgery (a few thought Jim might have surgical talent), Drs. Dallas Phemister and Lester Dragstedt's surgical research program was outstanding. The Douglas Smith Foundation research assistant, Dr. Ormond C. Julian, was also in the surgical program. Dr. Julian would become a very important part of the merged Presbyterian–St. Luke's Hospitals staff that Campbell organized some fifteen years later.

Campbell was now definitely directed in his career, and, although he was still a student, that he was to become a rising star in medicine should not have come as a great surprise to anyone. After he took on his crash course assignment at Knox and succeeded in getting into medical school, he made an exceptionally good account of himself as a student at the University of Chicago for three years, and then was able to transfer to Harvard, where he also excelled. He was now quite removed from the world of acting and the theater.

Dr. James Schoenberger attended the University of Chicago in the class one year behind Campbell's. He became chairman of the Department of Preventive Medicine at the reactivated Rush–Presbyterian–St. Luke's Medical Center during the time of Campbell's presidency and served as president of the American Heart Association and, in 1987, president of the Rush medical staff. Schoenberger's recollections of Jim are very vivid. He proctored pathology classes and examinations that Schoenberger was taking. Campbell, no question about it, had a presence and was noticed by everyone. As an upper classman, he kept his distance from these sophomore students underneath him. He was not "one of the boys," although occasionally he did kid around.

Jim Campbell had a mission, a serious one, a focus to his life and career that he never lost sight of. Classmate Bob Wissler remembers that Jim's passion for the rebirth of Rush might have gone back as far as the time when the two of them were students. There was a religious zeal in all of this. This highly unusual, high-minded goal was in many ways the same type of commitment that his father, Frank, had brought to the ministry.

Jim's natural acting ability, combined with this powerful sense of religious zeal, made him an individual who rarely went unnoticed. A magnetism was evolving in Jim that enabled him to engage others in his mission, often without question. And Campbell carried these sorts of leadership qualities with him throughout his entire career.

Jim Campbell was at the university all during the time of the breakup of Rush and the university. Rush's last graduation was held on the Midway campus in June 1942, shortly before Campbell moved on to Harvard. Although he achieved some recognition for his medical research work, his orientation very soon began to shift toward the clinical side, and somehow he sensed that he would eventually settle in the Rush clinical tradition.

In a sense, Campbell had to start all over again at Harvard. Boston was different. Many still took quite seriously Henry Adam's claim that Boston was not only a place but a state of mind. It was the hub of the solar system. Money was a good, a highly desirable, a necessary thing, but to make the pursuit of money or even the pursuit of happiness, which Mr. Jefferson laid down as a fundamental right, the chief end of man was to betray the spirit of Boston.[6]

To some extent, this philosophy could be extended to the hidden but well understood attitude of the medical school. Harvard Medical School regarded all its students as gentlemen until proven otherwise. You were not there for a meal ticket or to make money. You were a graduate student in the school of medicine – a very exclusive club.

Here was a new environment, with new colleagues and new friends, and Jim had to demonstrate that he could measure up to the standards of what was considered the country's best, if not the world's best, medical school. Anyone accepted at Harvard, it was assumed, could do the work, but Jim did a little better than that. When he finished his last year there, he graduated cum laude, ranking 25th in a class of 128, and was elected to the national medical honor society, Alpha Omega Alpha. This achievement is even more interesting considering that Jim barely passed organic chemistry in his junior year at Knox, when he was spending more time on advanced courses in Shakespeare and theater barnstorming than learning the formulations of the carbon ring in the laboratory.

All the students in the class lived in the medical school residence, Vanderbilt Hall. Being an outsider, Jim was on the one hand initially ignored by many of the establishment group who had already been there for two years and on the other hand closely scrutinized for any vulnerabilities. To make matters a little worse for Jim, trying to gain acceptance, many of the group at Vanderbilt had been together since college at Harvard across the Charles River in

6. Adams, *The Education of Henry Adams*, American Heritage Library (Boston: Houghton Mifflin, 1918).

Cambridge. Few among them would even admit that they had heard of Chicago, but clearly Rochelle and Galesburg were not familiar names for anyone in this group at Vanderbilt Hall.

Jim's Harvard classmates looked back on those times at Vanderbilt as among the happiest in their lives. Because of the war, the group was together virtually all the time, without even a break in the summer. They became very close. Few were married. Almost all were required to wear military uniform, of either the Army or the Navy.

Classmates Harrison Black, Joe Peden, Herbert Scheinberg, and Bob Glaser all refer back to the Captain Fairbanks story as the most vivid recollection of their days at Vanderbilt. Vanderbilt Hall was the only medical student dormitory in the country at that time, located immediately across the street from the Longwood Commons and the very beautiful Harvard Medical School campus. The student body at Harvard was comprised mainly of those from the privileged classes and from professional and well-to-do families. But there were also those of more modest circumstances with educational and religious backgrounds. Jim was in this latter group. Women were not permitted in the building. Poker games, drinking beer, water fights, and pitching pennies in front of Vanderbilt were indulged in by Jim's class and so memorialized many years later.

> So let the rafters ring with study and wit
> And let alumni everywhere prepare to do their bit
> And let the message spread to the corners of the earth
> That this is the center of gravity, but also a center of mirth.[7]

Suddenly the War Department took over Vanderbilt, the building was turned into barracks, and military rules prevailed. This change in lifestyle was not a happy one for many in the class. The group had to travel by rail to Fort Devens outside of Boston to train. There they learned the ways of army sex hygiene, the suggestion as to the military advantages of profanity, and the question of the advis-

7. Harvard Medical Alumni Spring, 1991

ability of ever volunteering. Forced marches both in the courtyard and outside of Vanderbilt went on for hours. When some murmuring occurred, the group was required to sweep up all the cigarette butts with a broom outside on Longwood Avenue. All the floors in their entire building had to be polished. The latrines had to cleaned, sometimes several times a day, and there was no time for the students to study.

Half of the Vanderbilt Hall complex was assigned to the Army and half to the Navy. Those on the Navy side could look out at night to the Army side where lights had to be out by 8 P.M., while activities on the Navy side went on as usual.

The Army commanding officer was Captain Russell Fairbanks, who, it was rumored, had been turned down for admission to Harvard Medical School. He seemed not to very much like the group of medical students at Vanderbilt and required what many felt was an unreasonable amount of military discipline. It seemed to bother Fairbanks a bit that these students were not drafted into the service like almost everyone else. In exhorting these future doctors on, he insisted on doing things his way so his disciplinary model could turn Harvard Medical School into the best in Boston. This sort of affront did not endear him to the class. A member of the woman's military corps known as the WACS served under Fairbanks, and she was required to do all of his work. Some in the class pointed this out to him and he did not take kindly to such observations. Some of the students had started to show more than a casual interest in the WACS, drawing Fairbank's wrath: "You leave my Wac alone." The students named a cat Fairbanks to express their displeasure and morale sank to a very low level.[8] As Jim records in the school yearbook, Vanderbilt had become a barracks full of sound and fury. A picture of Jim in the yearbook posing as Fairbanks appeared with the

---

8. Twenty years later in the *Twentieth Reunion Report* of the Harvard Medical School Class of 1943B, it was frivolously claimed that Fairbanks the Cat was the first female graduate of Harvard Medical School, although never officially recognized. In the interim of the twenty-year period, attention had been drawn to the scarcity of female students at Harvard Medical School.

caption "Bloody but unbowed." Somehow word of this situation got to the "brass" and shortly Fairbanks was replaced by Major Rosengard. From that point on, things went very well. Rosengard played Glenn Miller records for the boys to march to.

This story about Fairbanks and his pronouncements about making Harvard the best medical school in Boston appeared in an article of the 1944 *New Yorker Magazine.* Jack Graettinger, Jim's life-long friend was asked what his favorite Vanderbilt story or quote was. "They are unprintable, but fondly remembered," Graettinger replied. No doubt, there was some hyperbole in all of this.

Jim clearly made an immediate impression at Harvard and was accepted soon as one of the group. He was much admired for his great sense of humor, his brightness, and his obvious capability. His lifelong friend and classmate, the brilliant but shy Dr. Herbert Scheinberg, put it very simply: Jim was a star. It wasn't long before everyone in the class, many in the school, and many of the faculty knew who Jim was. Scheinberg many years later would have serious discussions with Jim about coming to Chicago to work at Presbyterian–St. Luke's Hospital. Scheinberg was graduated first in his class, magna cum laude.

Jim and his roommate Jack Taylor, also noted for his sense of humor, were very close. Both were elected to membership in the Aesculapian Club, a social club still in existence for promotion of scholarship and fellowship of prominent Boston physicians. Campbell and Taylor wrote the words and music for the follies in 1943 that involved an irreverent spoof of the Harvard faculty. Taylor went on to practice urology with his father at Ohio State University in Columbus.[9]

Jim's lifelong friendship with Dr. Robert Glaser started at Harvard. Glaser came from a well-known medical family in St. Louis and had gone to Harvard College. He went on to achieve distinction

9. Later Campbell was uneasy when Taylor's name came up, concerned that Jack might tell stories about the good old days that Jim would rather no one knew. Jim's suspicions were well founded. By that time Jim was more reserved in his humor and more mindful of his authority, careful not to appear the least vulnerable.

in medical leadership positions for the greater part of five decades; very recently his remarkable career was recognized when he received the Stearns Award for Lifetime Achievement from the New York Academy of Medicine for his work in transforming medical education and biomedical research.[10] Bob served with Jim on a number of national boards, including one that recommended that Rush be reactivated. Bob remembered how popular Jim was at Harvard, right from the beginning. A little serious on the outside, he would say, but with a wry sense of humor.

Although he would eventually end up in medicine, Jim did well in the surgical rotations and was very highly thought of by the surgical faculty. Excellent, industrious, and a clear thinker were his surgical evaluations from the noted Dr. Charles Mixter. Bob Glaser and Jim took a four-week externship at Beth Israel Hospital during their senior year. They took on the protective coloring of self-confidence and brashness that seemed appropriate for a surgical setting and had the time of their lives. Mixter's associate, Dr. Jacob Fine, would take extra time to point out to Jim his landmark findings during surgery. This was most unusual for these busy surgeons. They were in awe of this brilliant student, mature beyond his age and high-

10. Dr. Glaser was born in St. Louis, Missouri, and received an S.B. degree from Harvard College in 1940 and an M.D. degree magna cum laude from the Harvard Medical School in 1943. Trained in internal medicine at Barnes Hospital, Washington University Medical Center, and the Peter Bent Brigham Hospital (Harvard Medical School), he began his research career as a National Research Council Fellow in the Medical Sciences at Washington University, joining the faculty in 1949 and rising in the academic ranks to associate professor of Medicine and associate dean. Subsequently, he served as vice president for Medical Affairs and dean of the Medical School at the University of Colorado, as professor of Social Medicine at Harvard and president of the Affiliated Hospitals Center, a consortium of Harvard teaching hospitals. From 1965 to 1970, Dr. Glaser was vice president for Medical Affairs and dean of the Medical School at Stanford, leaving that post to become vice president of the Commonwealth Fund, then president and CEO of the Kaiser Family Foundation, and director for Medical Science and a trustee of the Lucille P. Markey Charitable Trust. In addition, Dr. Glaser served on various corporate boards including those of the Hewlett-Packard Company, the Equitable Life Assurance Society, and the First Boston Corporation among others. He was a charter member of the Institute of Medicine of the National Academy of Sciences, chairman of the Executive Council of the Association of American Medical Colleges, the recipient of numerous honors, and has received ten honorary degrees.

ly original in his thinking. Campbell had a way of impressing those senior to him, such as faculty and teachers, and he would continue to be successful in those kinds of encounters in other situations throughout his career. Campbell's brilliance at times could be so overwhelming that his senior colleagues were actually almost intimidated by him.

Jim had his moments in obstetrics and gynecology. He and Jack Taylor delivered babies at home, and not too adeptly. In spite of all the preparations for delivery learned in the classroom, the visualization of sudden crowning, along with the showering of generous quantities of fluid from both apertures of prospective mothers, was a bit much. Ob-gyne would not be in Jim's future planning. He did better than he thought, however, as he was elected to the Stork Club, an honorary group formed of notable medical students who had successfully completed their obstetric rotation, according to the yearbook, but in fact it was a social drinking club. The photograph of the Stork Club in the 1944 *Aesculapiad* showing each member with his hands positioned in preparation for performing a pelvic examination quite accurately depicts the mischievous nature of this group.

There were other clubs at Harvard, and Jim was in almost all of them, Alpha Omega Alpha, the Boylston Society, and Kappa Eta Pi, the honorary society for contributors of the *Aesculapiad*, the medical school yearbook. Jim, along with classmates John Nemiah and William Pollack, wrote the entire 1943–44 edition. So it was Knox College all over again for Jim.

Even before Harvard, Jim had intimations that internal medicine would be his chosen field. And in Boston, Jim trained under some of the world's most renowned men in the field of medicine, both as a student and later as an intern and resident. First and foremost, he had the makings of a good solid level-headed doctor. He got along well with patients, he could summarize their complaints clearly to his instructors, and he advised patients in a very reassuring manner. At the same time his knowledge of experimental immunology and pathology research caught the attention of several of the faculty. During his medicine rotation Jim's work impressed the hematologist, Dr. William Castle, at Boston City Hospital, where Jim would later spend three years after medical school training as an intern, resident, and finally a Thorndike Fellow.

The Harvard faculty claimed many famous physicians, and Jim was exposed to all these great men: Dr. John Enders in Bacteriology, who was awarded a Nobel Prize, along with two others, for isolating and cultivating the polio virus; Drs. Tracy Mallory, Shields Warren, and Sidney Farber in Pathology, as well as Dr. Granville Bennett, who later would work with Jim back in Chicago; Drs. Paul Dudley White, Fuller Albright, and Joseph Aub in Medicine; Drs. Oliver Cope, Robert Gross, and Leland McKittrick in Surgery; and many others who established Boston and particularly Harvard as the nation's leading medical center.

During the 1940s and 1950s, when confronted with medical problems of a particularly difficult kind, doctors looked to Boston as the source for answers. The "Boston school" referred to a group of institutions that were mainly affiliated with Harvard, including Massachusetts General Hospital, Peter Bent Brigham Hospital, Beth Israel Hospital, Boston City Hospital and Thorndike Memorial Laboratory, Boston Lying-in Hospital, and Boston Children's Hospital. The Case Reports of the Massachusetts General Hospital, which appeared each week in the *New England Journal of Medicine* were widely read by many students, interns, residents, fellows, and practicing physicians throughout the country. Boston, along with Baltimore, also established a tradition, particularly in medicine, of full-time appointees to head many of the departments in medicine, medical specialties, and to some degree surgery. This tradition was to be established for the first time back at Presbyterian Hospital in Chicago after World War II by individuals who trained in the Harvard-Boston system.

John Nemiah was another of Jim's many good friends. Later they interned together at Boston City Hospital. John related the story that while he, Campbell, and several others were still third-year medical students, they were recruited for emergency duty in November 1942, to help in the care, in any way they could, of the enormous number of severely burned victims of one of Boston's and our nation's most severe disasters, the Coconut Grove Fire. The fire, which occurred during a football banquet celebration, made newspaper headlines throughout the country. Hundreds died. Among the victims listed was a James Campbell, and when Jim's parents read of this back in Rochelle, they were, of course, frantic. They tried unsuccessfully to reach their son for several days. Jim didn't know the reason for their concern, so finally when Frank Campbell was able to find him, his family was greatly relieved. Jim reassured his parents, quoting from scripture, "Ye shall always have the poor with ye."

Jim's sense of humor was a great solace to his classmates as they struggled to learn some of the practical ways of medicine in their third and fourth years: "Most of us were spending our mornings in working up patients. People seemed to come in with almost every complaint, and our diagnoses were most ambitious. However, blood smears seemed to look less and less like leukemia, urine analyses revealed fewer and fewer casts; and we gradually began to blame cancer less and bad liquor more. It was interesting to find ourselves recommending the same vitamins that the LMD [local physician] had prescribed, to learn that little children who wet their beds could be cured by putting gold stars on their calendars following uneventful nights, and that menopausal females got phenobarbital in spite of all 'Albright's diagrams.'"

Many in Jim's class went on to excel in medicine. Gifted surgeon Harry Southwick became chairman of the Department of Surgery at Rush many years later. Jim's good friend Frank Trobaugh trained in both pathology and internal medicine at Boston City Hospital Thorndike Memorial Laboratory, served a stint in private practice in St. Louis, and joined Jim in Chicago as director of hematology in 1954, when Jim became chairman of medicine at Presbyterian Hospital. Eugene Poutasse continued his training in surgery in Boston and eventually pioneered and developed surgical techniques for the treatment of reno-vascular hypertension at Cleveland Clinic. Poutasse's work gained him worldwide fame. Faculty member endocrinologist Bob Williams was another good friend of Jim's. He later moved on to head the Department of Medicine at the University of Washington in Seattle. His leadership resulted in that department's elevation to an elite status. Bob tried to recruit Jim to head the cardiology program at Washington later in 1949.

Jim's good friend and classmate Joseph Murray probably would have to be considered the most accomplished of the class of 1944 (43B as they were called). As the friendly, down-to-earth Dr. Murray remembered about his class, there were no cars available at the time because of rationing so the group often rode bikes and the train together. They would go to the Ipswich beach for beer and poker and four-part barbershop quartet harmony.

Dr. Murray stayed on in Boston for his surgical training at Peter Bent Brigham Hospital and eventually became a plastic surgeon. He also was fully engaged in research at Brigham with a team that included Dr. John Merrill and Dr. Hartwell Harrison. In the late 1940s and early 1950s, a crude but workable artificial kidney had been developed at Brigham, but very little progress in the animal laboratory toward developing techniques for kidney transplantation was being made. The group was startled to learn that a human kidney had been successfully transplanted by a Dr. Lawlor in Chicago on the South Side at Little Company of Mary Hospital. This stimulated the Brigham group to perform nine cadaver donor kidney transplants to humans who were uremic and on dialysis. After the ninth transplant, it was learned that the report from Chicago had been a mistake, and the result had been retracted by the author in a subsequent publication. However, the transplanted human kidneys did a good deal better than the laboratory animal kidneys did. Two of the transplants survived for more than seven months. One explanation for the failure rate was that the immune system of the recipient was suppressed as a result of chronic illness.

Then in 1954 a uremic terminally ill patient was referred to Brigham. The patient had a healthy identical twin. It had previously been established that tissue grafts could be tolerated between individuals who had been exposed to donor cells in utero, and it was postulated that shared tissue such as a kidney from an identical twin might be successfully transplanted and might survive in the sick uremic patient. Clinically it had been established in Switzerland that skin grafts could survive between identical twins, whereas they would not between any other individuals. On December 23, 1954, Dr. Murray successfully transplanted the donor twin's kidney, removed by another member of the team, Dr. J. Hartwell Harrison, into the sick uremic patient. The transplanted kidney began to function immediately, and the patient lived in relatively good health for many years until the original kidney problem began to develop in the transplanted kidney. Dr. Murray established that surgical transplantation of the kidney was a technically feasible procedure and Murray was awarded the Nobel Prize in Medicine for this work, the performance of the world's first successful organ transplant.

Jim and his associates concluded the yearbook *Aesculapiad* with this thought: "This then is our myth; and our class, born of chance out of Harvard. Passing through the canal of three, if not four years of medical school, rotated by the promontories of the armed services, we were delivered by the grace of God, MD's and commissioned officers. God Bless our Alma Mater – may her lacerations heal."

There was no such thing as an intern matching program at that time. The selection process for both the student and the training hospital could be somewhat random and disorganized. However, both Harvard Medical School Service at Boston City Hospital and Columbia Presbyterian Hospital in New York City were interested in recruiting Jim. He chose "City," as it was called. The formal name for the internship program was the Harvard Medical Unit of the Second and Fourth Services at the Boston City Hospital.

Jim's class received their diplomas in December 1943. Virtually the entire class, which was all male, was in military uniform. Traditionally the ceremony was held on the lawn in the medical school quadrangle on the medical school campus. Facing the Commons opposite Vanderbilt Hall were the buildings of the remaining group, including the back of the beautiful medical school building. The front of this one hundred year old building, with its marble columns facing Shattuck Street, looks almost brand new today.

In addition to Campbell, many of the graduating Harvard classes from the forties eventually joined the staff of Presbyterian–St. Luke's Hospital in Chicago and included Louis Selverstone, John

Graettinger, Frank Trobaugh, Carl Hedblom, Robert Carton, William Shorey, Harry Southwick, and Henry Apfelbach.

In 1978, at the thirty-fifth reunion of the class of 1943B, in order to draw attention to and satirize a bit the changes that occurred over the ensuing years, Jim's classmate and friend John Nemiah described his medical school experience as having been received under the antiquated curriculum of anatomy, physiology, and bio-chemistry, rather than the modern one of business practice, person-nel practices, systems theory, and law. The old aim of providing patient care, thank goodness, would be replaced by a growing body of statutes which carefully defined such matters as the indications for treatment and the type of treatment to be employed, decisions that had previously been left to the arbitrary and capricious judgment of members of the self-serving medical profession.[11]

Harvard classmates John Nemiah and Bill Daughaday, along with Jim, were selected for the highly competitive internship training program at City. There were only sixteen selected out of two hun-dred who applied. There was no break after graduation. Jim received his diploma from Harvard on December 23, 1943, and started his internship at Boston City Hospital, Harvard service on January 1, 1944. The internship year had been reduced to nine months because of the war. Daughaday and Campbell were assigned responsibility for the entire Harvard services their first night of duty, New Year's Eve, starting at midnight. The outgoing groups of house staff were occupied with the traditional festivities of observing both the end of the internship year and New Year's Eve. So Bill and Jim were very apprehensive, as they were more or less totally on their own. Campbell and Daughaday were inundated with victims of the influenza epidemic and South Boston's weakness for alcohol. They managed to survive the night, and, despite a few mishaps, the patients survived as well.[12] John Nemiah, who served on the staff of

11. Harvard Medical School, 1943–1978, Thirty-fifth Reunion Report, Boston, Massachusetts, edited by John C. Nemiah, M.D.

12. Maxwell Finland and William B. Castle, *The Harvard Medical Unit at Boston City Hospital* (2 vols., [Charlottesville:] Distributed by the University Press of Virginia for the Francis A. Countway Library of Medicine, Harvard Medical School, Boston, 1982–83), p. 190.

both Harvard and Boston City many years later, remembered what an excellent intern Jim really was. He was extremely bright and very hard working. And yet through all the intensity of this time, Campbell would spend what leisure time he had reading detective stories. He didn't have to read medical journals more than once, since he remembered everything he read.[13] Dr. William Daughaday, originally a native of Winnetka, Illinois, moved on later to St. Louis, where he became a distinguished endocrinologist at Barnes Hospital and the Washington University Medical Center and eventually would serve as editor of the prestigious medical publication, *The Journal of Clinical Endocrinology and Metabolism*. In spite of his research interests, he was also regarded as an excellent clinician.

The life of the house staff at Boston City was rigorous. Almost unbearable work burdens were imposed on these trainees, and the stress level was extremely high. Two interns were assigned to a forty-bed ward. Their work was supervised by an assistant resident. The few medical students who were permitted to assist in the care of a few patients weren't much help because they needed time to study their cases. The interns were responsible for everything. All the patients were very sick. Ninety percent had infections: pneumonia, tuberculosis, general sepsis, and complications of these conditions. In the winter, the patient load vastly increased. Cots were crowded into the wards and corridors. Boston City refused admission to no one. There might be five to seven new admissions per day and the intern was responsible for carrying out a complete history and physical examination and for performing all the necessary laboratory studies by himself. A full resume of the patient's condition was required to be presented at rounds the following morning, completely written up in academically acceptable prose. The blood was drawn by the intern, and if transfusions were needed, the intern typed and cross matched, filtered and administered the blood. There were no technicians after 5:00 P.M. Daily blood counts and urine analyses were required on many patients and on all patients who were on new antibacterial agents like the sulfonamides. This, too, was the intern's

---

13. Finland and Castle, *The Harvard Medical Unit at Boston City Hospital,* p. 554.

responsibility. Use of the new wonder drug penicillin was just starting although explicit written permission for its use was required from
Washington. Those in the armed forces took top priority.

The interns considered their general status in the hospital to be
a step below that of the elevator operators. So it seemed even the medical students outranked them. Rounds started just after dawn, and
interns were on call every other night and every other weekend. There
was no time for sleep on night call, and they kept themselves going by
gulping down large quantities of coffee. Occasionally they administered intramuscular caffeine to each other at three or four in the morning. They managed to change clothes and shower every other day.
There was no time in between. The interns received no salary.

The pyramid system for appointment and selection of house
staff officers was still in effect at BCH, but eventually it was phased
out. The system was essentially to select for the next step or the next
year only a fraction of those who would be eligible to move up.
Many very good interns and residents did not make it and had to go
elsewhere or move on to other specialties to receive their training.
Part of the evaluation process for promotion involved the assessment
by the house officer above the level for which the trainee was hoping to be selected. Jim Campbell survived this system and was considered an "Iron Man" under the constant scrutiny of his senior
peers. When he achieved a certain elevation he also wielded authority. The dialogue among the trainees was very much more severe
than is the case today. Campbell was an excellent teacher, knowledgeable, incisive, very effective, and reliable. But interns trembled in
the presence of their senior peers, and the tone of the discussions
was much less confrontational than is the case today. The intern was
at the bottom of the pyramid system. "Perhaps" was not a widely
used expression. The answer was "yes sir" or "no sir." Campbell was
an outstanding role model and highly revered, but at the same time
he was feared. Like many others, he seemed omniscient, dominant,
and demanding, insisting on absolute loyalty and obedience.[14]

14. Personal communication, Dr. Walter Abelmann October 3, 2001.

And yet, these trainees made it and forged a bond like that of combat veterans. Each year as one advanced to assistant resident, senior resident, and so on, the number of patients under one's responsibility increased. Lou Selverstone was an intern under Jim Campbell, now an assistant resident. His demands for excellent patient care required almost complete perfection. There were no alibis. Campbell could get exasperated, however. On one occasion, he decided to stop giving blood to an old cirrhotic patient with bleeding esophageal varices, a condition frequently associated with alcoholism. Forty-five pints of blood had been administered and the blood bank was running out of supply. Immediately the patient stopped bleeding and left the hospital apparently a reasonably well man.

But the care of the patient was learned in the only way it could be. These young men learned how to look after sick patients in the very real world of life-threatening illness with all its accompanying chaos. There was, and still is, no other way. Their experiences would be the basis for a long and worthwhile career of service to their patients. These rigorous days of training would never be forgotten.

And Campbell, along with many of his fellow trainees, managed through all of this to donate a pint of blood occasionally. Twenty-five dollars was not easy to come by in those times.

All these trainees kept in touch in one way or another throughout their professional careers. There was that special feeling that the guys did it on their own. And there was also a friendly contempt for those Harvard trainees at Massachusetts General Hospital and Peter Bent Brigham Hospital, where less direct and more supervised training was the rule.

From January 1944 to July 1946, Jim Campbell spent all of his time in the service of Boston City Hospital and Thorndike Memorial Laboratory, first as an intern, then a resident and finally a fellow. It was here, more than anywhere else, that Jim's philosophy of medicine and medical education was formed. BCH, or City, in the mid-forties was at the pinnacle as an institution for training and research. It enjoyed equal renown with its sister Harvard institutions, Peter Bent Brigham Hospital and Massachusetts General Hospital. In the early twenties within BCH the world-renowned Thorndike Laboratory for Research was founded. And Harvard took over the responsibility for the care of patients as the Second and Fourth Medical Services at the City.

The hospital under the leadership of Mayor James Michael Curley was designed to take care of the medically indigent of Boston and was located in and adjacent to wards of the political constituency of the Boston Democratic party. The parsimonious Brahmins of Boston were not at all enthusiastic about the establishment of an institution that produced both municipal jobs and higher taxes. John "Honey Fitz" Fitzgerald, President John Fitzgerald Kennedy's grandfather, visited the hospital weekly as a ward boss, and this essentially political municipal hospital was regarded as one of Mayor Curley's greatest political triumphs. Yet, paradoxically, it is difficult to overestimate the value of the contribution of the city of Boston to clinical research and all that went on there. And it is so acknowledged by Boston medical historians.

It was at BCH during the great influenza epidemic of 1918 that the pneumococcal pneumonia antiserum was developed. Fatalities from influenza were shown to be caused by the pneumococcal pneumonia organism. The Thorndike Laboratory for Research was then established under Harvard sponsorship; its first director was Dr. Francis Peabody, who had trained in Boston, Baltimore, Berlin, and New York. Under Peabody's strong direction and that of his successors, Drs. George Minot, William Castle, and Maxwell Finland, Thorndike and BCH became the world's leading center for clinical medical research. The Boston School, as it was called, influenced medical training and research all over the world and at one time was responsible for the placement of over 25 percent of the medical school department chairmen and deans in the United States. Boston City and Thorndike were often referred to as the incubator of academic medicine for the country and known by many as the Harvard school of clinical laboratory medical science.

Francis Peabody, the author of the medical classic "The Care of the Patient," stated his beliefs: There should be no inherent reason why the professional standards of the public institution should be in any sense inferior to those of a private institution. "The secret in the care of the patient is in caring for the patient." He believed that all doctors, regardless of whether they were carrying out investigations in the laboratory, should have clinical responsibilities. The meeting place for all those involved was the patient's bedside and the ward. He set a remarkable example of the coexistence of medical research and the healing art.[15] This was the essence of Thorndike and the meaning of the role of a research laboratory in a clinical setting. Boston City and Thorndike attracted many people for training from other leading medical schools and centers throughout the world as a result of this.

Campbell worked closely with Drs. Minot, Castle, and Finland and was a guest on several occasions at the Minot home in Bar Harbor, Maine. One of Jim's most treasured possessions was an 1860 medical book authored by Oliver Wendell Holmes and signed, "To Jim Campbell, a Very Merry Christmas, from George Minot, December 25, 1944."

Minot was a frail youngster from a prosperous Boston family, a Brahmin. Somehow, despite his fragile health, Minot was able to get through Harvard Medical School and acquire additional training in Europe. He was also an amateur naturalist, with an interest in botany. In 1921, at the age of thirty-six, Minot almost succumbed to severe diabetes. In 1922, his life was saved when he became one of the first recipients of insulin under the care and supervision of Dr. Frederick Banting, the discoverer of insulin. Through the remainder of his life, he was maintained on a near-starvation diet. During all this time, while conducting clinical research at Thorndike, he was a great inspiration and attracted a strong staff. And in 1934, along with Dr. William Murphy of Harvard and Dr. William Whipple of Rochester, he was awarded the Nobel Prize for Medicine and Physiology for work on the development of an effective treatment for pernicious anemia, heretofore a fatal disease. Minot and Boston City–Thorndike were the darlings of Boston medicine.

15. Francis W. Peabody, "The Care of the Patient," *Journal of the American Medical Association* 88 (1927): 880.

Minot insisted, in spite of his own recognition as a "specialist," that all physicians view the patient as a whole and be involved in general medical practice. Doctors like Minot were part of a generation of physicians who, by their conduct, left an indelible imprint on their students and trainees, to whom they were figures larger than life. This was a time of heroes in medicine.

Some of the great leaders of medicine, Drs. William Castle, Chester Keefer, Soma Weiss, Maxwell Finland, and William Hale Ham, all trained under Minot. Dr. Castle, a giant of twentieth-century advances in clinical research in both medicine and hematology,[16] succeeded Minot as head of Thorndike. Castle's personal dedication to his work along with his modest ways endeared him to many of the trainees and in the eyes of many, his stature exceeded even that of Minot. Harvard recently established five honorary societies within the medical school for students to be assigned: the William Castle Society, the George Peabody Society, the Oliver Wendell Holmes Society, the Walter Cannon Society and the Harvard-MIT Society.[17]

Dr. Castle helped guide Jim on his career after he left Boston and many years later was a visiting professor at Presbyterian Hospital when Campbell was Chairman of the Department of Medicine.

Russian-born and Boston public school–educated, Maxwell Finland became a household name to all physicians in the middle third of the twentieth century, as America's leading expert on the use of sulfa and penicillin and other antibiotics in the treatment of infectious diseases.

The Harvard Boston City influence would continue to have an important bearing on Campbell's future. Dr. S. Howard Armstrong was a visiting physician assigned to the Harvard services at City at the time Jim was serving his residency. He was probably the best known of all the many young physicians affiliated with Harvard in the forties. In addition to being a brilliant and charismatic medical leader, a good solid teacher, and a very bright clinician, Armstrong

16. *Harvard Medical Alumni Bulletin,* Spring, 1991, Recollections at Memorial Church, Dr. William Castle, September 12, 1990, Harvard Medical Alumni Association, pp. 16–17.
17. Personal communication, Dr. David Fedderman, October 3, 2001

had a keen interest in psychiatry. He came from a prominent New York family, attended Princeton and Harvard Medical School, served his internship and residency at Columbia, and eventually returned to Harvard. From 1942 to 1947, he had been the recipient of the National Research Council Welsh Fellowship, an award made to a handful of doctors in the forties who showed exceptional promise for medicine. Armstrong was also selected to be a Junior Harvard Fellow, which provided the recipient financial support in any field of study of his choosing for three years. With this, Armstrong elected to work in the physical chemistry laboratory at Harvard under Dr. E. J. Cohn. Through this experience Armstrong developed a strong interest in plasma proteins and was involved in the process of separating blood products like plasma and platelets, which had life-saving implications for the wounded during World War II. This field of study was truly leading-edge technology for the time.

Armstrong was such a star that his flamboyant and eccentric life style was usually overlooked. He played music so loud in his apartment that his neighbors complained. He would sport old pants held up with a clothesline and, along with this, wear tennis shoes to the hospital. During the winter in Boston, he would ride around in his convertible with the top down, smoking a big cigar in his raccoon coat and frayed Princeton club tie. He was regarded as a kind of a crown prince.

After the war, when Armstrong accepted an offer to come to Presbyterian Hospital in Chicago to head the department of medicine, he recruited Jim Campbell to join him to help rebuild the department and develop a cardiac catheterization program.

There were many other Boston City Harvard doctors of that era who also settled in Chicago. Jack Graettinger, a senior student on Jim's service when Jim was an assistant resident at City, would eventually be recruited by Campbell as his replacement as chief of cardiology when Jim moved up to be department chairman at Presbyterian Hospital in 1954. Others with connections to Presbyterian or St. Luke's, even before Campbell's arrival, included Dr. Richard Capps and Dr. Norman Roberg, and later on Dr. Richard Carleton and Dr. Joseph Messer. Dr. David Cugell, another Harvard

Boston City protégé, joined the faculty at Northwestern University Medical School and went on to head its Section of Pulmonary Medicine.

Jim met Elda Crichton during his third year at Harvard while Elda was teaching school in Brookline. Elda was raised by her grandparents when her mother died in childbirth; she attended Wheelock College in Boston. Elda's grandfather, an immigrant from Scotland, started out working in the coal mines in Johnstown, Pennsylvania, and eventually the Crichton family owned the mine as well as a profitable ice business. The family became prominent in literary circles and remains so today. Kyle Crichton is a prominent writer and the head of the publishing firm of Little Brown.

Jim and Elda were married in 1944 when Jim was an intern. They left Boston after his residency was completed and moved on to start a new life together in a world that was no longer at war.

5

Rising Star

Edgewood Arsenal in Maryland was a major center for chemical warfare where bright physicians who excelled in science were often assigned. So, in 1946, Jim and Elda were off to live in a small home near the base. His old friend and classmate Herb Scheinberg, after having served his internship and residency at the Peter Bent Brigham, was also assigned to Edgewood. Herb spent many hours with Elda and Jim in their home and vacationed with them on furloughs. Jim and Elda were sporting a red convertible, a rare commodity in those days.

After their years of grueling duty as interns and residents, Campbell and Scheinberg, although still in uniform, found an opportunity to relax. They enjoyed playing with model trains on the floor and spent hours at it. Jim's banter consisted mostly of clever aphorisms: "Even if you are on the right track, but just stand there, you may get run over" (from Will Rogers).[1] Herb did not buy into this form of

---

1. Index card quotations, James A. Campbell, M.D., Box 35, File 4, C97-052, James A. Campbell, M.D., Papers 1924–1983, Record Group 002000, Office of the President, Rush–Presbyterian–St. Luke's Medical Center/Rush University Medical Center Archives, Chicago, Ill.

expression and insisted that Jim be more professional in his conversation. Jim would reply, "Chance favors the prepared mind" (Pasteur, inscribed on the ceiling of the entrance of Vanderbilt Hall at Harvard).

Campbell often carried a set of index cards with aphorisms and well-known expressions, ready for use at any time. Using his acting skill, Campbell sometimes spoke the words in a matter of fact way and sometimes with the same conviction that his father, Rev. Frank Campbell, would have used in delivering them to his Presbyterian congregation in Rochelle.

By this time Jim had passed through the beer-drinking stage of his Harvard Medical School years. For the *Aesculapiad* yearbook, Jim and his editorial staff were pictured in their army uniforms sitting at a table covered with beer bottles. After this time, probably when he started his internship, Jim became what he would be notoriously celebrated for later, a teetotaler. "Jim would take you out to dinner and offer you a martini," Scheinberg recalled. "Then he would sit back and make you feel like you were sinning when you drank it. He never, however, would say anything overt to force his Presbyterianism on you. Yet one felt at times like you were in the presence of the last day of judgment." This pattern of behavior perhaps suggested that during the early years of medical school Jim might be rebelling against his strict Presbyterian upbringing with its sense of morality and rigid discipline and now that he was maturing he was reverting back to a certain structure and rigidity.

Edgewood was considered a somewhat cushy assignment. Colonel John Wood, the commanding officer for the base, was so impressed with Campbell's talent for organization and his ideas about getting things done that he made Jim his right-hand man. Jim essentially ran the entire Army base. His title became Executive Officer of the Medical Division of the Army Chemical Center, Edgewood Arsenal, Maryland (Clinical Research Center). "Jim's presence even then evoked a sense of military bearing," Scheinberg recalled. "He simply took command and he was able to sell his talents so well to those in authority."

A military ship from Europe loaded with poisonous mustard gas arrived one day in Chesapeake Bay near the Edgewood arsenal.

The ship had been denied docking privileges at several other ports. During the ship's transit across the Atlantic, some leakage developed in the storage casing for the gas, so that gas was found in several areas of the boat. While authorities were trying to figure out just what to do about this problem, Jim and Herb were assigned the duty of "watching" the ship. This meant that for several days in the hot, humid summer of 1947, they would have to don heavy protective clothing, board the ship, and stay there for several hours at a time. They were also required to wear gas masks. All this was, of course, top secret at the time. Finally, the predicament was settled when a location in the southern U.S. was found to bury this material.

After they were discharged in July 1947, Scheinberg moved back to Harvard, where he took a three-year award as a Harvard Junior Fellow to study Wilson's disease. Over the years, Herb and Jim kept in close touch and they would get together whenever Jim visited New York, where Scheinberg eventually located. They loved going to the theater. On one of these evenings they went backstage to visit the famous acting duo, Hume Cronyn and Jessica Tandy. In 1948, after seeing Ray Bolger perform in the musical, *Where's Charley*, Jim expressed to Herb his fantasy of dancing down Broadway with a pretty girl on each arm, not noticing his acne-scarred face, and singing "Once in Love with Amy." Scheinberg was a guest at Campbell's well-known and popular medical grand rounds in Chicago many times over the years.

Jim and Elda didn't have to move very far from their home in Maryland, when Jim was appointed a cardiovascular fellow in the research laboratory of Dr. Richard Bing at Johns Hopkins Hospital in Baltimore, just some fifteen miles away. Jim would no longer be required to wear military garb, something he had done off and on for thirteen years going back to his freshman year at Knox College when he served in the ROTC.

Johns Hopkins Medical Center, like Harvard, was one of the world's leading centers for medical advances and research. There had been several interchanges of each center's top physician-scientists during the first half of the twentieth century. The renowned surgeon Dr. Harvey Cushing, considered the greatest neurosurgeon of the twentieth century, was one such individual, having first trained at Hopkins and then moved on to Harvard. Francis Peabody, the founder of the Boston City Thorndike, had some of his training in Baltimore at Hopkins. And while the Campbell team that Jim originally brought to Chicago to reorganize the Department of Medicine later in 1953 was primarily from Boston, there was one exception, the endocrinologist Dr. Theodore Schwartz, who was recruited from Hopkins and Duke.

In the United States many of the rapid advances in medical sciences and research that occurred in the late 1940s and early 1950s were directly or indirectly funded from Washington. The development of cardiac catheterization was just such an example.

The technique of radiographic demonstration of the blood supply of the heart itself, the coronary arteries, had originally been developed in 1929 by Werner Forssmann, a young surgical resident in Eberswald, Germany. He catheterized himself in his antecubital vein (adjacent to the elbow) and safely passed a ureteral catheter into the right atrium of his heart and documented the position by X-ray. This proved that a catheter could be safely passed into the heart. The ureteral catheter is about 18 to 24 inches long and about the diameter of a strand of spaghetti. Even today, the ureteral catheter remains the primary device for the evaluation of the ureter, particularly in patients with urinary tract stones. This technique became the forerunner for intravenous direct access to the general circulation for placement of fluids, drugs, and further monitoring of cardiac function.

The original work was carried out in a completely darkened room as Forsmann positioned himself in front of a mirror across the room so he could see himself while he was being fluoroscoped. In essence the patient was the doctor as he studied his own circulation in mirror image. Forsmann was dismissed from his position in Germany for self-experimentation and nothing further developed from this work for well over a decade.

When the United States became involved in World War II, the government developed a crash program for studies on shock, its physiology, and how to treat it. A number of leading medical institutions were commissioned to do this work and in the process rediscovered the work of Werner Forssmann. Eventually a workable technique for cardiac catheterization was developed. Dr. Andre Cournond and Dr. Richards Dickinson, of Columbia University on the Columbia Bellevue Hospital Service in New York, and Dr. Forsmann were awarded the Nobel Prize for this work. After having been dismissed from his hospital position in Germany, Forssmann continued his interest in self-catheterization, attempting the procedure on himself seventeen times. He eventually switched to urology and later became a country doctor. Cournond also studied himself by cardiac catheterization. About the same time a training protégé of Cournond, Dr. Richard Bing, started doing these studies at Johns Hopkins Medical Center in Baltimore. The support and funding for this pioneer work was undertaken by the noted Hopkins surgeon, Dr. Alfred Blaylock, who, with Dr. Helen Taussig, then applied this technique to the evaluation of blue babies in the mid 1940s. Eventually operative procedures were developed to treat this and other congenital heart conditions.

This important development caught Campbell's attention, and after his discharge he was appointed the Harvey Cushing Fellow in cardiology at Hopkins. Dr. Bing's department and laboratories provided a very open and stimulating environment for Campbell and others from the many medical and surgical specialties who came from all over the country to Hopkins to train. Chicagoan Dr. Margaret Hanlon, then in training and later a pediatric cardiologist, worked with Campbell. Hanlon followed Campbell's career as they both eventually ended up back in the same city. Hopkins surgeon Jack Handelsman was another. The Handelsmans and Campbells became good friends and often vacationed together. Like so many others, Jack liked and admired Jim a great deal. In addition to being very smart, he was very sure of himself and expressed a firm sense of direction and commitment in what he was doing.

So Campbell was introduced into yet another new type of medical environment. And here he also did well. Dr. Bing, who was recently honored for his contributions at Hopkins on the occasion of his ninetieth birthday, remembered Campbell very well: He was an excellent trainee and performed many cardiac catheterization procedures during his year's stay at Hopkins and was the senior author on two of the scientific papers that came out of Bing's laboratory in 1948 and 1949. Campbell was, by that time, clearly considered almost a pure clinician with a flair for organization and administration, not a pure researcher, as Bing hoped he might be.

In May 1948, Campbell's nine-year period of training had come to an end and he was on to his new assignment to work with Dr. Howard Armstrong and to develop a cardiac catheterization laboratory in Chicago at Presbyterian Hospital. In those nine years of formal training, Campbell was exposed to many of the world's most brilliant medical minds. Among Jim's mentors were outstanding educators, Nobel Prize winners, Harvard junior fellows, and many other highly respected clinicians and surgeons. And many of Jim's peers and friends from medical school, internship, residency, and fellowships would also make their mark in their profession. Jim related well to all these individuals, and they held him in very high regard. His star was rising, and a great future career was expected of him.

Much had happened to Campbell since he started his career in 1939. Even for the industrious and highly focused Campbell, the intensity of this nonstop training over so many years would be more than almost anyone could handle. In an ideal world he might have benefited from a little time and space away from it all, a little time to catch his breath so to speak and, in the process, to mature a bit. But just as for millions of others in the world, the time of World War II was extremely disruptive and chaotic, and people simply had to adjust to these realities and keep going.

Campbell developed many good friendships during this time and maintained them throughout the rest of his career. Jim related to his peers quite differently from those colleagues with whom he later worked. He always maintained a certain distance with this latter group, but with Bob Glaser and Herb Scheinberg, he was very easygoing and completely comfortable. His new Chicago colleagues and friends immediately noticed this collegiality with his old school chums. Was it an expression of what was called the Harvard syndrome? By their mannerisms and body language, Harvard people expressed their inner sense of superiority, or so it seemed. And Jim's standard throughout the rest of his career would be Harvard and everything that that implied. Toward the end he once commented, however, that some people go to Harvard and never get over it.

The professional and social life of the Presbyterian Hospital community was something quite new to the Campbells. They had originally intended to live in Park Ridge, a northwestern Chicago suburb where many of the hospital staff were living, but when nothing was found to be available, through a hospital connection, they found a home for rent in the northern suburb of Lake Forest. Jim and Elda liked the community and stayed. Their first two children, Jamie and Bruce, were born in 1949 and 1951.

Jim and Elda's next door neighbors were the Cyrus Adams family and as the Adams and the Campbells got to know each other, Elda and Mary Adams Young, Cyrus's daughter, became lifelong friends. Cyrus Adams, a lawyer, was also a good friend of the prominent New York lawyer Sinclair Armstrong, who happened to be the brother of the flamboyant and eccentric Dr. Howard Armstrong, of Boston City Hospital, who brought Jim to Presbyterian. Soon Jim Campbell became acquainted with George Young, Mary's husband and they too became lifelong friends. George was Jim's first friend in Chicago who was not a doctor. Young, a brilliant lawyer who had availed himself of the opportunity for an education at Yale through the G.I. Bill, had come from a strong educational background: his parents had doctorates from Yale and Wisconsin and had taught in college. The Adams family had served on the St. Luke's Hospital Board for many years, and Cyrus had been chairman at one time. St. Luke's Hospital was, like Presbyterian Hospital, one of Chicago's best-known and most venerable hospitals, dating its founding back even before Presbyterian, to 1864.

George Young was appointed to the St. Luke's Board in 1953 at about the time the board was looking to the future and making long-range plans. Young discussed all of his ideas with Campbell including the idea of merging the two institutions, Presbyterian Hospital and St. Luke's Hospital, long before it became a reality many years later. Jim would say that it was George who had the idea, and George would say that it was Jim. Thus the seeds were planted very early in Campbell's career at Presbyterian Hospital for development and expansion.

The almost immediate entry of the Campbells into the world of Chicago's high social circles and hospital trustees was significant. The original connection came through Dr. Armstrong, Campbell's chief at Presbyterian, whose brother was a good friend of Cyrus Adams, George Young's father-in-law. Elda Campbell fit in very well socially among the elite of Chicago society. She was modest about her affluent background. Jim's good friend and roommate from his Boston City days, Dr. Dick Eckhardt, remembered how apprehensive Jim was about just how he might be perceived in a social sense because of the great disparity in their backgrounds.[2] Elda downplayed these concerns of Jim's very effectively.

At the time of Campbell's arrival, Presbyterian Hospital was in the process of planning for expansion after World War II. It was no longer the major affiliate and teaching hospital of the venerable and oldest educational institution in the state, Rush Medical College. Presbyterian was Chicago's leading hospital but the loss of identification with the now inactive Rush was a blow to the morale of the staff. Rush students, the lifeblood for new ideas and innovation, were no longer present. There was also a perceptible but unspoken sense of humiliation among some over their dismissal by the University of Chicago. However, an equal or greater number of physicians were glad indeed to escape the university's influence, which they regarded as impractical and unrealistic for educating doctors.

In order to maintain a professional university affiliation, Presbyterian entered into a new arrangement with the University of Illinois School of Medicine, its neighbor on the West Side. The affiliation would be clinical so as to allow University of Illinois students in their third and fourth years of medical school to rotate through Presbyterian Hospital for their clinical training. Neither institution entered into any budgetary agreements with the other. And Presbyterian Hospital and Rush would no longer be granting med-

2. Personal communication, Dr. Richard Eckhardt, October 29, 2001.

ical degrees. These rotating students received their diplomas from the University of Illinois.

Presbyterian had incurred a loss of a few important staff members to the University of Chicago and Billings Hospital in the 1930s, particularly younger ones. Additional losses were sustained as Rush physicians moved to other medical centers in Chicago such as those associated with Northwestern and Loyola. And just about the time that plans for developing and incorporating the University of Illinois affiliation into its educational program and recruiting for new staff, the onset of World War II severely disrupted these plans. At that time also, some consideration was given to an affiliation with Northwestern University.

Presbyterian Hospital doctors were recruited as a group during the war, designated the 13th General Unit (later another, the 25th Portable Surgical Unit was also organized). The 13th, one of fifty-two such units organized during the war, served in New Zealand, Australia, New Guinea, the Philippines, and Okinawa. Members of the unit were among the first Americans to enter Japan after VJ Day in September 1945 and set up the first American hospital in Tokyo. At one time the 13th General was composed of more than 25 physicians and 100 nurses, all from Presbyterian. There were also former Rush physicians who had left to go to the University of Chicago in the 1930s in the group. Those Presbyterian staff members who stayed behind on the civilian front, many of whom were very senior, also served heroically, working long hours at the hospital with very restricted support services.

At war's end, many of the nationally recognized and prominent physicians on the staff were nearing retirement, and there was a strong sense within the institution that an infusion of new energy was needed. For some of those physicians returning from the war, the aging of the staff was quite striking. Conflicts then developed because it was difficult for the senior staff to give way to the returning young veterans who demanded more hospital beds and operating time for their patients.

Dr. James Herrick, the first physician to describe coronary occlusion in 1912, was still prominent and active. Even in his later years, Herrick was astute and his appearance was striking. Here was a short slender man with thinning gray hair, a Van Dyke beard and mustache, trimly tailored gray suit and starched collar with cravat. His very presence radiated the Rush tradition. Dr. Earnest Irons, dean of the Rush Medical College from 1923 to 1936, had gone on to become president of the American Medical Association in 1949. The renowned clinical insights and teaching ability of Drs. Irons, Roland Woodyatt, and Ralph Brown were still attracting bright young trainees for the hospital. Dr. Herman Kretchmer, a pioneer in urology, maintained a very active practice. He had served as president of the AMA in 1943. The gifted surgeon Dr. Vernon David had succeeded Dr. Arthur Dean Bevan as chief of a strong surgical department. Dr. David represented the medical staff on the hospital Board of Trustees. But the number of those in the next generation coming along with the promise and potential for achieving national stature had thinned considerably.

The management of the hospital was carried out by a small staff. Hospital superintendent Mr. Asa Bacon would meet with members of the medical staff as well as some trustees. Bacon was just completing over forty years of service to the institution. One of Chicago's most prominent lawyers, Presbyterian trustee Alfred Carton, father of a later Rush faculty member, Dr. Robert Carton, devoted his entire Friday each week to meeting with Bacon and others to provide guidance and advice on problems and policies for the hospital.

In 1946, Carton, Mr. A. B. Dick, Sr., and several other trustees undertook a study of long-range plans for the institution and retained the management consulting firm of Booz, Allen and Hamilton. For a hospital board to take such a step was quite unusual for the time. The trustees, on the one hand, had been through an ongoing controversial struggle with the University of Chicago in the thirties regarding employment of a totally full-time medical staff and the university's demand that the hospital be relocated to the South Side, a dispute that would result in the termination of this forty-four-year-old affiliation. On the other hand, times were changing and many of the eastern medical centers in Boston, New York, and Baltimore now were engaging medical leaders to head their major departments on a full-time basis. The board was anxious to expand the number of top-notch doctors within the institution, and, in 1946 and 1947, after a detailed search, appointed the first full-time doctors to head key departments: Dr. George Hass in Pathology, Dr. S. Howard Armstrong in Medicine, and Dr. Douglas MacFaydean in Biochemistry and Laboratory Services. Armstrong, from Harvard, brought new ideas and attracted many promising new recruits, including Jim Campbell. MacFaydean, from the Rockefeller Institute in New York, worked to develop the laboratory, now emerging as a critical element in modern medicine. These appointments were the first of many such over the years that would result ultimately in the development of Rush University Medical Center as we know it today.

Strong departments of internal medicine and pathology are most important. Most or all of the other hospital departments look to these two for basic scientific and professional support. Internal medicine leads the way for the training in diagnosis, and pathology answers the critical questions with direct tissue assessment of what is going on with the sick patient. These departments would set a standard that the rest of the departments within the institution would have to follow. With the development of medical technology during and after the war, laboratory services were expected to have increasing importance as time went on.

In 1946, Dr. Hass was the first of the appointments as chairman of Pathology and remained in that position until his retirement some thirty years later. A Midwesterner by birth, Hass left his native Iowa for Harvard while he was still a teenager. He was considered a child prodigy and was included in sociological studies of such children that were first carried out in the 1920s. He had to delay taking his internship for one year because he finished Harvard Medical School before reaching the requisite age of twenty-one. For that year, 1929, he stayed at Harvard as a research fellow in physiology.

The Harvard Junior Club of Fellows was started in 1933 by a wealthy benefactor, and Hass was the first physician to be selected. Harvard fellows themselves are the University's Board of Trustees.

Three individuals within the university would be selected each year, and such an individual would receive unlimited financial support for a period of three years to engage in any scholarly endeavor of his choosing. A selectee could come from anywhere at Harvard: humanities, medicine, or any other discipline. After this three-year period, the selectee would be elevated to a Harvard Senior Fellow and participate in the selection process for future junior fellows. There was no degree awarded for this, but the initials J.F. could be placed after one's name. This hugely prestigious award was, of course, highly coveted. Not even the renowned Dr. Harvey Cushing could claim that distinction. Fellows met on a regular basis in Cambridge, to discuss their work and problems as well as future selectees. By 1950, five of the awardees had received Nobel Prizes. Dr. Howard Armstrong was also a junior fellow, as well as Campbell classmate, Herbert Scheinberg.

George Hass remained in Boston for ten years in departments of pathology at Harvard, Thorndike Laboratory, Boston Children's Hospital, and Peter Bent Brigham Hospital. His basic significant scientific work included the first characterization of the chemical composition of amyloid and the description of disseminated herpes simplex infection in the newborn. During his training he worked extensively with surgeon Dr. Harvey Cushing and pathologist Dr. S. Burt Wolbach. Hass then moved on to the New York Hospital and Cornell University Medical School from 1939 to 1942 and then was appointed chief of Pathology at the United States Air Force School of Aviation Medicine. It was here that he designed the program of airplane accident investigation adopted first by the Air Force and later by the Federal Aviation Administration. He also first proposed the development of the ejection seat in military aircraft after interviewing pilots so as to understand the gravitational forces pilots experienced during flat spins, immobilizing them and pinning them to the walls of their cockpits.

After the war, he was offered the chair of Pathology at Harvard, but he declined. His brother, also a physician, had urged George to take the job, offering to help him financially, since salaries for such positions were paltry at that time. Harvard's misfortune turned out to be Chicago Presbyterian Hospital's good fortune. A national reputation for excellence in pathology training was established as evidenced by the fact that twenty-eight of Dr. Hass's first thirty-five trainees became professors and department chairmen.

George Hass was brilliant: he read everything and forgot nothing. His insistence on excellence influenced professional conduct and professional policy throughout the entire institution. In one way or another, virtually all new appointments to chairmanships for all hospital departments needed to be blessed by Dr. Hass. His quiet and modest manner of expressing his insistence on excellence and institutional good were never dismissed or ignored. He was most unassuming about his own accomplishments and his influence.

His days at the Thorndike provided Dr. Hass, a great storyteller, with hours of material, and then he would suddenly change the subject and inquire how your research study was going. He was very perceptive and when you were in his presence, he knew exactly what you were thinking. Yet, he was very kind and loyal. He was an outstanding departmental administrator. Each and every person he hired, from his staff of physicians to the most menial technician, was selected with the idea that the individual would devote his or her entire career to his department. He planned for each and every person to stay. And many did.

Hass served on a number of important national medical committees and headed a study section of the National Institutes of Health for pathology grants, which decided how and to whom large amounts of research funding would be awarded. Yet, many were never aware of this because he did not boast of this sort of thing.

Hass's continued personal commitment to research was his greatest strength as he set an example in motivating his trainees and members of other departments within the institution to develop their own investigative protocols. His work in growth factors and transplantation were well ahead of its time and he was one of the first to use the electron microscope.

George Hass, like Jim Campbell, never quite forgot that he came from Harvard Medical School. There was a sense or a feeling that Hass and Campbell simply had no peers. In many things, perhaps in all things, they knew best. This way of thinking would eventually lead to some problems for Hass. He never had taken his pathology specialty board examination, nor did many of his trainees. Although no one would ever say why publicly, the implication was clear: they didn't need to. On occasion Hass was known to quietly reflect to his associates that we at Harvard didn't read books, we wrote them.

But when the merger of St. Luke's and Presbyterian occurred, the agreement between the two institutions called for all department chairmen to be board-certified. There were other candidates to consider for the merged institutions' departments. So Hass had to be temporarily appointed as chairman of the Research Department within Pathology while he prepared to take his Anatomic and Clinical Pathology Specialty Board examination. Jim Campbell attempted without success to grandfather Hass's position. This humiliation, with its political overtones, was graciously endured by Hass. Dr. Phil Coogan, one of his colleagues, tutored him in preparation for the tests while Dr. Hass was recovering from a mild heart attack. Hass went on to achieve one of the highest grades ever recorded for the examination.

As Hass and Campbell were both very strong minded, they had many conflicts. Hass, the pure scientist, had a tendency to look down on Campbell as too political. In 1964, when Campbell was elevated to the office of President of the newly formed Presbyterian–St. Luke's Medical Center, Hass commented, "Now it's official," the implication being that he was that all along. And in many ways he was entirely correct, for Campbell had by that time established his power and authority throughout the institution and was duly feared by all, except Dr. Hass.

At that time, the Clinical Pathological Conference, or the CPC, was considered the most important component in a teaching hospital's educational curriculum. A case was presented, discussion was then opened to both the attending and the house staff, and finally the autopsy findings of the pathologist were presented. The entire staff attended. Campbell, drawing on his experience conducting autopsies as a student resident at Billings Hospital at the University of Chicago under Dr. Cannon, sometimes challenged Hass's method of conducting post mortem examinations. Campbell after all was board-certified. Both men were department chairmen and in a sense professional competitors. Campbell was a proponent of the professorial method, in which the examination was conducted almost entirely by the teacher. Hass on the other hand was of the Dr. S. Burt Wolbach school, which called for the trainee to conduct the examination as far as he could.

And yet while there was a public image of antagonism, at the same time Hass and Campbell had the very highest respect for each other, but were of very opposite temperaments. Hass was shy and soft spoken. Campbell was quite aggressive and assertive. Hass in his later years would come to regard Campbell as the person most responsible for the medical center's growth and development, and Campbell would say virtually the same thing about Hass. Paradoxically, the gentle and retiring Hass and the pragmatic rough-and-tumble Campbell were very similar in their enduring commitment and efforts for the institution to rise to new levels of excellence. Their focus was exactly the same.

After the war private medical practices expanded and grew. A healthy tension developed between the medical staff of the physicians who conducted these practices and the three new full-time salaried departmental chairmen as each side struggled to adjust to these new realities. At the same time, the staff and the institution were seeing revolutionary breakthroughs in scientific medicine that signaled the beginning of what would be described as medicine's "golden era." Federally funded medical research was clearly in the ascendancy. If science could develop the means of preventing new wars through the development of nuclear weapons, then the hope was that medical science could develop cures for many of mankind's major causes of death and chronic illness. The achievements in medical research were remarkable: the birth of molecular biology, the expansion of knowledge in immunology, and the development of the technique of radio-immunoassay (the use of radioactive materials to detect and measure very small amounts of protein particles, an analytical technique of great importance to medical and biological research).[3] An array of new antibiotics was developed to add to the dramatic introduction of penicillin and sulfonamides that had occurred in the decade before. The polio vaccine, cortisone, and new drugs for the treatment of high blood pressure and certain types of cancer were developed. Cardiac catheterization, the technique that Jim Campbell brought to Presbyterian, was also considered a major breakthrough. A little later on came open heart surgery, organ transplantation, the heart-lung pump, renal dialysis, and the mechanical ventilator. The recruitment of Hass and Armstrong and those who followed would enable Presbyterian to participate in this exciting time and to keep the institution in the forefront of medical advances. This is particularly noteworthy since Presbyterian was no longer a university hospital directly connected to a medical school where the bulk of federal monetary support was being awarded at this time.

Following the war an expansion of residency training for the specialties provided the nation with an abundance of well-trained medical specialists within a relatively short period of time. The Departments of Medicine and Surgery at Presbyterian contributed their fair share to this effort. Dr. Oglesby Paul, a protégé of the famed Dr. Paul Dudley White of Boston, was a leader in cardiology. Dr. Steven G. Economou, one of America's leading surgeons several years later, was a trainee of that era.

The Schweppe-Sprague Nursing School and Residence on Harrison Street was constructed in 1950 and a half century later was razed and replaced with the Robert and Terri Cohn Research Building. A time capsule in the cornerstone of Schweppe-Sprague was opened at the dedication ceremonies of the Cohn building in the year 2000, and a viewpoint of the world of Jim Campbell and Presbyterian some 50 years before could be determined from the records preserved in that capsule. Campbell was an assistant attending under Dr. Armstrong in the Department of Medicine and in

3. Kenneth M. Ludmerer, *Time to Heal: American Medical Education from the Turn of the Century to the Era of Managed Care* (Oxford and New York: Oxford University Press, 1999), p. 146.

some ways low man on the totem pole, just getting started. The trustees were embarking on a $5 million expansion program for buildings and improvements. The construction of Schweppe-Sprague was required in order to replace the older nursing building, which stood in the way for the newly proposed Congress Street Expressway. Expansion and remodeling of the Rawson, Jones, and Murdoch buildings was being undertaken to provide greatly needed space for the growing research and teaching programs. The first artificial kidney in Chicago had been installed recently at Presbyterian, again very much leading-edge technology for the time, just as cardiac catheterization had been.

The demand for beds was extreme. A waiting list of more than one hundred patients and delays of as long as two weeks for hospital admission were common. A new facility to increase bed capacity was planned where the existing Kellogg Building is located, but for six stories, not thirteen as it eventually worked out. It would be several years before that facility was completed, however. The expansion of research facilities was not delayed as it was a high priority for the trustees. Research and an expansion of the teaching program with the University of Illinois Medical School were important to the hospital's leadership community.

The University of Illinois Medical School, Presbyterian's neighbor as well as its affiliate, was headed by the world-renowned leader in clinical research and physiology, Dr. Andrew C. Ivy. Ivy was executive director of the National Cancer Advisory Council and served on many other important national committees. He also served as a member of the Nuremberg War Crimes Trial commission. Ivy was at that time held in the highest esteem professionally. Among the other University of Illinois faculty leaders of that time were Dr. Warren McCullough in the Department of Neurology and Dr. Warren Cole in the Department of Surgery. McCullogh did not stay long at Illinois, but Dr. Cole played a major role in the development of surgery both in Chicago and throughout the nation.

The Illinois Medical Center District, a combined private and governmental effort, was organized to develop the area in and around Presbyterian on the near West Side. It was given the power to buy and clear slum properties. The purpose of all this was to restrict growth of this entire area to the development of medical facilities and in the process identify this entire area as the world's largest medical center. In addition to Presbyterian and the University of Illinois, the district included Cook County Hospital and all its adjacent facilities, Loyola University Medical and Dental School, the University of Illinois Dental School, Chicago Medical School, the West Side Veterans Administration Hospital, and the Medical Center YMCA. As it turned out, some but not all of these expectations would materialize. Both Loyola and Chicago Medical School left the area to relocate. Presbyterian and the University of Illinois underwent major expansions over the next half century, and Cook County Hospital continued serving the underprivileged but only in very antiquated facilities.

It was not anticipated that the area around the West Side Medical District would deteriorate and become riddled with crime, poverty, racial tension, and general neglect. The forced displacement of middle-class neighborhoods caused by the construction of the Congress Expressway and later the University of Illinois Circle Campus added significantly to these problem. Although they could have moved away from the area, Presbyterian Hospital and later Presbyterian–St. Luke's Hospital decided to stay and, in doing so, helped stabilize the area. Patients from all over the metropolitan area continued to come to Presbyterian for their medical care and the medical center went on to become one of the city's largest employers.

Students in their third and fourth year at the University of Illinois rotated through Presbyterian for their internal medicine clerkships. Dr. William Deutsch was then a University of Illinois student rotating through Presbyterian.[4] Everyone was impressed by the teaching services of Howard Armstrong and Jim Campbell and the rotation through their services was highly sought after. The training

4. Dr. William Deutsch later became chairman of the Department of Ophthalmology at the reactivated Rush, and his son, Dr. Thomas Deutsch, succeeded his father in that position, until 2003, when he was appointed dean of Rush Medical College. Dr. William's father, Dr. Emil Deutsch, had been an ophthalmologist at the old St. Luke's Hospital.

both academically and clinically was top notch. Armstrong and Campbell along with another Harvard recruit, Dr. Louis Selverstone, were known as the triumvirate. Word of the serious, highly focused professional rounds and conferences taking place at Presbyterian spread like wildfire in the medical student community throughout the city. The flamboyant Armstrong knew the medical literature so well that he could quote a reference, sometimes several, on a case being presented without any previous preparation. Armstrong was also an astute clinician and a good solid well-balanced doctor. Campbell was similarly regarded. Dr. John Long, then a young obstetrician and gynecologist, remembered seeing Campbell write out the entire Krebs Cycle for glucose metabolism from memory on a blackboard during a teaching conference. No one could imagine such a feat.

Selverstone, one of three brothers who attended Harvard Medical School, was a protégé of both Armstrong's and Campbell's. He had completed his training at Boston City just after Campbell and then moved on to Chicago. After Campbell left Presbyterian to become Dean at Albany Medical College in 1951, Selverstone took over direction of the cardiology laboratory. He was then recruited for Albany, the University of Illinois, and the University of Washington cardiology programs but decided to return to Boston to head the cardiology program at Tufts.

But it was Campbell who stood out most in the memories of his contemporaries. Dr. Peter Farago was an intern when Campbell arrived at Presbyterian in 1948. From the first day, Campbell was very serious, all business, and even, at times, a little dour. He would grill the house staff to within an inch of their lives on the condition of the patients for whom they were responsible. But right from the start, he showed great compassion for patients. One patient who underwent cardiac catheterization incurred complications immediately afterwards, and Campbell stayed with him all night, sleeping on a cot next to the patient, and getting him through satisfactorily. Although he had a sense of humor, under the surface was the strength of an individual who seemed to feel himself invincible. This bearing often frightened people who felt threatened by his determination. Here was the power of a preacher. A certain intensity, mistaken for meanness, was sensed by many, but Farago, who knew Campbell very well for many years, insists that deep down, Campbell was not that way.

Campbell cardiology trainee Dr. Daniel Donovan depicted Campbell as the truly "All American boy" in the Department of Medicine. He developed an excellent research program and was a prime mover in stimulating research among his trainees. He was also an outstanding clinician. He had enormous energy and, along with Armstrong, initiated evening and Saturday teaching rounds, which greatly enhanced the training program. Campbell's meteoric career came as no surprise to Donovan.

Markel Scholar Dr. Robert Grissom was another Campbell trainee. A former general practitioner, Grissom had received this highly prestigious award, given to an individual who exhibited exceptional promise for pursuing a career in academic medicine. Grissom was seeking out the newest and most technically advanced field to study and heard about the Campbell program at Presbyterian. Grissom later went on to be chairman of Medicine at the University of Nebraska Medical School in Omaha. Grissom's praise of Campbell was absolutely unequivocal. Jim Campbell was brilliant, honest, scholarly, and above all, a first-rate physician.[5] Campbell and Grissom presented scientific papers together on cardiac atrial-septal defects at the Central Society for Clinical Research Meetings in Atlantic City.

A bright young female medical student rotating on the Medical service, Janet Wolter, caught the attention of both Armstrong and Campbell. She was encouraged to lengthen her training to include an internship at Johns Hopkins and a residency at Duke, in addition to her required graduate training at Presbyterian and the University of Illinois. Dr. Wolter initially went into physical medicine and then later medical oncology. She became one of Rush University Medical Center's brightest stars. Her long and distin-

5. Personal communication, Dr. Robert Grissom, October 19, 1999.

guished career was recently recognized when she was elected president of the medical staff at Rush.

Campbell's cardiac catheterization laboratory by today's standards was primitive. The equipment was composed mainly of previously used X-ray fluoroscopic machines with dubious radiation safety features. Large lumps of solidified barium sulfate had to be chiseled away from the bottom of the tables. There were rumors of image intensifiers being developed but none were available for a long time. When Jim tried to have the procedures carried out in the operating room, he incurred the displeasure of the chief of Surgery, Dr. Vernon David. Finally a room on the sixth floor of the Murdoch Building adjacent to the operating room was provided to do these studies. All other regular X-ray studies for patients had to be completed before the catheterization procedures could begin. But Campbell's laboratory setup was good enough to impress his former mentor, Dr. Richard Bing when he visited Presbyterian.

These studies were done primarily on children for evaluation of congenital cardiac diseases, and many cases were referred to Campbell from Children's Memorial Hospital. The widespread use of this revolutionary technique for adult studies would not come until many years later when it could be applied to evaluate cardiac conditions potentially amenable to surgical correction.

Pittsburgh cardiologist Dr. Donald Fisher, a Campbell trainee remembered the excitement of that era.[6] The procedure had to be performed in a dimly lit room and only after wearing red-lens plastic glasses for twenty minutes so as to make the appropriate visual adjustments. The first catheterization that Fisher attended was performed by Campbell and two of his associates. Campbell manipulated a catheter into the basilic vein, near the right elbow. There was silence as the catheter was advanced along the veins of the right arm and shoulder; then the catheter could be visualized fluoroscopically as it moved down into the superior vena cava. Then very slowly

6. Dr. Donald Fisher, "In Memory of Dr. James A. Campbell, Chicago, 1948" (manuscript, February 27, 2001).

Campbell demonstrated the technique to his trainees explaining as he went along as he passed the catheter into the right atrium and right ventricle within the heart shadow and then turned upward into the main pulmonary artery, into either the right or left lung. At each location, a blood sample was drawn into a syringe for measurement of oxygen content, and the pressure pulsations were recorded. After all the data were tabulated a diagnosis of congenital heart disease could usually be documented and the patient might then be amenable to corrective surgical repair.

In 1950, resuscitation for cardiac arrest was in a very early state of development. A few medical reports had demonstrated successful ventricular defibrillation in experimental animals and in a very few patients by using 60 cycle 110 volt alternating current and electrodes applied directly to the heart for 0.1 second. In such instances the heart was exposed by incision (thoracotomy). The original studies came from the surgical laboratory of Dr. Claude Beck in Cleveland. Fisher had improvised a similar device by connecting a 10 amp 110 volt isolation transformer from an electronics store along with a knife switch and heavy-gauge electrode cord with the tips soldered to handles with plates of galvanized iron. Selverstone thought the home-made device belonged in a popular mechanics magazine rather than a scientific medical journal.

Before Fisher, Selverstone, and Campbell could even try the equipment out in the laboratory, an emergency call was received from the operating room. A patient, a student nurse, in preparation for surgery was given intranasal epinephrine as premedication for a nasal procedure and went into immediate cardiac arrest. There was loss of pulse and respiration. A general surgeon had opened the abdomen and was giving cardiac compression with one hand under the left diaphragm and the other over the front of the heart. This maneuver did not work. Then the chest was opened and the heart directly massaged and good pulses obtained. The heart would not beat independently, however, and the EKG (electrocardiogram) showed continued ventricular fibrillation. Word of the device that Fisher, Selverstone, and Campbell had put together was passed on to the surgeon and they were asked in to see what they could do. Their home-made device was plugged into the wall, the electrode placed on each side of the quivering heart, and activated momentarily. The heart started to contract briefly, then resumed a slow regular beat, then faster until a normal heart rhythm was sustained. The patient made a normal recovery and was the subject of a national story in the media.

In looking back, these methods would be considered crude by today's standards. But Campbell had established an atmosphere of inquiry and innovation in his training program, and this way of thinking encouraged his trainees to move forward to initiate new procedures, many of which benefited patients.

The cardiac catheterization laboratory at Presbyterian was not only the first established in Chicago, but one of the earliest organized in the Midwest, well ahead of the Mayo Clinic. Presbyterian was becoming known again all over the Midwest for this work. Armstrong has to be given credit for the vision to move forward in this area, and, of course, Campbell did the work. And in doing so, by example, Campbell was making a personal statement of commitment to the study of advances at the forefront of medical technology. This mind-set influenced the habits and attitudes of those who would work with and follow him over the years at the medical center

Dr. Howard Armstrong was going about the work of building up the Department of Medicine. His charisma and brilliance attracted many capable young trainees including future Rush staff member, Dr. Robert Felix, then a student from Cornell Medical School, who took his internship at Presbyterian primarily because of Armstrong's reputation. Although Armstrong was considered a brilliant educator, he had an eccentric side to his makeup that did not sit well with many of the more conservative members of the medical staff. Moreover, at one time he was believed to have taken a rather dim view of private practice and suggested the establishment of a full-time medical practice plan, which was in actual fact a plan for salary and limitation of income for physicians.

Armstrong had been provided with an expensive laboratory for research on plasma proteins to further develop this innovative technology. But then he became interested in psychiatry and little further development came out of his laboratory. Armstrong and Campbell soon began to have some basic disagreements about the role of public versus private hospitals in providing medical care. Campbell eventually left Presbyterian, but it seems unlikely that it was because of any issues between him and Armstrong. Not long after Campbell went to Albany Medical College to assume his new job as dean, Armstrong left Presbyterian and became chief of Medicine at Cook County Hospital. Tragically Armstrong developed severe hepatitis shortly thereafter and eventually succumbed to his illness.

Jim Campbell's singular ways did not escape the notice of his good friend, Lou Selverstone. He was extremely honest, highly moral, and fun-loving, truly an utterly fascinating individual. When he was having a good time, he may have been struggling to overcome a rigid Presbyterian Calvinistic conscience. On the one hand, Campbell had been raucous and bawdy when he produced the faculty follies with Selverstone for the Aesculapian Club at Harvard. There was absolutely no reverence in these productions. Yet, on the other hand, Jim kept a strict façade among the righteous, and, so to speak, on Sunday, he was right there in the first pew, all stiff and formal.

Campbell, Selverstone, and some of the others in the cardiac cath lab managed to find time to place bets on horses. Campbell made a scientific study of the process by looking at genealogy charts and racing forms, so he was eventually able to predict winners quite well. Here again he applied his computerlike mind to the task at hand and came out on top.

Selverstone was impressed with the Rush Library, located on the first floor of the Rawson Building. The room was beautifully appointed with wood paneling and richly endowed with medical publications. Several of the national specialty board examinations were held there. Selverstone and Campbell talked about the library a good deal. Campbell would then reflect on the past glories of Rush and would say, "This library is a relic of a first rate top notch medical school. Wouldn't it be nice if, someday, I had a magic wand and could get it going again?" So Campbell had it in his mind that somehow someday maybe Rush might come alive again.

Yet Campbell was well aware of some of the deficiencies at Presbyterian and took a dim view of some of the practices of the very well established practitioners. But he kept his thoughts to himself and a few trusted colleagues. When he wasn't able to do this, it was clear to many that here was an individual who was quite outspoken. Or as Selverstone put it, he had not yet learned to call a spade an instrument for removal of dirt rather than a manure shovel.

After he had been at Presbyterian for about two years, Jim began to think about his plans for the future. By that time he was completely committed to clinical practice. After establishing a high priority for research among his trainees, he showed little further interest in developing more investigative research protocols in conjunction with his cardiac catheterization laboratory. One of Campbell's habitual quotations from Alexander Pope (1775), "Be not the first by whom the new are tried, nor the last to lay the old aside," may have been a mindset for him in that time.[7]

Campbell had now reached a plateau. To have established oneself as an expert in leading-edge medical technology and to develop a training program for other physicians to learn this skill and apply it to other patients would be a great deal more than even the most idealistic and dedicated physicians could hope to accomplish in a lifetime. His former mentors at Harvard were impressed by what he had done. A Harvard faculty member when Jim was a student in Boston, Dr. Robert Williams, seriously recruited Jim to relocate to Seattle and head the new section of cardiology at the University of Washington, where Williams had just been appointed chief of medicine. Campbell gave this offer very serious consideration but decided not to accept.

Campbell was getting to know a good deal about Chicago and Chicago medicine and was ambitious for advancement. But he was

7. Index card quotations, James A. Campbell, M.D., Box 35, File 4, C97-052, James A. Campbell, M.D., Papers 1924–1983, Record Group 002000, Office of the President, Rush–Presbyterian–St. Luke's Medical Center/Rush University Medical Center Archives, Chicago, Ill.

still very young and, at Presbyterian, still close to the bottom of the medical hierarchy. He began to make connections with many of the leadership trustee community of both Presbyterian and St. Luke's Hospitals and had discussions with George Young, now his good friend, about a possible merger between the two. The Chairman of the Board of Trustees of Presbyterian Hospital, Mr. Franklin Snyder, and Jim became good friends. Jim also talked about the idea of the revival of Rush Medical College at that time to a few of his medical colleagues, Selverstone, Fisher, and Donovan. Apparently he did not express himself in those terms to the trustee leadership community with the possible exception of George Young.

To become a medical leader who could influence patient care, guide physicians and trainees and others, and develop a medical center in the emerging golden era of medicine was a fascinating challenge that Campbell was considering. His educational background would make him quite suitable for such an undertaking. Campbell was among the higher ranks in his class at the best medical school in the country. He had advanced professionally in a very definite, directed, and important way since he completed his formal medical training. Being married to Elda provided him with a degree of financial security and flexibility in considering what he might do regarding his career. He had been introduced to the highest levels of the social and business world in Chicago, understood it, and related to it well. He sensed that he was capable of accomplishing almost anything, which indeed he was. Here was a poor boy from respectable poverty who was making good. The powerful factors that make up strong human ambition were all there. The sky would be the limit, and he was saying to himself, "Let's go for it."

Campbell envisioned his own "empire" to be one of high clinical excellence, somewhat at variance with the developing trend of identifying with research expertise. And quite opposite to the medical philosophy he was originally exposed to at the University of Chicago. His idea was the Francis Peabody philosophy of the patient coming first. Support for research was fine, and teaching was an absolute necessity, but in the last analysis, the patient must come first. This demanded, in his view, the continued development of private practice, but in a carefully controlled and supervised, peer-reviewed fashion. The doctor must first and always consider the welfare of the patient; other considerations such as social and economic status were secondary.

The doctor caring for the patient under the scrutiny of peers and trainees was motivated to do his very best. If a doctor had no other peers around and was only exposed to trainees and students, then ongoing mature peer critical assessment would be lost. Such were the shortcomings of the full-time university professor system. No one, not even the professor, had all the answers, particularly when it came to human illness. If, on the other hand, the doctor had no students or trainees around, the patient might suffer because a sense of idealism and new innovative ideas might not emerge. Such could be the setting in a community hospital without the questioning attitude of bright and highly motivated students and trainees. So, on the one hand, Campbell was very much for the private practitioner and held the "good doctor" to be the ideal for all his trainees. On the other hand, when private doctors, and all other doctor groups for that matter, got together politically, they had a tendency to become a little too strong and had to be reigned in. The role of the private doctor and his place in an expanding medical world continued to be a focus of thought and action for Campbell throughout his career.

Among the other opportunities that were presented to Jim was one in a path away from clinical medicine, but one that nevertheless had interested him. In the late forties, Albany Medical College was undergoing an expansion of its medical center and was looking for a dean to strengthen the medical education program. Albany was a smaller program compared with many of the prestigious eastern medical centers, but it had the nucleus of what was considered to be a solid school. Among the leaders there were Dr. Richard Beebe, who had trained at the Thorndike Boston City Unit in the 1930s, and Dr. Carter Davidson, who was president and chancellor of Union College of Schenectady, New York, Albany Medical College's general educational affiliate. Beebe had heard about Campbell through his Harvard connections. Davidson had known

Campbell since he was a student at Knox and had nurtured his educational development.

So in some ways, it was no surprise that Jim at the age of thirty-three was appointed dean at Albany. He was the youngest medical school dean in the nation at that time. Campbell may have sensed an opportunity to influence his profession more broadly than he might had he stayed in clinical medicine. Others suspected it was a move on Jim's part to be a big frog in a little pond rather than a small frog in a big pond. Another factor regarding the move to Albany may have been location. Elda had come from the East, and Jim and Elda had spent many years in that part of the country, so in some ways it was like returning home again. Campbell would later reflect on the decision to go to Albany. Davidson had sought Campbell for the job. "You know it's really a timing world. And I was very fortunate in having good friends."[8]

Jim's decision to leave clinical practice was not viewed favorably by his peers at Harvard, particularly his old friend, Dr. Bill Castle. Campbell had exceptional clinical skills that, in Castle's opinion, should not be wasted. Eventually Jim would return to clinical medicine primarily as a medical educator, not a practitioner, as chairman of the Department of Medicine, but for now, apparently the lure of establishing himself as a medical educator was too compelling for Campbell to turn down.

On his first day on the job at Albany, Campbell was asked to park in the back of the hospital and not to come around to the front for four years, until after he graduated from medical school, whereupon he said, "I'm the new dean, where do I park?" Jim barely looked his age. But he got right into rearranging and changing some of the private practitioners' ways of doing things. His new ideas, such as making medical rounds more educational, were met with some resistance. This may have been due to Jim's level of impatience. As his lifelong friend, Dr. Richard Beebe, recalls, "Jim's strengths were in

8. Jack Starr Interview and Bruce Rattenbury Commentary, Fall 1973 and 1991; folder 22, Box 4, C97-052, James A. Campbell, M.D., Papers 1924–1983, Record Group 002000, Office of the President, Rush–Presbyterian–St. Luke's Medical Center/Rush University Medical Center Archives, Chicago, Ill.

clinical medicine. He was not suited for a deanship. Even when deal-ing with the board, he wanted things done his way, and quickly." The rigid unyielding approach simply was not acceptable. Jim was very young to be a dean. However, he was beginning to gain experience and developing administrative skills.

Jim and Elda's stay in Albany was a happy one. They were raising two young children. They kept in contact with Chicago with visits from Dr. Janet Wolter, who was now training in Baltimore at Johns Hopkins and Jim's friend George Young, now a board member at St. Luke's Hospital. George and Jim continued to share their many ideas on education, and medical education in particular.

In 1951, the search committee for the Medical Department chairman to find a replacement for Armstrong was formed and Campbell was offered the job. Armstrong had come under some crit-icism for a number of things at Presbyterian, even before Campbell had left to go to Albany, but Campbell would not participate in any activity that would undercut him. He was very loyal to Armstrong, who had brought him to Presbyterian in the first place.

Dr. Edward Irons, a member of the search committee and son of former Rush Medical College dean, Dr. Earnest Irons, traveled to Albany to present the offer to Jim. Irons was particularly high on Campbell, feeling that he would relate extremely effectively to the out-side world. So Jim and Elda returned to Chicago and Presbyterian after a short stay of less than two years at Albany. They were now well con-nected socially and professionally in Chicago, and happy to be back.

The people at Albany had hoped Jim would stay. Despite stormy moments, many realized that they were losing a valuable asset. For Jim, the experience at Albany was a maturing one. He gained valuable insights into medical education, quite different in scope and breadth from both his experiences in Boston and in Chicago. He began to realize that he must be a little more patient, a little more understanding and tolerant of people and their short-comings. If you were always running ahead of the pack, sooner or later you had to slow down and give your colleagues a little time to catch up. Jim may have developed an unconscious attitude of intol-erance toward those less gifted than himself. He may have taken a bit too seriously the doting of those leaders in academia who admired Jim so much.

The conflicts that inevitably develop between practitioners, researchers, and administrators can be difficult and complicated. Jim may have been a little too young to deal with these issues, but Albany was a training ground that enabled him to handle them more effectively at a later date. "Jim in his earlier career had a tendency to walk away from difficult problems. He wasn't as disciplined as he later became," Bob Sessions recalls. "But, later he developed the discipline to deal with these serious issues as he grew."[9]

9. Personal communication, Mr. Robert Sessions, October 15, 1998.

6

A New Era

When Presbyterian Hospital orthopedic surgeon Dr. Fred Shapiro was asked what the most important consideration in the development of a first-rate hospital was, he replied without any hesitation, "What you need in a hospital is quality in the doctors, any old warehouse will do." Yes, first-rate scientific facilities, good location for accessibility, and many others factors would also be needed, but without the doctors, nothing would happen.

Jim Campbell was quite aware of this when he returned to Chicago, and so developing and reshaping the medical staff of Presbyterian Hospital would be of the highest importance to him as soon as he took over as chairman of the Department of Internal Medicine at Presbyterian in 1954. Campbell then went on to become the single most important force in medical staff development as he continued to dominate this process over the next thirty years.

Campbell did not personally rebuild the staff, nor did he ever make that claim. But his powerful presence was so overriding that virtually all appointments for medical staff physicians would eventually pass his desk for review. Jim would not interfere with selection of individual physicians to various departments or pass judgment on their professional qualifications or usually their personal attributes.

This was clearly the purview of the search committee if it involved a new department chairman or the department chairman if it involved an appointment within his or her department. This was not Jim's job.

Although he would disclaim any role in the formation of various search committees, it was no secret (as a matter of fact, it was taken for granted) that Campbell had a great deal of influence over who was and who was not on these committees. As one colleague put it, Campbell liked to have people on these committees that he could work with. Stated another way, those selected for committees were people who shared Jim's vision of what the medical center was trying to grow into over the long haul. Jim was often "asked" by chairmen of these search committees to appear personally to address them. Perhaps a better way of stating it might be that Jim directed the chairmen to extend an invitation to him to attend. Then Campbell would appear, give his thoughts on the committees' deliberations, and leave. He usually didn't stay for the whole proceedings. In this way he was saying, "I've had my say, now let's get to work." He didn't intrude on any specific deliberations, but the committee knew there were limits because of him. It was almost like the military. This type of exchange in which Campbell effectively restricted accessibility was experienced in other settings as well. Without actually coming out and saying so, he let you know that you better be very careful in how you proceed because in the end he might not approve. There might be some fear in asking too many more questions. And so he was able to control the content of such dialogues and exchanges in these kinds of situations.

When individuals for key appointments had interviews with Jim, he was well prepared and intensely focused. Candidates often came away from such interviews very impressed with his vision of the medical center, and such an encounter could turn out to be the deciding factor in the decision-making process for the applicant. At other times, after interviewing a candidate, Jim would immediately get on the phone to call the next interviewer to have the candidate questioned on a subject, perhaps a sensitive one, that Jim felt it would be inappropriate for him to broach. This signaled to the next interviewer the importance of the upcoming encounter and triggered the interviewer's concentration and perceptions.

But much to the consternation of many, Campbell could also be cold and distant, even nasty if the interviewee was not what Jim wanted or expected or sometimes, it seemed, for no reason at all. A prominent member of the medical staff was told by Jim when he was interviewed for an internship position many years before that he should not come to Presbyterian Hospital. The reason given was that the training provided at the time wasn't good enough yet for the candidate who was trained at a prestigious eastern Ivy League medical school. This was clearly not the case. No one but Jim will ever know why this might have happened. Or if the interviewee was sent by someone on Jim's "list" (of those with whom he was not on good terms), the Campbell charm very well might not be forthcoming at all.

So the character of the staff both as a whole, and to a significant extent individually, had the clear imprint of Campbell's approval and indeed his values. And Jim's intensity of involvement in this and so many other areas of medical center activity led to criticism that his style of management was too fine tuned. He engaged in too much micromanagement, was too involved in detail, didn't delegate authority, and surrounded himself only with people who shared his views. Or as one administrative associate pointed out who worked later with Campbell when Rush was reactivated, people who didn't share Jim's values and singular focus on the patient could not stay at Rush. Jim's values became part of one's fiber. Most institutions of its size could tolerate a few outliers, but Rush could not.

And yet several of the key people in the Campbell story, Lepper, Oder, Hass, and Julian as well as many others were strong-minded independent thinkers in their own right. Campbell listened to all these people and learned from them, even some people of seemingly eccentric political views and persuasions. And they, in turn, became engaged in the vision and the mission that Jim believed in. In truth, of course, nobody has all the right answers and Jim knew that. Although he seemed to be rigid in his convictions, in the long run he was flexible enough to listen to other people's advice and to act accordingly.

Although the importance of a quality medical staff was self-evident, Jim emphasized that all the other components of the medical center – nursing and the other allied health sciences as well as administration, in fact all the personnel in the medical center – were vital as well. And Jim could make decisions and took actions that were intended to cut the medical staff down to size. This perceived intrusion on the prerogatives of the doctors and the medical staff was not well received by many and became one of the main reasons that many doctors did not like Jim, did not quite trust him, and indeed feared him.

And yet individual physicians were almost universal in their praise of Campbell's leadership of the medical center. In addition to its impressive growth and the reopening of the medical school, success of their individual practices followed right along with these developments as well as successful outcomes of several other initiatives undertaken by Campbell. Many physicians regarded Jim as one of them, a doctor who wore a white coat, when earlier in his career he was engaged in clinical practice. In almost every address delivered by Campbell at literally hundreds of medical staff meetings over the years, Jim would single out the outstanding work of the medical staff for special recognition

On the other hand when he might like to think that he was conveying to the doctors the message, "I'm one of you," he was really projecting to them by his body language the notion that "this is my hospital, and you are very welcome here, provided you play by the rules, which incidentally, may I remind you, I make up."

Jim related to a few close associates over the years, not his medical colleagues, that he had some real regrets about his decision to leave clinical medicine for administration. He was a very good doctor, an astute clinician, and committed to the work ethic that is essential for a practicing doctor. Jim felt and understood always that the patient comes first because he truly believed in this. And, in addition to this, since Campbell had established himself as a premier clinician when he performed the first cardiac catheterization in Chicago, this would turn out to be a great strength and add significantly to his power as he assumed more and more responsibility in leading the institution.

At the time of Jim's return in 1953, Presbyterian Hospital was struggling in many ways. The Department of Medicine was in a state of turmoil as it had gone almost a year without a permanent chairman when Dr. Howard Armstrong had gone on to Cook County Hospital. The institution too was without any strong leadership. The staff had become very senior, and no one was clearly in charge. Surgeon Dr. Vernon David was making valiant efforts to lead the institution through this difficult period. Many of the institution's long-range plans for professional development seemed to be in shambles. Recruitment for the house staff, the interns and residents, was being affected by this situation. In the extreme, one young trainee of that time made the observation, "Here was a not very big hospital that was long on pride, but very little else."[1]

The relationship with the University of Illinois had changed as a result of the controversy surrounding its involvement in the Krebiozen-Ivy story.[2] Dr. Andrew C. Ivy had become an internationally known leader in the field of medical research and was the author of more than 2000 scientific articles in the field of gastrointestinal physiology and pharmacology, the physiology of reproduction, applied physiology (aviation medicine), and physiologic resistance to cancer.[3]

In 1949, a Buenos Aires physician, Dr. Stevan Durovic and his brother Marko, an industrialist, brought a substance, Kositerin to the

1. Personal communication, Dr. H. A. Paul, 5-24-99.

2. James F. Holland, M.D., "The Krebiozen Story," http://www.quackwatch.com/01 QuackeryRelatedTopics/Cancer/krebiozen.html, January 19, 2002.

3. Ivy had trained at the University of Chicago, where he received his Ph.D. degree in 1918 under the renowned physiologist A. J. Carlson and his M.D. degree from Rush Medical College in 1922. He went on to teach and do research at Loyola University School of Medicine, then the University of Chicago, and in 1926 he was appointed head of Physiology and Pharmacology at Northwestern University Medical School. He remained in that position until 1945, when he was appointed vice-president for Medical Affairs at the University of Illinois. Ivy was regarded by Dr. Carlson, his mentor, as his greatest contribution to medical research.

United States, which was claimed to be useful in the treatment of high blood pressure. It is not clear whether animal or clinical trials were ever conducted on the substance. The Durovics were introduced to Dr. Ivy and presented him with information suggesting that another substance, Krebiozen, extracted from the serum of horses inoculated with a fungus, actinomycoses, was effective in treating cancer in experimental animals. Dr. Ivy found the idea attractive since he held that chemical substances must be present in the body to control cancer growth and presumably this substance Krebiozen, or Substance X, as it was called, influenced this mechanism. Ivy later admitted that he accepted this information without ever having heard of Durovic as a scientist, without repeating the experiments, without having seen analyses or manufacturing records, and without knowing what the substance in the ampoules was.

Ivy then treated the first human with this substance in 1949 and announced the results of his clinical trails in 1951. The announcement was not presented to a group of peers, but at a press conference held at the Drake Hotel in Chicago in which four science writers for Chicago newspapers, the mayor of Chicago, two United States senators, potential financial supporters, and a few doctors were invited. The results of the study in 22 cancer patients disclosed that eight patients had died but none as a result of cancer and dramatic clinical improvement was reported in one.

The story, because its claims were so promising and because Dr. Ivy was involved, was carried in the headlines of newspapers throughout the world. And as the story would unfold, it held the attention of both the public and the medical scientific community for several years. Immediate attempts to confirm the observations reported by Dr. Ivy were undertaken by cancer research centers and universities throughout the country. No evidence of cancer activity or cancer control by the substance was found; and the results of a multi-institutional study were published in the *Journal of the American Medical Association* in 1951. A friend counseled Ivy that he should correct or retract his erroneous position. This did not happen. Instead Krebiozen backers howled conspiracy. They said that the American Medical Association and the American Cancer Society were conspiring to keep Krebiozen off the market, either to delay the advent of effective cancer treatment or to force the Krebiozen Foundation to cut them in on the windfall that was to be expected.

Public controversy regarding Krebiozen continued for over a decade. Patients continued to be treated. Claims of efficacy from its backers could not be substantiated by an FDA study that examined the records of 1526 patients and found that in only 3 patients could evidence be found for partial tumor regression. The Durovics were very reluctant to have Krebiozen subjected to laboratory analysis. Eventually a National Cancer Institute and FDA study disclosed no evidence of any tumor activity. Dr. Stevan Durovic came under indictment for evasion of income tax and the Durovics and Dr. Ivy were brought to trial for violations of FDA regulations and fraud. The trial, held in Chicago, resulted in acquittal by a jury of laymen.

The Krebiozen storm hung like a dark cloud over the University of Illinois Medical School for years and clearly had a negative effect on faculty recruitment for the institution. Moreover, the affiliation with Presbyterian Hospital was subtly but definitely affected. The enthusiasm among many of the doctors on the staff for further developing and enhancing that affiliation for the future was significantly diminished.

At the same time, sentiment was growing among Presbyterian staff members who had recently trained in the East at Boston, New York, and Baltimore that the situation for training at the hospital required a major overhaul; clearly there was now a need for development of some type of full-time system for medical education and training. In the ongoing struggle of Rush with the University of Chicago in the thirties over the issue of the complete conversion of the Rush faculty to a full-time system, Presbyterian Hospital may have overreacted by rejecting the concept of any full-time faculty and staff. As a result the institution's philosophy for training had fallen behind the times and, once established, was difficult to change.

It isn't clear just how Jim Campbell viewed the hospital when he returned in 1953. He had been exposed early in his medical training to the total full-time system at the University of Chicago. Apparently he never bought into this approach, and this in itself would make Jim unusual. Many of those students exposed to the sup-posed superiority of the full-time system at the University of Chicago often became zealots of this educational philosophy throughout their career. Dr. James Schoenberger, who attended the U. of C. one year behind Jim, was so thoroughly indoctrinated into the full-time U. of C. system that he experienced extreme pangs of guilt when he devel-oped a private practice in suburban Hinsdale. Schoenberger recalls that when he encountered his teachers from the U. of C. later, he felt clearly their sense of disapproval of his career path.[4]

Campbell had been inspired by his teachers on the faculty at Boston City Hospital and Harvard Medical School. They were ded-icated practitioners of the art of laboratory and clinical medicine and were regarded as such in the highest circles of medical education and practice throughout the United States. Some of these men engaged in private practice and some did not. It didn't seem to make much difference either way. Campbell may well have thought that, in the development of Presbyterian and his plans to restore it to a high level of eminence, as long as the leadership was committed to his ideas about patient care, research, and education, everything else would fall into place. Campbell was also of the opinion that the medical staff at Presbyterian at that time were highly devoted to their patients, greater in fact than in any other place he had been.[5]

And yet during this time Campbell did not think highly of these physicians in private practice. In his mind, taking money from the patient for providing care tarnished them. These doctors were to be tolerated because they were necessary. Later on, Campbell would soften this harsh view. But this seemingly con-temptuous attitude toward the physician in private practice was not well concealed and was another reason why Jim was not well liked or trusted by many doctors.

4. Personal communication, Dr. James Schoenberger, May 19, 2000

5. Jack Starr Interview and Bruce Rattenbury Commentary, Fall 1973 and 1991, fold-er 22, Box 4, C97-052, James A. Campbell, M.D. Papers 1924–1983; Record Group 002000, Office of the President; Rush–Presbyterian–St. Luke's Medical Center/Rush University Medical Center Archives, Chicago, Ill.

When Jim accepted the job as chairman of Medicine, however, he agreed to respect the established tradition of private practice. But at the same time he was also given approval, financial support, and encouragement to proceed immediately to develop the professional and educational program to move the institution forward as rapidly as possible.

That Campbell would agree to respect the established tradition of private practice at Presbyterian came as a surprise to many who were there in those early years. The search committee chairman, Dr. James Eyerly, insisted on this provision. Campbell very likely had bristled over such a restriction, but over time, he honored it. The threat of requiring the medical staff to forgo the traditional private practice fee-for-service system and become salaried employees of the institution was a constant fear for many of the members of the medical staff in those years. And Campbell indeed did make decisions and formulate policies that were designed to "cut the medical staff down to size." But the traditional fee-for-service system for physician compensation was preserved. Dr. Ted Schwartz, a "full-time salaried" recruit of Campbell's, who eventually became chairman of the Department of Medicine has verified this. In all the years of deliberations, not once was the notion of eliminating the fee-for-service system ever seriously brought up for discussion.

As soon as Campbell took charge, dramatic changes were made. Three top-flight doctors from the outside were recruited to strengthen the professional training program and several more followed. And virtually all those recruited stayed most or their entire professional career at Presbyterian. These appointments were not stopgap measures, but were made to fit into a plan for the long run.

Dr. John (Jack) Graettinger came from California. Both of Jack's grandfathers were doctors. He was in the class at Harvard Medical School two years behind Jim and was a student at the Boston City Hospital when Jim was in his residency training. After Jack's training in cardiology at the Massachusetts General Hospital under the world famous cardiologist Dr. Paul Dudley White, he was assigned to the Pensacola Naval Station and participated in important cardiac research studies involving physiologic changes in the heart that occurred at high altitudes. Medical corpsman Bob Sessions served under Jack at Pensacola and later worked in Jack's department at Presbyterian as a technician, where he invented a number of cardiac monitoring devices. Sessions also went on to play a special role in the development of the medical center when, as a successful entrepreneur-inventor, he funded the construction of the Sessions Presidential House at the corner of Loomis and Harrison streets.

After he was discharged from the Navy, Graettinger was recruited for the cardiology program at the University of Washington but decided to accept the offer from Presbyterian to become chief of the Section of Cardiology in Jim Campbell's new Department of Medicine, which was in effect Campbell's previous job at Presbyterian. Betty, Jack's wife, had family roots in the Presbyterian community that went back as far as her grandfather, Mr. William Angus Douglass, who served on the Board of Managers for more than forty years; Betty's mother, Mrs. Elizabeth Douglass Shorey, volunteered for over sixty years and served as president of the Woman's Board on two separate occasions.

Next came Dr. Frank Trobaugh, also a classmate of Jim's at Harvard and a fellow intern at Boston City Hospital. Frank first went into pathology and served in the armed forces as a director of laboratory services in Europe. He then returned to Boston to complete his training in internal medicine and hematology, where he met his future wife Marge, a key staff member in Dr. Bill Castle's laboratory. Frank was appointed chief of Hematology.

Dr. Theodore Schwartz was then appointed chief of Endocrinology. Ted came from Duke, where he worked under endocrinologist Dr. Frank Engel. He had received his training at Johns Hopkins in internal medicine. Jim recruited Ted at the annual Atlantic City scientific meetings. As Ludmerer describes it, "clinical scientists would gather each spring for their most important meetings (the Association of American Physicians, the American Society for Clinical Investigation, and the American Federation for Clinical Research). This was where all the best in internal medicine came together to present papers, engage in intense discussions and often stay up all night probing the meaning of the latest reports."[6] The best and the brightest were there, and recruitment of promising young clinical investigators was carried out openly in this setting. As Dr. Don Fisher recalls, "I never saw Jim Campbell seated in the audience during any of these meetings. He was always outside moving about, politicking and conferring with various individuals."[7]

Ted Schwartz recalls his impressions of Campbell at that time. "Here, I thought, was somebody effective, and that is why he chose Presbyterian. He was very direct. He avoided nothing. This is the way it is. He had some money, and he could afford to pay whatever the figure was for the time, which could be enhanced with fees from consultation. He seemed to know what the hell he was doing, and what his plans were. Here was a rather modest-sized hospital in Chicago at the moment, but there was a Rush Medical College Trustee Board that he intended to do something with. He did mention at the time that Chicago was a bit behind for the times, and it was time to catch up. This change was something that was necessary, and it was time for full-time people, salaried people to come in and straighten out the training programs."[8]

"Suddenly," Dr. Robert Carton then a young attending physician recalled,[9] "we had a modern twentieth-century Department of Medicine. We had some people on our staff who were good in the three specialties that were brought in, but they were more or less self-trained, and bringing in these three full-time people made a dramatic statement that a new era had arrived." Dr. Sam Taylor, who had been in Endocrinology, graciously moved on into Medical Oncology and established the first hospital section of Medical

6. Kenneth M. Ludmerer, *Time to Heal: American Medical Education from the Turn of the Century to the Era of Managed Care* (New York: Oxford University Press, 1999), p. 46.

7. Dr. Donald Fisher, "In Memory of Dr. James A. Campbell, Chicago, 1948" (manuscript, February 27, 2001).

8. Personal communication, Dr. Theodore Schwartz, June 28, 1998.

9. Interview of Robert W. Carton, M.D., by Evan W. Barton, M.D., Stanton Friedberg, M.D., and Stuart W. Campbell, Ph.D., February 5, 1992. Oral History Collection; Rush–Presbyterian–St. Luke's Medical Center Archives, Chicago, Ill.

Oncology in the United States. Soon afterwards, Dr. Robert Kark, a world-renowned nephrologist and another former colleague of Jim's from Boston City came on board. Kark introduced the technique of renal biopsy to clinical medicine, an important diagnostic tool.

Recruiting individuals rooted in the newer concepts of full-time medical education did not, however, automatically restore the medical center's reputation back to the very top right away. Although changes were necessary it was clear that the existing medical staff was doing a very fine job of providing excellent care for patients. Some things were working well at one of the oldest university hospitals in the United States. Individual practices were flourishing, and many of the old Rush faculty were still active. Although they were very senior, their instincts for training young men and women in the art and science of medicine in the Rush tradition were still very much alive. This was a staff that had obligations in their own mind and had been dislocated by circumstances of the two-decade-long conflicts with the University of Chicago. But the staff was in need of a re-infusion of enthusiastic leadership with a different perspective to engage all the newer scientific forces that were coming together in the second half of the twentieth century. Herrick, Irons, and Woodyatt among others were proven leaders, but their time was rooted back at least a decade or more from before the early 1950s. Now exciting new things were taking place at a breathtaking pace.

So although Campbell's mandate for change was self-evident by the appointment of Graettinger, Trobaugh, Schwartz, and others, these individuals would still have to prove themselves and they would have to do very well indeed to match the professional respect that many of the existing staff had earned. Jim Campbell knew and understood this. To preserve the best elements of the old system was the objective. His ambivalence toward private practitioners notwithstanding, Jim insisted that these so-called full-time men start at the core of all medical training, the patient and the bedside, just like the private practitioners were doing every day. They were to establish themselves as top clinicians, not exclusively laboratory doctors. By fostering such an attitude, Campbell was saying to his new staff that the existing staff was by no means second rate, and he discouraged any attitudes that would lead to a destructive hostility of the sort that can develop between academicians and practitioners. These full-time people were to treat the existing staff with respect and get along with them. When they were called into consultation for a patient under the care of a private doctor, great efforts were to be expended to communicate with the patient's doctor, and sometimes no fee was submitted for the service. The full-time men could have bettered their income by rendering a fee in these situations but chose not to. Every effort was made to convey to the private practitioners that these new full-time doctors were there to help the patients with their specialized knowledge, not to compete with the patient's primary private doctor. In this way, a growing mutual sense of trust developed, and staff morale improved very considerably. The full-time staff was to be a resource for the private doctors. They were not intended to be competitors. This policy was fully supported by a very knowledgeable hospital Board of Trustees.

Campbell thus avoided the hostile elements of the "town-gown" syndrome wherein distrust by the practicing physicians over the fear of perceived intrusion of the salaried academic physicians "stealing their patients" was prevalent.[10]

As things turned out, these newcomers in no time became very busy because of requests for consultations by the private medical staff. Graettinger, Schwartz, Trobaugh, and the others were regarded with a good deal less suspicion, and they soon became known as Jack, Ted, and Frank. The private practitioners, instead of resisting change, supported many of the Campbell initiatives. These attitudinal changes, so hard to measure, meant a great deal. The changes were noted everywhere in the hospital. A new era was clearly underway.

An important innovation instituted by Campbell, now taken for granted in today's hospital environment, was the geographic location of patients in the hospital by service, Medicine, Surgery, Pediatrics, and the like. Such was not the case at Presbyterian in the

10. Ludmerer, *Time to Heal*, p. 117.

early fifties. The same would also be true for Presbyterian's new part-
ner in the future, St. Luke's Hospital. Patients admitted to the hospital were assigned a room anywhere in the hospital that might be
available, regardless of their diagnosis. They could be stratified by
location as to whether they were paying or non-paying and whether
they were teaching or non-teaching. Campbell insisted on changing
this. Patient care would be considerably improved if patients with
similar illnesses were all treated on the same floor. Medical patients
would be assigned to a medical floor, surgical patients to a surgical
floor, and so on.

All patients were to be teaching patients. They deserved to have
the advantages of being assignable to a staff of inquiring medical students and residents. These bright people might pick up on something
that had been missed. Segregation of patients as charitable or paying
was discouraged. Campbell would insist on the benefit to the trainee
of this type of encounter. In the classic charity hospital encounter, the
patient would usually listen to the advice from the trainee and seldom
say anything. They were grateful for any kind of advice whatsoever. At
Presbyterian, the student had to learn to deal with paying patients who
would often talk back and ask questions. And if not satisfied, the
patients would relay this back to their personal physicians.

For those patients without a doctor, one was assigned from the
private attending staff. The staff doctor would oversee the work of the
interns and residents in the care of the patient, engage in dialogue on
all aspects of the case with house staff, and countersign all orders.
Thus, the charity patient would be receiving the same care as the private patient. Furthermore, the old system exposed the trainee primarily to diseases of poverty. And this would be the first step in
Campbell's attempt to develop a single standard of care for all patients.

Campbell's ideas about a single standard of care cut across the
lines of traditional thinking in medical education. Patients were stratified into two types in terms of their educational value for the training of students, interns, and residents.[11] There were those of the
"ward type," usually of lower economic and social class found in

11. Ibid, p. 120.

large municipal hospitals such as Cook County Hospital, New York's Bellevue Hospital, and similar institutions across the country. The other types were the "private patients," those found in the private hospitals. A classic example of this system would have been when Rush Medical College was affiliated with Presbyterian Hospital and Cook County Hospital. Trainees and the faculty of the Rush system understood that the hands-on experience for training would be emphasized at County and the Rush Central Free Dispensary, whereas a less active, more observant posture for training was encouraged at Presbyterian. Countless similar educational systems were in place across the United States. It was held that a dual system for training was absolutely necessary for high-quality medical education. An exception to this system was that of Boston City Hospital, which more consciously aspired to the ideal that the poor patient should receive the same care as the paying patient.

Campbell intended to do away with the old ward system altogether. After World War II, as the indigent hospital population began to decline for a number of reasons, the most significant being the enactment of Medicare in 1965, medical educators feared that quality medical education could not be maintained without an abundant supply of "teaching patients" provided by public hospitals. The indignities that public patients suffered in the hospital were significantly greater than those of private patients. And Campbell fought this tendency every inch of the way throughout his career. He never accepted the argument that private patients objected to having students, interns, and residents involved in their care. He insisted that the trainees be involved in every aspect of their care although he met great resistance from the old guard at Presbyterian. Paying patients actually were for the most part pleased and receptive to this new approach. The private attending doctors rarely "lost" their patients as a result. Patients tended to regard the trainees as their private physicians in a somewhat different sort of way. Campbell and his associates pointed out that exposing the students, interns, and residents to private patients really presented them with real-world experience. An overemphasis on exposure to the illnesses of the poor would not be realistic training for those who would eventually settle in practices serving those in mainstream America, where illness often presented itself in a very different way.

The view expressed by educators that the loss of the "ward patient" would spell the doom of residency training programs was unacceptable to Campbell.[12] The medical center worked out ways of compensating for the perceived lack of hands-on experience that turning away from the "ward" system implied and never sustained a decline in their ability to recruit high-quality trainees.

Later on, Campbell eliminated the old Central Free Dispensary system altogether, and he, Dr. Joyce Lashof, and others converted this facility into a modern state of the art complex where all patients were assigned to a private physician. Dr. Bruce Campbell, his son wrote his doctoral dissertation on the subject of conversion of a public hospital-based clinic facility to a private one. The next logical step in this process was the development of the Mile Square Health Program, which provided for the medically indigent on the West Side adjacent to the medical center, an alternative to public care at Cook County Hospital. Patients on the West Side were provided with a medical center physician, and when hospitalization was required, they were admitted to Presbyterian–St. Luke's Hospital like any other private patient. The poor were no longer being isolated and put off in a corner, but brought into the mainstream of care.

Many have high ideals and good intentions for social betterment, but Campbell provided more. He did more than sit in his ivory tower devising social schemes. He figured out a way to get it done and, once accomplished, vigorously supported it. Campbell's willingness to persevere in his belief in a single standard of care in the face of much skepticism and opposition eventually led other medical educators to follow. He was far ahead of his time, a true visionary. His policy of a single standard of care for everyone was well understood and admired by many of the public in Chicago. The medical center would be regarded as going beyond the current way of doing things and, while maintaining excellence in medical education and patient

12. Ibid., p. 174.

care, was attempting to deal with a serious social concern. Everyone could hold his or her head up a little higher as a result of this.

Next in organizational change came the assignment of the house staff, residents, interns, and students to a particular floor, not to an individual private physician. In the extreme in the old system, the trainee would greet the private physician at the entrance to the hospital, help remove the doctor's coat, and assist him as the attending physician saw fit in helping him see patients around the corridors throughout hospitals. A trainee could be essentially just an errand boy. There would be the Irons service, the Woodyatt service, and so on. This was the old apprentice system, and, as might be expected, it was not discarded without a good deal of grumbling. But in due time the private attending doctors went along with Campbell's changes. The attending doctors now had the benefit of having their patients on a particular floor, where everybody, nurses, interns, and residents would be involved, which actually made the doctor's conduct of his practice considerably more efficient, better organized, and far easier and safer.

Another step, symbolic but important in Campbell's mind, was to have all attending doctors in private practice attired in white coats. Heretofore, the private physicians made hospital rounds in business suits, and the so-called full-time doctors made rounds in white laboratory coats. There had been a tendency on the part of private physicians to regard with some contempt those who were wearing white coats as being symbolic of "hired hands." The visible distinction between the two groups disappeared. And yet the individual fee-for-service private physician system continued the way it had been before. Campbell had intended no change in this system. A unity of purpose was projected, and, again, Campbell was working toward the concept of a single standard of care for all patients.

Recruitment of the most highly qualified trainees was an item of uppermost priority for Campbell. A number of Presbyterian trainees at the time when Campbell took over were not recruited from the higher ranks of the more highly regarded medical schools. On their rotation during medical school, University of Illinois students were not enthused about going to Presbyterian for further training because of the apprentice system. They seldom voluntarily selected Presbyterian for their rotations. Something had to be done about this. The first step was to abolish the old system. Jim accomplished this in a dramatic fashion, as he was wont to do, to help spread the word that a new era was now in place at Presbyterian, and news of this traveled rapidly in the medical student and house staff training community of the West Side.

In the first year of Jim's term as chairman of Internal Medicine, only six of the twelve spots for internship were filled. Jim became very visible on the floors right away. As Dr. Harold Paul, then a third-year medical student at the University of Illinois assigned to Presbyterian recalled, "here was this stiff somewhat formal figure with a brush haircut, very youthful in appearance but with an intense body language speaking out with a most impressive voice, 'which one of you is Dr. Paul, which one of you is Dr. Farrell? What are you doing? Good.' He took a look at the patients' charts, walked down the hall, and turned back and said, 'I'll meet you in the office at one o'clock.' Farrell took one look at the new guy and said, 'who are you, the senior resident?'" Jim had been used to this sort of thing. When he was at Albany, he had been mistaken for a medical student.[13]

Jim then made an arrangement with the University of Illinois to allow them to be externs. That is to say, they would be paid an intern's salary and be given responsibilities almost equal to that of interns. Jim then personally trained these students and supervised virtually all their activities. He was on the floor with them at all hours of the day and night, just as if he were back in his days as a resident at Boston City Hospital. He took these trainees away from following the attending doctors of the old apprentice system around and assigned them to a specific floor. Jim didn't wait for his future staff recruits, Graettinger and the others, to appear on the scene several months later.

A patient was sent in to the hospital from one of the doctors' offices on Michigan Avenue with a complicated heart rhythm problem. The extern called the doctor at his office and suggested he

13. Personal communication, Dr. H. A. Paul, May 24, 1999

institute a newly developed intravenous medication that required constant monitoring. The doctor cleared his throat over the phone and said, "Well, go ahead." The extern then proceeded with the treatment with Campbell standing by to supervise the whole extended effort. Jim took the role of responsible supervisor and gave medical student H. A. Paul a lot of leeway. Several untoward events occurred, but Jim was there to change the treatment to obviate these problems. As he was doing this, the trainee was being grilled by Campbell, saying "Why are we doing this? What were you thinking? What could you have done different?" He was being critical in a very good sense. His thinking was always logical and easy to follow. You learned very quickly in this sort of environment.

Campbell eventually took over and stayed with the patient well into the night until the arrhythmia had stabilized. He rarely left the bedside in a ten-bed ward in the old 3 Jones section. As it would turn out in this case, only one with the skilled cardiac training that Campbell had could have done the job. And Jim never sent the patient a bill for his services.

As a result, Jim Campbell developed a strong loyalty among these externs. They were learning from a master and having the time of their lives. Now they walked the halls with the swagger of interns. Presbyterian's recruitment problems suddenly became a thing of the past. It wasn't long before University of Illinois students were requesting a rotation through Presbyterian, and the next year a full quota of interns was recruited. Here was Campbell making the best of things, by being a creative and exemplary leader. And word spread quickly in the hospital community of this amazing and rather outspoken doctor, who was smarter than hell, and whom you could also learn a lot from.

As the era of testing and new procedures for the benefit of patients evolved, certain tests were developed that had great potential benefit. But not all of these so-called breakthroughs materialized, and many were exceedingly uncomfortable for patients to go through. Campbell encouraged his trainees not to take everything they read in the medical journals at face value, but to be critical. Very little was published in the "Journal of Negative Results," when in truth this sort of journal should contain countless articles every month.[14] Campbell would insist that his trainees be as sure as they could possibly be that, by doing these new procedures, the information obtained was important enough to make the patient suffer. For example, passing a tube into a patient's stomach through the nose became rather commonplace. Yet valuable information such as analysis of the gastric secretion might be overlooked as this procedure was being done. Jim would become outraged if the trainee had overlooked such things. He would stress again and again, "Whenever you make a patient suffer, you better be sure you get all the information you can to justify making the patient endure all this misery."

From the beginning Campbell had to confront objections from the attending staff about the way he was rearranging things in the teaching program. They were certain that they knew best. Many doctors were exceedingly uncomfortable with the notions and philosophy that Campbell espoused. His goals were for the betterment of the institution. Yes, there was an enterprise here, and yes doctors were an important part of this enterprise, but not the only part. Doctors in general were somewhat against hospitals at that time, and the issue of geographic full-time people such as Jim represented was also very disconcerting to them. From his previous three-year tenure at Presbyterian, Campbell knew he had embarked on a huge undertaking in bucking the circumstantial inertia that had existed for the better part of two decades.

Campbell brushed aside the objections from the established senior staff and moved forward rapidly in reorganizing the department. He organized teaching conferences and rounds, and many of the objecting private practitioners enthusiastically participated in these sessions. Before long there was standing room only in the audiences of trainees and private physicians.

After Graettinger, Schwartz, and the others arrived and began to develop their respective sections, the quality of the training programs began to improve even more. Expansion of residency

14. Ludmerer, *Time to Heal*, p. 310.

training programs, initiation of fellowships, and development of important research programs funded by National Institutes of Health (NIH) grants fostered an atmosphere of inquiry. The NIH funded the training of five fellows in cardiology. Eventually, the number of applicants for training positions in the Department of Medicine far exceeded its capacity to handle the interest. Presbyterian now was considered one of the top ten internal medicine residencies in the United States; it became known again in this new era as one of the strongest and most progressive in the Midwest. In one year, seven trainees were recruited from Harvard. The University of Illinois now regarded Presbyterian as its strongest affiliate. The university no longer had to assign students because the majority of them wanted their medical clerkships there and not at the other affiliated hospital rotations.

The principal individual in all this activity was the departmental chairman. Campbell led the way. He established guidelines for teaching all the trainees. Didactic lectures were deliberately avoided. Training was always centered around a given patient, and how one's expertise might be applied in this particular situation. These exercises were extremely educational and forced the professorial types on the faculty to come down to earth and apply their expertise in the challenging world of the unpredictable patient.

"Campbell's way was always direct – there was no wasting time." As Dr. Guy Matthews, then an intern, recalled,[15] "one didn't even have to look up to know that Campbell was appearing for his afternoon rounds. You could hear . . . the clicking of his heels as he approached. Dr. Joe Muenster would straighten his tie and button his collar . . . Everyone stood at attention. If their preparation for the visit was thorough, they would volunteer to Campbell that they didn't need the charts as they made their way around the hospital floors. They then would be grilled within an inch of their life by Campbell regarding every last detail of each case. The trainees were scared to death. Campbell always found something they didn't know, and it

15. Personal communication, Dr. Guy Matthews, February 24, 1999

wasn't usually something minor either, no matter how well prepared the interns had been. Campbell might say in certain instances the response 'I don't know' is not acceptable when it comes to a patient. After he had worked over the group and if they had done pretty well, he would express himself in his body language meaning 'A job well done.' There was nothing quite like this subtle expression of approval from Campbell. It provided a real sense of palpable pride. But at the next encounter with Campbell, wherever it might be, it was all business again, and the intern would have to prove himself all over again. Campbell might recognize who you were by asking you what you thought about the White Sox seven-game losing streak."

Although Campbell's trainees could be quite fearful of him, virtually all the interns and residents that he trained during his tenure as department chairman from 1953 to 1964 regarded him as absolutely extraordinary. He maintained a profound professionalism along with a terrific sense of humor. The patient was number one. He drilled this into his residents, and many held Campbell to be the most influential professional force in their entire career.

Jim would stress in his daily reports in the afternoon that one shouldn't get too complex in evaluating patients. Many of the great discoveries in medicine occurred when people stumbled onto something right in front of them. If a patient presented with congestive heart failure, he wouldn't ask for a complicated formula but he wanted to know what the patient's weight on admission and after bed rest overnight was, knowing that this in itself could produce a significant diuresis, or water loss. Jim often referred to the "joy of medicine." He loved his profession and engaged his trainees with his enthusiasm. He found fascination in medical phenomenon like the term "shingles," from the Latin, *cingula*, meaning a layer, a band, or a girdle. What a total bore all of this would be if you couldn't enjoy these things, he would say. Let's have fun. Everybody got caught up in it. People loved to go to afternoon report, even though he could be severe on them. There was on the one hand the element of fear, and on the other hand people enjoyed it. Campbell and his audience both loved the banter of it all.[16]

16. Personal communication, Dr. Bernard Blauuw, June 18, 1998

The genius of Campbell was that he could make complex medical things fairly simple to understand. If you weren't thinking, he might give you an assignment, and then not ask you about it until several weeks later. Then he would say, "Hey, Matthews, how about what I tripped you up on a while back. He never forgot."

Campbell could be devastating when something was presented at rounds that wasn't accurate or even worse, perhaps made up a bit. He would sense this almost immediately, and allow the presenter to dig himself into a hole. As Dr. Richard Sassetti recalled,[17] "bluffing through or fabricating an answer was lethal – leading to a slow painfully inexorable exposure of the dissimulator's ignorance." Jim would string you along on the rack, and then crucify you slowly and devastatingly. On one occasion, Dr. Ernie Fordham,[18] then a student, finally gave up and said he simply didn't know what he was talking about. The residents in the background were laughing. They had set up future intern Fordham with a deliberately difficult case in which Campbell had particularly extensive knowledge. Campbell sensed this and might make the chastisement a little lighter in this instance or even very occasionally make light of it. But if the presenter continued, he would be annihilated verbally by Campbell.

One of Jim's loyal trainees was just such a victim. He had been giving Jim and those in attendance at the conference an explanation of what happens regarding blood vessel spasm as it occurs in hypertension. As the presentation continued, his concepts about the process became more vague and his knowledge base thinner by the second. Finally Campbell became infuriated, and threw a book on hypertension at the trainee. And he then added, "Don't come back until you know what you are talking about." Yes, Campbell had literally thrown the book at him.

As exasperated and short-tempered as Jim could be with an attending physician who didn't measure up in one way or another, he was exceedingly kind, gracious, and thoughtful to his trainees. He

17. Personal communication, Dr. Richard Sassetti, February 10, 1998
18. Personal communication, Dr. Earnest Fordham, September 8, 1998

might be presented with a personal problem or a question. He wouldn't give an answer, but you knew what you had to do when you left. He only asked a few questions because he had the ability to guide you to make your own decisions without being dogmatic. He would answer a question by asking another question. And then perhaps on the way out, he might pass on another of his favorite quotations and sayings, "Not everything that can be counted counts. Not everything that counts can be counted."[19]

Campbell's unpredictability protected him from petty infighting. Just when Jim was on the rampage about one of the more high-profile attending men who were particularly arrogant and abusive of their prerogatives, he would step in and defend him. One of his trainees who later became a leading Chicago cardiologist had sensed that Jim had a particular dislike for one of these "attendings," as they were called, and complained to Jim about him. He was loading up the floors with borderline admissions that might be handled just as well at home and so on. Jim replied, "Doctor, several training positions are now available at Cook County Hospital if you don't like the way things are done around here." This instance was an example of one of Jim's great strengths. He balanced people's views and kept everybody on their toes by refusing to get caught in polarizations. He began to develop a pattern of management for the future. The many constituencies that he would deal with would at times perceive themselves to be decidedly in his favor and at other times decidedly not in his favor.

Another incident reflected his usual demand for respect of attending physicians by the house staff. One afternoon at residents' reports, a resident disclosed that a certain attending man had admitted a patient with ulcerative colitis and had ordered gum aramanth enemas. A number of residents chortled and made disparaging remarks. While the banter was going back and forth, it was noticed that Campbell was writing something on a card and putting it in his pocket. He interrupted the teasing to ask if anyone had heard of gum

19. Index card quotations, James A. Campbell, M.D., Box 35, File 4, C97-052, James A. Campbell Papers 1924--1983, Record Group 002000, Office of the President, Rush–Presbyterian–St. Luke's Medical Center/Rush University Medical Center Archives, Chicago, Ill.

aramanth. No one had. He commented that in light of our ignorance we (residents) should cease the nasty comments and withhold our judgment. As soon as rounds were over, Campbell was seen to head immediately to pharmacist Louis Gdalman's office and Louis looked it up in a book. It was an ancient remedy, which indeed turned out to help the patient. Two weeks later Campbell asked the same group the same question. Of course, no one knew. But Campbell did.

At one time, salaries for the house staff had become decidedly substandard; in fact some of the interns' families needed food stamps to get by. When Campbell learned of this, he moved quickly to correct it. Although Campbell projected himself as the champion of the house staff, he could turn right around and make it perfectly clear, in no uncertain terms, who was boss. One month, the resident call schedule was changed from call every third night to call every second night. Apparently there was a temporary shortfall in the house staff manpower allotment. The house staff was up in arms and requested an immediate meeting with Campbell. The meeting was held in the old cafeteria. Campbell reiterated that the call schedule was to go on as scheduled. He said that if the residents had any problem with it, he had brought with him a stack of papers which were thought to be resignation forms that they could sign if they so wished. He may not have actually had them in his possession, but it reflected his self-assurance that no one would dare take him up on it and imperil the rest of his career. That ended the meeting.

To protect the private attendings' prerogative and yet foster teaching, Campbell instituted the regulation that attending physicians on the medical service could not write orders on their own patients. This was not intended to restrict in any way the authority of the private physician but forced interaction between the attending and the house staff, which Campbell felt was a vital component of house staff training. His aim was to give those in training the widest possible exposure to the spectrum of attendings, not just those they happened to like or were comfortable with.

Campbell also had a rule about rounds on floors. All house staff rounds had to be done by 9:00 A.M., and no attending men were to make rounds before 9; this way the house staff could be fully

informed about their patients and could interact in the most beneficial fashion with the attendings.

But Campbell wasn't always tactful and patient with attending
physicians. One afternoon when the hospital census was overflowing
and not a single bed could be found, not even in the basement, an
affluently dressed attending whose practice filled a lot of beds objected to his patient being placed in a four-bed ward. He demanded that
the patient be moved immediately to another floor and a private
room. It turned out that the doctor, not the patient, was upset
because one of the patients in the four-bed ward was black. Jim
Campbell was livid. He said, "Don't you ever threaten me again like
that. I will be happy to support your application to any other staff in
the city if you so desire." The attending doctor, clout and all, backed
off. Everybody on the floor had witnessed this confrontation, and
greatly admired and respected Jim's stand. And many never forgot.

So within a short period of time, Jim had instilled new life into
the Department of Medicine. Surgery and all the other departments
within the institution were forced to take a look at what they were
doing. Were they measuring up to the pace of change and innovation developed by Campbell? Hospitals may be big places but when
it came to the things that Jim was doing, the news traveled exceedingly quickly. Jim had very little patience with those who had not
kept up. Campbell would not hesitate to be critical whenever he
observed situations that were not first rate in his view, whether within his department or outside of it. To be on the receiving end of Jim's
incisive, biting, and outspoken criticisms could be an unnerving and
even a devastating experience. Even to be on the receiving end of
one of Jim's stares was not something one forgot quickly. It could
depress one for weeks. Campbell could be a very tough individual to
deal with, and many found it exceedingly difficult to measure up to
his expectations.

New discipline was brought to the staff, and a new atmosphere became evident. Jim's actions in retrospect were often more
symbolic than substantive. Was it really important whether a doctor
wore a white coat or a business suit while making rounds? Maybe

not now in the present era, but to those at the time it was. It also signaled the notion that someone here was in charge.

Besides Campbell's recruits for the Department of Medicine
from outside the institution, others in the institution involved in
training benefited greatly from an overall upgrading of the hospital
as it made their recruitment programs more effective. And of course,
many, if not most, of the trainees within the Department of Medicine
during the time that Jim was chairman stayed on the staff and
became the nucleus for its future department. Richard Sassetti, James
Clark, Bernard Blauuw, Harold Paul, Ernie Fordham, and others
were just a few of the many who would devote their entire professional career to the medical center. And most of these Campbell
trainees would be engaged in the traditional private practice settings.
This Campbell legacy is often overlooked, as it seemed to be dwarfed
by some of his later achievements. But it was there, and clearly needs
to be reiterated. He had restaffed his Department of Medicine with
his own "boys."

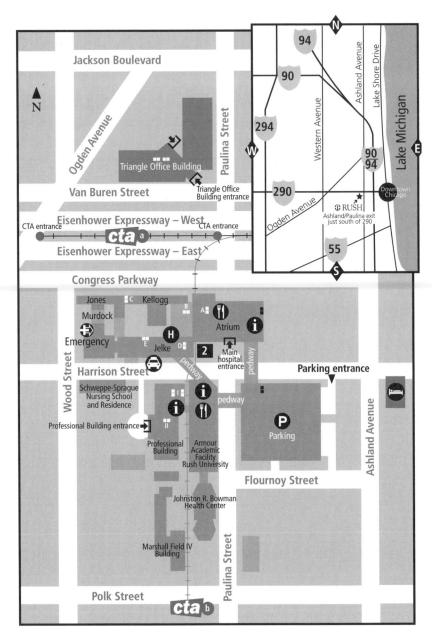

Campus of Rush–Presbyterian–St. Luke's Medical Center, 1986
(modified with permission of Rush University Medical Center)

7

The Merger

The development of the Department of Medicine opened the door for Jim Campbell to extend his connections to the entire Chicago medical community and gain new knowledge and information about what was going on medically throughout the city. There were contacts through physicians who referred patients to Campbell's department, contacts through his active involvement in medical organizations like the Chicago Society of Internal Medicine and the Chicago Medical Society, as well as contacts through his introductions to key medical leaders in Chicago arranged by members of the Presbyterian Hospital medical staff. Nothing that transpired in these encounters escaped his perceptive observation. In these types of settings, less reserved and more frank conversations tended to be the rule, and Jim began to have a better understanding of what was good and what was not so good in Chicago medicine.

Campbell projected a strong identity with Harvard Medical School and its affiliates. He frequently talked about what was happening at the Thorndike and about his mentors and colleagues like Drs. Maxwell Finland and William Castle. Similarly he often referred to his days at Knox College in Galesburg. But he rarely made any reference to his time and experiences at the University of Chicago, where he spent three years in training a decade before. Many of those interviewed for this book were surprised to learn that Campbell had taken part of his medical studies at the Midway. Some who looked upon Campbell as overly ambitious explained this as merely another expression of his intense pursuit of advancement, identifying with the nation's most highly regarded medical school, Harvard, and downplaying his connection with the University of Chicago, very good but not quite Harvard.

Campbell continued to carry on his private discussions about medical center development with George Young, who had now become a member of St. Luke's Hospital Board. Young's immediate concern was the rapid deterioration of the neighborhood around St. Luke's Hospital. Campbell had no official connection with St. Luke's Hospital, but that did not stand in the way of Young and Campbell formulating ideas and plans for both hospitals and where the ensuing product might fit into the medical scene in Chicago. With his experience in medical education for over ten years in Chicago, Albany, and Boston, Campbell communicated his ideas to Young, who was also experienced and understood the subtleties and challenges of academic education that a hospital merger might involve.

Young and Campbell's thinking in many areas was quite similar. Night after night, they discussed their ideas. George was able to enhance Jim's effectiveness by adding tact and diplomacy to Campbell's convictions about medical education, some of which might have seemed unacceptable in their formulation and presentation. Out of these discussions emerged the idea of establishing a superlative medical center for Chicago. Young and Campbell then presented their plan to the chairman of the board of St. Luke's, John Bent. Although startled by the idea, Bent did go along with it, adding some ideas of his own, before further consulting with his counterpart, fellow Presbyterian board member John Simpson, who also provided input for the proposal. Bent and Simpson, also next door neighbors in Lake Forest, fully understood the difficulties that would lie ahead in merging these two strong institutions, each with its own longstanding traditions, into one cohesive unit.

A factor that helped bring about the eventual merger of the two hospitals was that both the sponsoring members of the Presbyterian and Episcopal faiths got along well together socially. There were, of course, some differences, but not any serious barriers to their working together. The more church-going Presbyterians might make a humorous comment, for example, "whenever you find four Episcopalians together, there is always a fifth." And the Episcopalians might return this barb by making the traditional observation about the rule of Presbyterian morality, that you can do whatever you wish as long as you don't enjoy yourself.

St. Luke's Hospital, like Presbyterian, enjoyed a long and distinguished tradition and it dated back even earlier than Presbyterian, to its founding in 1864, when it was originally opened as a hospital for Confederate prisoners. It had been founded by the ladies guild of the Grace Episcopal Church on the near South Side. The founding director, the Reverend Clinton Locke, nurtured growth of the hospital, attracting leading doctors to its staff, including many from Rush Medical College. It also attracted the interest of many of Chicago's most prominent community leaders, including Nathaniel K. Fairbanks, George Armour, George Pullman, Charles Walgreen, and Marshall Field. St. Luke's was also noted for its excellent nursing school. By 1950 St. Luke's, at its location on Michigan Avenue between Fourteenth and Fifteenth streets, had grown to a bed capacity of over 500 served by a strong medical staff and engaged in a considerable amount of charitable medical care, which regularly produced deficits that were generously covered by the Board of Trustees. Like Presbyterian, St. Luke's staff had been severely impacted by the Second World War. Many of its staff were gone for several years, and although, like Presbyterian, it returned to some semblance of normalcy after the war, the hiatus of several years in recruiting made its staff, again like Presbyterian, rather senior in overall makeup.

The idea of merging hospitals at that time was virtually unheard of. As Jim Campbell's friend Dr. Robert Glaser, himself a medical educator, reflected on this, he couldn't imagine anything harder than to join two equally strong medical staffs together. As a consultant Glaser experienced a great deal of difficulty in attempting to bring about the merger of the hospitals of the Brigham complex in Boston into one entity, and he eventually resigned in frustration because he could not get the people involved to come to an agreement.

The merger of Presbyterian and St. Luke's did not happen overnight. It was first discussed in 1950, before Jim Campbell moved on to Albany but did not physically take place until 1959, almost a decade later. When the proposal to merge was first made public in 1954, it was big news both in Chicago and throughout the country. Mergers in the business world usually take place between two unequal enterprises, one clearly dominant and the other a lesser but still important one. Such was not the case here. Both institutions were considered more or less equal in stature. The recollections of distinguished University of Chicago professor Dr. Joseph Kirsner were that the merger represented the coming together of "the cream of the crop of top medical staffs."[1] Subsequent hospital mergers were not nearly as successful as this one, which became one of the most harmonious and durable in American history.[2]

Both institutions were forced by circumstances to react to changes in the Chicago inner city itself, to provide for upgrading their facilities which were becoming obsolete, and finally to deal with the more subtle but real problems in the restructuring and reorganization of each hospital's medical staff. Their difficulties, in order of priority, involved location, facilities, and staffing. Had both hospitals been ideally located with modern facilities, the idea of a merger might never have been proposed. The trustees of both hospitals were enlightened businessmen committed to making whatever changes were necessary to keep their respective institutions in the forefront of medical advances that were going on every day. In those times, boards of trustees were more heavily engaged in the day-to-day operations of hospital management than is the case today. Hospital administration, as we know it today, was just in its infancy.

1. Personal communication, Dr. Joseph Kirsner, June 4, 1998.
2. Personal communication, Dr. Leo Henikoff, May 14, 2000.

Alfred Carton, Albert Dick, Jr., and others on the Presbyterian side and John Bent and others on the St. Luke's side devoted a great deal of their time helping the hospitals manage.

The neighborhood on the near West Side where Presbyterian Hospital was located had been considered an elite residential section up through the 1920s. Chicago's mayor lived there. But the Great Depression resulted in a severe decline in real estate values, and plans for further improvement never materialized. Slumlike conditions developed, and further neighborhood disruption took place when the Congress Street Expressway was constructed and the University of Illinois at Chicago moved from Navy Pier to its present location a mile or so east of the hospital and just west of Chicago's business district. These changes led to the flight of a large number of middle-class families away from the West Side. Plans for an expansion of the University of Illinois Medical School, including a new hospital and construction of a new state-of-the-art federally funded Veterans Administration Hospital, were also undertaken. Although the construction of the Congress Expressway was severely disruptive to the area for several years, it was advantageous in the long run because of its ideal geographic location for the entire Chicago Metropolitan area.

St. Luke's misfortunes of location in 1950 were not unlike Presbyterian's. South Michigan Avenue and the Prairie Avenue neighborhood once constituted a prime location. But it, too, had become run down. Most of the St. Luke's Hospital buildings were very old, but it had recently built a new nursing residence. To connect its old five-story building on Michigan Avenue to the newer fifteen-story building one block east on Indiana would require a very expensive structure. Equipment within the hospital was going to have to be completely replaced, and the design for traffic flow and fire safety was not ideal. So the St. Luke's board had to consider building new facilities and was reluctant to do so because of the neighborhood change. Although many of Presbyterian's physical facilities were also old, its board had recently invested a considerable amount of its endowment in upgrading the laboratory and research facilities at about the time that merger discussions began.

St. Luke's finances were strong enough to proceed with their own building program. Rumors that the Michigan Avenue facility was in financial distress were not true. But both Presbyterian and St. Luke's were supported for the most part by the same philanthropic constituencies. Presbyterian already had funds committed for the construction of the new six-story East Pavilion Building (later renamed the Kellogg Pavilion). The design of the new building also allowed for the construction of eight additional floors, which could accommodate the expansion needs of St. Luke's if they should decide that they could move over to the West Side. The resultant hospital complex would be huge, with over 900 beds, larger by far than any other private hospital in Chicago, and its combined staffs would also be the largest.

The financial benefits from the elimination of duplicate support facilities made the idea even more attractive. And furthermore investment in expensive hospital equipment and instruments might be possible when neither institution on its own might be able to afford them.

The decision by the board to proceed evolved gradually. The idea had been considered by only a few trustees of both groups after Campbell returned to Presbyterian Hospital in 1953. It was then presented for the first time late in 1954 for full board consideration but was not formally approved until April 1956. The actual move of St. Luke's to Presbyterian did not occur until 1959, when construction of the thirteen-floor East Pavilion Building was completed.

The rationale for the merger was almost entirely the creation of Jim Campbell and George Young. Neither hospital on its own had the critical mass of top-flight doctors to develop a truly superlative medical center. Both staffs to some extent had become too senior. They were both bogged down with many old ways of doing things and were less receptive to new and innovative ideas than they should have been. This was reflected in the difficulty of recruiting consistently high-quality interns and residents at both institutions. But both staffs liked to teach. They had been brought up in this tradition. Yet there seemed to be too much inbreeding. And circumstances had allowed some very big egos to develop. Once the merger took place these petty considerations were forgotten and instead of quibbling over old ideas and old ways, both sides had to compete with and adjust to each other. If there were some who could not adjust to this new reality, they might even have to move on and go elsewhere. The patient would be the beneficiary. A new discipline would be brought to both staffs.

At the same time, both staffs served a large clientele of loyal private patients, and if St. Luke's patients found it difficult to accept going to another hospital, there were some incentives in the proposed state-of-the-art facility to persuade them. The resultant large patient base would support full-time consultants, which were now necessary to make the hospital flourish in the new scientific environment. The private fee-for-service system necessary to keep this new 900-bed behemoth financially afloat would at the same time be preserved. Both hospital staffs were in need of more hospital beds for their practices. This was particularly so at Presbyterian, where physical expansion had been planned since the end of the war, but other more pressing priorities had been dealt with first.

Some of the trustees on both sides were skeptical about Campbell's plans. In their view both hospital staffs were top notch. Of course, there are always problems, but in the eyes of many, nothing especially severe. But when doctors on both sides were assured that elimination of the fee-for-service system was not being considered and that the new hospital would be a state-of-the-art facility that would provide the environment for attracting top-notch new recruits for the internship and residency programs, many softened their objections. However, no doctor from either staff was enthusiastic about the whole idea. It seemed highly unlikely that any medical staff on its own would ever have initiated such a proposal. In some ways doctors and hospital departments are just like other people: they have a tendency to resist disturbing the status quo.

Objections to the merger were somewhat less so on the Presbyterian side. But when taken to a vote, the proposal passed by only a small margin. Had the action not been favorable, the merger could have been blocked legally since some of the Presbyterian doctors had fiduciary leverage through philanthropic funds that they had attracted for their ongoing research programs.

On the St. Luke's side there was even less support. Many on St. Luke's staff were quite concerned about the future of their hospital because of the changing neighborhood. They had come to realize that they had to move. Where would they go? If they moved to the Northwestern Medical School campus or even to the University of Chicago, they might be swallowed up and lose their independence and their identity. While many of St. Luke's staff members were affiliated with Northwestern and quite satisfied with the arrangement, many were also affiliated with the University of Illinois. Presbyterian staff members were similarity affiliated and seemed to be getting along well enough in this circumstance. Moreover, many of the St. Luke's staff knew the Presbyterian staff on a close personal basis. Dr. Frank Billings, back in the early part of the century, had established offices on the fourteenth floor of the Peoples Gas Building on Michigan Avenue and shared them equally throughout the many following years with the Capps Internal Medicine group from St. Luke's and the Irons Internal Medicine group from Presbyterian.

Both staffs were served by several of Chicago's most respected physicians and community leaders, including Dr. Egbert Fell, of Presbyterian, who in 1956 performed the first open-heart operation in Chicago using a heart-lung machine, and Dr. Eric Oldberg, of St. Luke's, who, in addition to being considered the founder of neurosurgery in Chicago, served as president of the Chicago Board of Health.

As the time came for the trustees to vote on the proposal, George and Mary Young entertained a number of doctors from both hospitals at their home on Lakeview Avenue to reassure them that the trustees fully understood the issues involved. Young was key with his diplomacy and sophistication in negotiating fairly the objections that were brought forth by each group. Jim Campbell lost some of his abrasiveness and learned a good deal from Young as he struggled with both trustees and doctors to convince them of the wisdom of such a move.

The vote to merge was approved but it was never unanimous. On the morning of the vote, each of the trustees received telegrams from many of the St. Luke's medical staff urging them not to vote for the proposal. It was described by some resentful doctors as being tantamount to a shotgun marriage, forcibly arranged by the trustees. The trustees did understand just how hard it might be for two staffs to merge. This would be particularly so for those from St. Luke's who had to leave the hospital where they had spent their entire professional lives and, in a sense, start all over again.

Considerations of other components of both organizations, such as nursing, administration, the Women's Board, and the like had to be dealt with and major adjustments were necessary. Each place had its own way of getting things done. Each place was justifiably proud of its traditions. Now both were introduced to a fresh but unfamiliar way of doing things. In the long run, these challenges were beneficial to both groups, but for the short run, it wasn't easy.

The attractive fourteen-story nursing residence on Harrison Street, the Schweppe-Sprague Building, constructed in 1950, highlighted the importance of nursing to the whole scheme of things. The St. Luke's Training School for Nurses was established in 1885, and the Presbyterian Hospital School of Nursing in 1903. Both were top quality nursing schools with proud traditions. But there were differences, small by today's standards but, nevertheless, important for the time. The nursing uniform, the nursing caps, the curriculum, and policies for both schools were different. So when the two groups first came together, there clearly were some adjustments to be made for both sides.

Sylvia Melby, Presbyterian's director of nursing, was near retirement, so it fell to Edith Payne of St. Luke's to lead the new merged organizations. Payne moved her office from St. Luke's to Presbyterian as soon as the merger was official in 1956, but three years before the actual merger took place so by the time of the merger, many of the problems had been resolved. As Ruth Schmidt, a leader in nursing during that time recalled, both groups were beginning to fall behind the times. Payne stepped in and initiated a number of reforms that were totally new to both groups. New changes in curriculum and modern procedures were instituted. An experimental floor, 2 Jones, in the old section of Presbyterian was utilized as a model for these changes, which were eventually applied to all the hospital floors. Social programs for students of both schools were developed, and the strong alumni groups from each school were integrated. Payne opened enrollment to minorities and to males, something almost unheard of for the time, and she also worked hard for raises in the salary structure.

Much of the credit for the successful union goes to Payne, who in addition to her professional qualifications knew a surprising amount about finances and had a good business head. She got along well with Campbell, and their alliance marked the beginning of a long and fruitful relationship, which ultimately resulted in the elevation of the standards of nursing at Rush University Medical Center to among the highest in the nation.

The traditions of both Woman's Boards and volunteer organizations also started at the beginning. Ladies from the Grace Episcopal Church and St. Luke's Hospital started the Camp Douglas Ladies Aid Society to help sick victims of the Confederate prisoner of war camp. During the Second World War, hospital volunteers at Presbyterian worked directly on hospital floors because the nursing staff was so shorthanded. Many of the Woman's Board members served for their entire lives as volunteers. Mrs. Virginia DeYoung, from St. Luke's, began serving in 1932, each Monday, and continued for sixty years. Mrs. Clyde Shorey, daughter of founding Presbyterian board member, William Douglas, first became involved in volunteer work in 1912 and continued in this capacity for seven decades. The socially prominent Mrs. Fentrees Ott was elected first president of the combined boards in 1956, and the cordial and friendly way in which each group got together at the time of the merger greatly reinforced a positive image for success of the entire undertaking.

The Rush University Medical Center Fashion Show, started in 1927 by the St. Luke's Woman's Board, has been an annual event since its inception and the only one of its kind in the nation. Development of the gift shop, the art carts, the patient library, the beauty shop, the chapel, the Smith Lounge (the waiting room for families of patients undergoing surgery), an endowed chair, scholarship funds, and a Cancer Treatment Center are just some of the important services and programs that have been provided by the Woman's Board's fund-raising efforts through this event.

After the merger, the volunteer component of the Woman's Board became a separate department, headed by Jane Warren. The volunteer service is now the largest by far of any hospital in Chicago. Over five hundred men and women serve quietly and unselfishly, providing an extraordinary amount of service in countless ways in virtually all areas of the hospital. Interest of the public in serving is at an all-time high. The volunteer service is an essential and integral part of the medical center operation and the institution could not do without them. Several volunteers and Woman's Board members serve on a number of hospital committees.

Jim Campbell never lost sight of these contributions. When he walked by the volunteer office, people would say, "Here comes the boss!" A leader with verve and sparkle, Campbell also manifested charm with his powerful inspiring voice when he addressed the organization at their annual meetings. No one left these meetings feeling less important or taken for granted. Campbell made sure of this. The audience felt they were an integral part of the team. And they were. And are.

Very few on either medical staff realized that Jim Campbell had such an important role in the creation of the merger and had it been known, his influence might have been resented, and the entire effort could have been compromised. As far as the medical staff in general was concerned, it was all the trustees' work and the trustee's decision.

And indeed the trustees were the ones who approved the merger, but it was Campbell, along with a few key trustees, George Young, John Bent, and Ralph Bard, who formulated all the details of this huge effort, and it was Campbell to whom the trustees looked for guidance on medical staff matters. Campbell worked with the trustees in a very deferential manner. He would say it was their hospital, their medical center. He might be suggesting to them that an idea was their idea, when in fact it was probably his own. His sense of mission was contagious, and one could not resist getting caught up in it. Not even the practical-minded leading members of Chicago's business community, the boards of both hospitals, were immune to his brilliant persuasions. Campbell communicated to the trustees in their language, language that they could understand, a rare quality in a physician. He also began to develop a sense about things financial, again most unusual for a physician. Here was an individual who earned by his scientific achievements the highest regard from his professional peers and at the same time was beginning to understand the real intricacies of finance and the business world. Campbell was a rare individual, indeed.

A fund-raising campaign for $7.5 million was launched to finance the cost of the eight-floor hospital addition, an amount larger by far than either hospital had ever attempted before. The committee was headed by Ralph Bard, Jr., and included John Bent, leading businessman Philip Clarke, insurance executive Donald McLennan, Jr., and Mayor Richard J. Daley.

Additional funding was provided as the merged institutions floated a hospital bond issue, a newly created financial product for the time. It was subscribed fully within a few weeks. This new mechanism for financing began to be employed frequently for interim financing and was used subsequently for construction of additional new buildings, such as the Kidston House Residence for interns and residents, the McCormick House for nursing students, and the Jelke Building for laboratories.

The groundbreaking ceremony for the new thirteen-story Pavilion Building (later to be renamed the Kellogg Building) was held outside on a cold, damp, and windy day in April 1957. The backdrop for this event was the noisy newly constructed eight-lane Congress Expressway (later to be renamed the Eisenhower Expressway) located just north of the ceremonial stands. The noise of the CTA elevated trains going east or turning south interrupted the proceedings of the ceremony until they passed by. There were derricks and construction equipment close by and looking on from several directions were deteriorating buildings and decaying neighborhoods.

President John Bent presided at the ceremony with prominent civic, medical, and community leaders. Presbyterian Hospital chaplain Reverend Louis Sherwin delivered the invocation. Then Board

Chairman Ralph Bard addressed the gathering and said that Chicago and the Midwest would be provided with one of the nation's outstanding hospitals for patient care, medical education, and research. Richard J. Daley, then in the first of his five terms as mayor of Chicago, voiced the same sentiments saying that the occasion was a great day in medical history, not only for the West Side, but for the whole of Chicago. After the cornerstone was laid, the ceremony ended with the Episcopal Bishop of Chicago Charles L. Street delivering the benediction. The clergy were dressed in ecclesiastical robes, and banners for both the Presbyterian and Episcopal churches of Chicago were presented, adding a certain appropriate solemnity and pomp to the occasion. A sense of mission and high purpose was unmistakable. The medical center was dedicated to the Glory of God and the Service of Man.[3]

This sense of theatre, of the dramatic, and the ceremonial religious pageantry had all the earmarks of a Campbell-orchestrated event. This was the first of many public events, groundbreakings, dedications, and graduations that would become trademarks of his long tenure as leader of the medical center. There was no detail that was unimportant for these occasions, as Campbell oversaw the entire production.

Variations of this scene would be repeated over and over again during the next twenty-five years as the new medical center on the West Side was being put in place. A quarter century later the culmination of the Campbell expansion program, the new Atrium Building, known as the New Footprint of the West Side, would be the largest hospital addition ever built in the state. Many of its rooms faced an inside garden so that one got the sense of no longer being on the West Side. Things had changed that much over the ensuing time period.

Mayor Daley's presence at that event was the first of many appearances for him at Presbyterian–St. Luke's functions over the years, and support for the medical center by the Daley family and the Mayor's office has continued right up through the accession of

3. The Latin inscription of this, "Ad Gloriam Dei Hominumque Salutem," is inscribed on the mace of Rush University used at commencement exercises.

Mayor Richard M. Daley, who presided over the dedication of the new Robert and Terri Cohn Research Building forty-one years later in 1998.

In the early years of his mayoral tenure, Richard J. Daley was confronted with the exodus of many businesses and civic institutions from the city, which led to numerous problems of unemployment, deterioration of neighborhoods, erosion of the tax base, and a general decline in the central city. But here were two of the city's leading institutions deciding to stay in the city rather than move to the suburbs. And not only deciding to stay, but expanding very considerably the scope of their operations. In time, the medical center would become one of the city's leading employers and a beacon of hope for the future of the near West Side as neighborhoods around the medical center began to revitalize dramatically many years later.

In 1977, Mayor Daley underwent successful carotid artery surgery under the direction of a team of medical center doctors, led by Drs. Hushang Javid, Thomas Coogan, Jr., and Floyd Davis. This procedure, elective in nature, was performed on Sunday morning in an effort to keep news of the event from leaking to the press prematurely. The effect was to deflect much of the commotion that attends the presence of reporters everywhere in the hospital, in the elevators, on the stairwells, and calling and paging any and all of the doctors involved in the case. The media was nowhere to be found on Sunday because they had expected the procedure to be carried out on Monday and were totally taken by surprise when announcement of the successful surgery was made late Sunday afternoon. All of the operating room staff were called in and surgery was performed in the old operating room number 8. Citizens of Chicago, and yes even many throughout the nation, followed this story with great interest. Daley by that time had become one of the country's most respected and admired political leaders.

The merger was expected to be more difficult for those coming from St. Luke's. Jim Campbell had a lot of new ideas, and he wasn't bound by petty ties to the old guard of either place. Yet, when necessary, he could deal with the big egos in a politically respectful way. His ideas were not "Presbyterian" or "St. Luke's" but "we" ideas.

Both sides could look to him for leadership because he made cohesiveness a primary value of new programs as everyone moved forward. It was the perfect opportunity to initiate new ideas and innovations. Even those already at Presbyterian experienced "newness" as they saw the East Pavilion Building undergoing construction.

Each medical staff had elected its own officers and department chairmen, so clearly this could not continue. In the instance of the medical staff, the two staffs elected their own officers in 1957 and 1958, but then held a combined election in 1959 in which Presbyterian internist Dr. George Stuppy was elected as the first president of the combined medical staff in a tightly contested race. In the following year, St. Luke's Dr. Thomas Coogan succeeded Stuppy. Stuppy and Coogan were both bright and moderate thinking people whose leadership posture elevated the prestige of the office. Both staffs were represented fairly, and a precedent for orderly elections for the future was established. For many years, medical staff meetings were held at the Guild Hall of the University Club downtown. They were well attended, and many subjects and issues were vigorously debated but virtually without any hint of acrimony. It took a lot less time than was expected for the doctors to drop their claim that they were from Presbyterian or St. Luke's, and soon they were from Presbyterian–St. Luke's.

Some of the medical staff's problems with the merger were in the long run not substantive but for the time, they were very real. St. Luke's internists were used to the apprentice system; they were greeted at the front door by their assigned house staff. (The apprentice system in a modified form persisted for many years on both sides in surgery.) The house staff was now being directed by the "hired hands," the full-time people Campbell had brought in. St. Luke's Medical Department had no full-time people. So the Campbell system prevailed, but the St. Luke's internists quickly began to see the advantages to such changes, which, in fact, proved very helpful for their practices.

St. Luke's doctors sensed that Presbyterian doctors were a bit pompous. They seemed to take their University of Illinois titles as Rush professors a little too seriously, as they did the notion that

Presbyterian Hospital was founded by a medical school. But that had happened some seventy-five years beforehand, and Rush as a practical entity did not exist.

The fear and anxiety of some physicians, that they would be "squeezed out" at the West Side, were instrumental in the establishment of Skokie Valley Hospital (later renamed the Rush North Shore Medical Center). They could then practice and bring patients to this new hospital. Eventually, a few of the doctors from both staffs did relocate there, mostly as a second location, but kept their primary activity downtown.

Some staff physicians objected to the rule that the house staff had to write orders on their private patients, always, of course, in consultation with the attending private physician. Campbell acquiesced to these objections eventually but insisted that these doctors in return carry out their own history and physical examinations for their admitted patients. These ensuing disagreements eventually led one or two doctors to relocate elsewhere. Campbell's regulations in retrospect seemed quite reasonable, but he demanded that they be adhered to. Through all of this, a message was sent that Campbell meant business, he could be tough, and he played for keeps.

A seemingly petty annoyance to Presbyterian doctors was the term "St. Luke's section," used in referring to the entire newly constructed East Pavilion Building. The implication was, of course, that the older sections, those that appeared obsolete, that is, the Pavilion Building and the Jones Building, were the Presbyterian sections and, therefore, in some way second rate. Patients admitted to the hospital often requested the new section, the "St. Luke's section." There was very considerable depth of feeling about this because the Presbyterian doctors, along with the Presbyterian Board of Trustees, had worked hard for many years before the merger to raise the money for the construction of the first phase of the new building, and here St. Luke's seemed to be getting all the recognition.

Many years later, in describing what took place during the merger, one St. Luke's doctor described its success for the St. Luke's side in terms of "we took over." The resultant merged institution was, of course, an entirely different entity. A dynamic symbiosis had transpired, in which the sum of both hospitals' achievements could not equal the achievement of the merged complex. As time went on, one side would have greater strengths in one department or activity than the other, but there were no losers, only winners, particularly patients who benefited from all this friendly and highly professional rivalry. From the standpoint of the St. Luke's staff, whose practice patterns were more disrupted by the merger, the practice of every doctor, including those who were very opposed to the merger, prospered and grew. Most later were glad "they came over." Virtually none of the Presbyterian practices were adversely affected by the merger.

Referral of patients between staffs took a while to develop, but eventually the distinction between a St. Luke's referral and a Presbyterian referral began to disappear. Large St. Luke's medical groups such as the Capps, the Roskelly, and the Coogan groups began sending some of their patients to specialists on the Presbyterian side. And the same thing occurred in the opposite direction with the DeYoung, Kirkland, and Kesler groups from Presbyterian. Cross referral seemed to occur less from individual doctors in solo practice, and a few on both sides held out to the very end of their career only referring to those doctors from their original staffs.

A difficult and even greater challenge was in selecting a leader for each department. The major departments were Medicine and Surgery, but those were by no means the only ones; on the surgical side there were also separate sections for Orthopedics, Urology, Neurosurgery, and the like. Both hospitals also had their own Department of Obstetrics and Gynecology, Pediatrics, Psychiatry, and Pathology. And both hospitals had leading doctors in each section or department, so choosing one among them was not always easy. The future of the institution depended on the right choices. Whoever was selected had to be committed to setting a standard for the department or section to keep it in equal stride or ahead in medicine's rapid progress.

In the case of the Department of Medicine and the obvious recognized need for a full-time salaried person at the chairmanship level, the decision was relatively straightforward. Jim Campbell had been doing an extremely good job as chairman at Presbyterian since his return in 1954 and was recognized throughout the city's medical community for this. He had also established several medical subspecialty sections such as Hematology and Endocrinology. On the St. Luke's side several highly qualified internists had served from time to time as chairmen without salary, but all were engaged in active private practices that left them with little time to develop the areas that a leading hospital department now had to have. Subspecialty section development at St. Luke's was behind that of Presbyterian. So the selection of Jim Campbell as the first chairman of Internal Medicine of the new Presbyterian–St. Luke's came as no surprise and was widely supported by both staffs.

On the surgical side at the time of the merger, things were different. In 1951, at about the time that Jim Campbell was winding up his first tour of duty at Presbyterian, the hospital board appointed Dr. Edward J. (Ted) Beattie to a full-time position to develop Surgery and eventually lead the department. This appointment in 1954 was every bit as important for the time as that of Campbell in Medicine. Surgery, too, had been in need of reinvigorating. Beattie had attended Harvard in the class of 1943A; Campbell was in the class of 1943B. After his training at Peter Bent Brigham Hospital in Boston, Beattie was appointed a Markel Scholar for three years, during which time he developed the modern structure for the Department of Surgery at George Washington University in Washington, D.C. By that time he was regarded as one of the nation's most promising surgeons and surgical educators. In addition to possessing very excellent surgical skills in his specialty of chest surgery, Ted Beattie was a highly energetic organizer and an inspirational teacher. When he arrived at Presbyterian, he immediately injected new life into the department, reorganizing the training program to begin to attract top-quality trainees and initiated a surgical investigation research program that was able to carry out credible research. In addition to all of this, Beattie had developed a busy surgical practice His elevation to be the chairman of Surgery, first at Presbyterian in 1954 and then at the merged hospitals, was widely supported by both staffs.

Beattie ran the department very fairly – not an easy job at all when it involved so many strong-willed individuals. There were constant conflicts and fighting about whose patients were to be admitted and, once admitted, when surgeons could get operating room time. As soon as the new hospital had opened, a shortage of beds developed, and surgeons had to wait days and sometimes even weeks to get their patients admitted. Many operating rooms were busy from early morning until the late evening. Beattie then set up a priority system to help circumvent this problem. Everybody grumbled, but they adhered to his rules. Perhaps no one but Beattie could have kept people in line and made the merger in surgery work. Dr. Pen Faber, a trainee at the time and later one of Rush's premier stars in surgery (chest) as well as associate dean for Surgical Sciences and Services, characterized Beattie's work as almost in the realm of a superhuman accomplishment.[4]

At the time Campbell and Young were planning the merger, another physician, Dr. Ormond C. Julian, was in the early years of his brilliant surgical career. When Campbell was a medical student at the University of Chicago, Julian was also in training and received a Ph.D. degree in surgery from the university in 1942. Julian served his internship at St. Luke's hospital in 1934 before starting his residency at the university. He later served in one of the St. Luke's affiliated military units and was awarded the Soldiers Medal for his participation in a rescue effort of several aviators who had been shot down in the China-Burma-India theater.

Julian had hoped to return to the university after the war but was told there were no openings available. He started a general surgical practice and spent the next several years doing surgery at several smaller hospitals in Chicago including South Chicago Hospital and Chicago Memorial Hospital. Julian became very busy and performed many surgical procedures at night and on the weekends. Many years later, even after he had established the cardiovascular surgical program at Presbyterian–St. Luke's and demands on his time

4. Personal communication, Dr. L. Penfield Faber, November 5, 1998.

were extreme, Julian was quite reluctant to give up performing these general surgical cases such as hernia repairs and removal of gallbladders as he was an outstanding general surgeon. Julian's pioneer work would become instrumental in establishing the specialty of cardiovascular surgery, which did not exist at that time.

During this time, Julian was also serving as a surgical consultant to the Hines Veterans Hospital, where he worked with the pioneering surgeon in vascular research, Dr. Geza DeTakats, who was conducting the only vascular clinic of its kind in Chicago. In this clinic, chronic problems like varicose veins were evaluated and treated, but there were also other vascular problems seen, like vascular insufficiency, that were often treated by amputation, such was the state of treatment at the time. University of Illinois Departmental Chairman Dr. Warren Cole recognized Julian's brilliance and brought him into his program and DeTakats was able to secure a staff appointment for Julian at St. Luke's as well. Julian developed techniques for treatment of hypertension and peripheral vascular disease by sympathectomy, surgical treatment of portal hypertension, surgical treatment of aortic and iliac artery occlusion by replacement bypass graft, and devised the sternum-splitting incision that became the standard approach for heart surgery. He also helped develop synthetic arterial grafts.

In 1951, Julian did the first mitral commisurotomy for rheumatic heart disease in Chicago. This courageous pioneer endured consecutive failures in his early experience with this procedure, which carried an extremely high mortality rate at that time. Only very severely ill patients could be considered for this procedure. Julian could be found retching in the operating room lavatories in the morning before undertaking these difficult operations. No one could qualify as a real hero more than Ormond Julian. All these efforts eventually resulted in the saving of many lives and restoration to good health for many others.

Julian inspired many other talented individuals to follow in his work. First came Dr. Sam Dye, then Dr. Hushang Javid, and finally Dr. Jim Hunter. Many others would follow. Julian was such a good surgeon that he was never afraid that someone would overshadow him. So all of his associates were top notch. Javid, particularly, made surgery look easy. Among many of his contemporary surgeons, Javid may have been regarded as the most gifted and skilled surgeon in the history of the entire modern medical center. Julian eventually established a cardiovascular surgical training and trained dozens of skilled heart and blood vessel surgeons. All the best nurses wanted to scrub with Julian. All the best students and young people wanted to train under Julian. Later on, he was instrumental in bringing about the first heart transplant in Chicago performed by his associate Dr. Hassan Najafi in 1968.

Julian's requirements of his staff were very high, but he never asked anybody to do anything that he himself wasn't willing to do or had not done. My first experience with Dr. Julian came when, as a resident, I arrived in the operating room at the University of Illinois one morning about 6:00 A.M. Julian was just finishing a case, an emergency repair of a ruptured aortic aneurysm and was on his way across the street to Presbyterian–St. Luke's to start another case at 7:30. Julian constantly kept after his trainees and associates to go to meetings and write scientific papers. The type of training that he espoused demanded a very high level of commitment.

One of Julian's "boys," a junior resident, had been given a weekend call assignment that was brutally, almost inhumanely tough. The call schedule had been made out by the senior resident. The junior resident talked to Julian and complained about it. Julian listened sympathetically but, with a gentle smile and a soft glint in his eye, said to the junior resident, "You understand, I have to back the senior resident."

Julian was always fair, but his expectations were very high. The nature of the work required it. Many of the cardiovascular cases in the operating room went on for seven or eight hours, even longer. There were no stops for coffee breaks, and the subsequent care and monitoring of these patients afterwards required the same kind of intense vigilance. All this became routine. For him and for what he was trying to accomplish, there was no other way.

Julian's career was in ascendancy at the time of the merger. He organized and effectively led the group practice of cardiovascular surgeons known as JDJH (Julian, Dye, Javid, and Hunter) and it became the premier practice for heart surgeons in Chicago for many years. Julian's hospital service might occupy eighty or ninety surgical beds at one time. Since many of these patients had complicated non-surgical or medical problems, an equal or greater number of consulting physicians from other hospital services were also needed. The Julian service in itself could almost be reconstituted as a separate hospital. At the same time, the medical cardiovascular group headed by Dr. John Graettinger was also rapidly expanding, carrying out more procedures, and training more fellows, so that the synergy provided by these two closely allied programs for the newly created merged hospital also was extraordinary: One plus one was equaling three, four, and sometimes five.

The magnitude of the work being done by the Julian group astounded the rest of the hospital community and indeed all of Chicago medicine. In a new time and a new era, Presbyterian–St. Luke's was establishing a preeminent position for itself just as each hospital in another time and another era had done. The field of cardiovascular surgery was still in its infancy and future growth could be expected. Cardiac bypass had not yet been developed. Patients from all over the Midwest were referred in, and the hospital census for the Julian service was so large that a daily or twice daily bulletin was printed to help his huge staff keep up with the entire goings on. Julian recruited cardiovascular nurse Mr. Jack Theil to help coordinate this colossal effort. The Julian group was particularly careful about communicating with referring doctors and Julian would take particular note when patients were referred in from the University of Chicago, where he had trained originally and had wanted to return after the war.

The Julian team also went out to outlying hospitals to do emergency surgery, bringing their own instruments and staff along with them. One night, after a surgical procedure had been performed at one hospital, a call was made for an emergency from another hospital. So the team had to wait for the instruments to be sterilized before moving on to the next emergency.

Julian's career continued to skyrocket. A separate section of cardiovascular surgery was established, and in the mid-1960s Julian was made chief of all of Surgery, after Dr. Ted Beattie moved on to New York City, where he was appointed medical director and chief of General and Thoracic Surgery at the Sloan-Kettering Memorial Institute. Julian continued on until 1972, when health forced his retirement. In 1974, he underwent a coronary artery bypass procedure performed by his associate, Dr. Hushang Javid, a procedure Julian himself had been instrumental in developing and survived for another 13 years.

With such an extraordinary program developing when the two hospitals merged, this left no doubt about the wisdom of Jim Campbell's long-range planning. But the Julian cardiovascular phenomenon was not without its problems. Some doctors sensed that Julian and his group were selected out as favorites and regarded as Campbell's golden boys. The Julian program was attracting patients, outstanding trainees, and generating innovative research. From his position as chairman of Medicine, Jim was doing all that he could to foster this success. But the enormous activity of the Julian group put a strain on the resources available for the rest of the medical center to grow and expand. Other doctors had greater difficulty getting their patients admitted because so many beds were taken up by the cardiovascular group. Campbell would talk to Julian about getting his patients discharged earlier so beds might open up sooner. And occasionally these and other similar discussions escalated into very heated exchanges between the two.

Campbell and Julian were both very bright Type A personalities, but Jim was interested in the long view, Julian in the present. Both were considered expert in heart disease, and they would disagree at times. Campbell took a rather dim view of surgeons, saying that if you want to hide a hundred dollars from a surgeon, just put it in a book. A sense of the internist's clear-cut intellectual superiority was reflected in this barb. Then Julian would say to one of his residents that it interests him (Julian) as a surgeon that he is capable of knowing everything that Campbell knows, but in addition he possesses all the surgical skills. One morning, when Campbell appeared in a scrub suit in the operating room to be on hand for a surgical procedure in which a new heart-lung machine was being used for the first time, Julian asked him why he was there. When Campbell responded that the surgeons had requested a bright cardiologist to be there in case they needed any advice, Julian replied, "So why did they send for you?" Campbell was obviously insulted and left in a huff.

More may have been made of the Campbell-Julian differences than was actually there. In retrospect, Julian and his associates claimed that admission and hospital policies were tilted against the JDJH group, restricting its growth. But many other doctors, particularly surgeons, would complain that Presbyterian–St. Luke's was becoming the "Chicago Heart Institute," and not much of anything else was being promoted and supported. Campbell and others in administration were caught in a bind trying to balance all these considerations.

In formulating how the merger could result in the development of a truly superlative medical center, Campbell and the trustees no doubt envisioned an institution with strengths that would enable it to achieve a desired status within a given frame of time. It was expected that two very good staffs would become greater together than they were apart. In fact, where one hospital staff might be weak in one area, this could be made up for in strength from the other. Then this newly created institution would be well ahead of many others throughout the country. But, still, no one could be sure just how it would all work out. That the merger would work, there would have to be no doubt. Both from the Presbyterian and the St. Luke's sides, there were too many professional assets for it not to work. Perhaps it might, however, take a while. Because of Julian, it happened right away. And because of Julian, instead of getting a double or a triple, the newly merged institution scored a home run.

And most important and vital to the success of the merger was the positive attitude of both hospital and professional staffs in adjusting to make it all work out. Trustee support was also very important. And it wasn't easy. Everyone sensed that, through it all, the final product was very much worth working for. And, indeed, it turned out that way.

After the merger took place, things settled down, and a new era had started. Most recalled that the whole time of adjustment was very short. It was the best thing that ever happened to both places. One of the nation's leading medical institutions was being created as new ideas and innovations were being introduced. One highly respected senior surgeon from St. Luke's many years later recalled, "I didn't want to come over, but I'm glad I did. Although he was never very popular or well liked by the Presbyterian staff, Campbell really put the place together. It was good because the old goats had to get out with their little kingdoms and give up their corner."

8

The Educator and Scholar

Overseeing the Department of Medicine, particularly after the merger, when its size vastly increased, was a large undertaking. The department was also composed of sections: cardiology, gastroenterology, rheumatology, as well as many others. All doctors on the medical staff belong to a department and sometimes to a section within that department. The chairman of the Department of Medicine then has the responsibility for the overall direction of General Medicine as well as its internal sections. Thus, the chairman has to attend to organization, supervision of physicians in training, and ongoing disciplinary matters. This included review of all diagnostic and treatment methods as to their appropriateness and an insistence on initiating new advances and new treatments whenever applicable. Corrective measures could also be extended to include attending physicians, those in practice as well as those in research. A section might meet only once a month or even quarterly, but the larger departments met once a week and preparation for the event was a major undertaking that required the participation of several people.

Over the past five decades at Rush University Medical Center, the departmental meetings considered the very best were those con-

ducted by Jim Campbell when he was chairman of the Department
of Internal Medicine. These events, known as Medical Grand
Rounds, were the highlight of the week. Every Friday at noon in the
A. B. Dick Amphitheater, people from all over the hospital would
gather. Students, interns, residents, consultants, specialists, basic scientists, attending physicians from the Department of Medicine as
well as many other departments, nurses, virtually everybody in the
hospital came. All age groups were represented. Even the hospital
chaplains attended as part of their program for improving patient
understanding. The room, with a capacity of about 200, filled quickly, so unless you got there early, you had to stand or sit on the steps
leading from the entrance at the rear of the auditorium down to the
front below next to the stage. On the left was the podium where the
case was presented by the intern. Sitting stonelike in the first or second row on the right, with arms folded, legs crossed, and a straight-
ahead stare, concentrating on getting ready for his "show," was Jim
Campbell. If Campbell relaxed, turned his head to the side or back
toward the audience and smiled, the tension in the room eased. If he
rose to speak with a critical, questioning, judgmental, harsh, and incisive tone, everybody tightened up, wondering just how they would
respond if they were on the receiving end of one of his penetrating
questions or comments.

The A. B. Dick, as it was called, had been constructed in the
middle of several larger buildings, and it had no direct exit to the
street from its ground entrance. Its location may have been an afterthought. There may have been no other space available. It became
the central meeting location for all major hospital events in the fifties,
sixties, and even as late as the seventies. Albert B. Dick III, known to
his friends as "A. B.," provided the necessary funding for it, and it was
named for his father, who had been active on the Presbyterian board
in the 1940s and early 1950s. A. B.'s grandfather, Daniel Jones had
donated the money necessary for construction of the Jones Pavilion
Building at the beginning of the century. A. B. and Jim were good
friends, and Jim was persuasive in getting A. B. and his family to come
through once more for the support of this much-needed facility.

The larger departmental meetings had previously been held in the old North Amphitheater of the Senn Building, now hopelessly outdated and much too small. Eventually, the size of the medical center professional staffs expanded so much that the A. B. Dick wasn't even large enough. Campbell helped design the facility. It had an elevated stage in front, so Jim could, if he so desired, recite a few lines as Brutus in Shakespeare's *Julius Caesar* or play a part in a Brooke Pemberton Broadway play. He never quite did that, but for those who attended, it wouldn't have come as a total surprise. Campbell was an actor of supreme ability. He really knew how to do it and he was most effective in holding an audience. He was now in his glory, as the consummate actor, wizard physician, and severe fire-and-brimstone preacher.

Anyone not interested in joining in this extraordinary hour-long exercise in which medical practitioners attempted to define as precisely as possible the scientific principles to apply to the inexactitudes of clinical practice had better leave. While he never came out and actually said it, the message was clear: he was ready to take on all challengers. People from many of the city's other medical institutions were also frequently in attendance.

Campbell started out with an explanation of the ground rules. "If you have questions at any time, please feel free to address them to any one of us. In turn, any of us will feel free to address questions to you." But Campbell was completely fair as a moderator. This rule of Campbell's was meant to minimize grandstanding or the exercise of ego. But it was a chilling reminder that anyone who attempted to embarrass any attending or house staff physician involved in the case presented for some oversight or who wanted to pontificate or who said something irresponsible ran the risk of being skewered by Campbell.

The case was presented by an intern; the patient would be ushered into the room from the back onto the stage, usually in a wheelchair or even on a gurney, and then introduced to the audience by Campbell. The patient could be private or clinic, have a classical common or some exotic puzzling problem, and the case could also have surgical implications. Questions would be asked of the patient, and then the patient was excused. The resident would then continue the presentation with X-rays, scans, lab results, and the like. After the patient left the conference room, Jim would say to the smokers in the audience, "Now, you can light it, if you can stand the risk."

At the start, Campbell announced that no eating would be permitted. If he heard the crinkling of a lunch bag, he would stop the proceedings and ask without naming a person that whoever was creating the distraction to please stop. If it occurred while the patient was present, he would wait until the patient left and then deliver a short sermon on all that the patient was contributing for the training program and, hence, the degree of respect and consideration we owed them. It was a good reminder that in addition to revenue, the patients contributed a great deal to the staff's professional life by what they allowed us to learn from them.

Exhaustive preparation for Grand Rounds were made by everyone involved in the presentation and its subsequent discussion. The intern or resident presenting the case worked all week to put it together. You had to be extremely well prepared. Nothing could go wrong. You had to do better than the last one on stage from last week. You had to be organized because Campbell was very critical. You absolutely had to do well. Campbell discouraged and even belittled lecture-type discussions. It didn't mean a thing, unless it could be applied to this particular patient at this particular time. As the conference went forward, the entire audience was stimulated to join in. You had to think on your feet. Campbell seemed to have superior knowledge on the subject at hand, no matter what it might be. Experts from the attending staff were called on to comment, and if the responses were not pertinent, appropriate, or accurate, God help them. Even the best and brightest were pushed to their limits of knowledge and experience. Campbell encouraged others to rebut what was presented. But Campbell elicited comments from the most experienced and highly respected in attendance to provide a rounded and balanced viewpoint. In this sense he wasn't the show. It was the patient and all the meaningful information that came from these conferences. So Campbell was both moderator, conductor, referee, and interlocutor. His deft handling of the discussions drew to the surface the many pieces of the jigsaw puzzle of diagnosis, suggested treatment, and the physiological alterations in the course of the disease or diseases that were being presented.

He thus provided character and personality for Grand Rounds. It stood out as one of the finest exercises of its type in the country.[1] His colleagues from Harvard, Bob Glaser and Herb Scheinberg, were most impressed when they attended. Little reverence could be shown, however, to many of the distinguished guests. One such individual, an expert in radiation therapy from a prestigious Ivy League medical school was asked to interpret a chest X-ray. The guest declined saying that he didn't specialize in this; he was a therapeutic, not a diagnostic radiologist. Campbell went ballistic over this response. "Well," he said, "spoken like a true specialist. You won't even make a comment about something like a routine chest X-ray." Campbell was nasty as he could be. After attending Grand Rounds and seeing Campbell in action, a member of the hospital Board of Trustees commented that he had never encountered such a tough character, not even in the business world.

There could be great fear at these events. When the exchanges became a bit too heated, Campbell would lighten up and perhaps even tell a joke. He also could be compassionate with someone doing his best, but just not coming across. But as biting as a criticism might be, it was always in the spirit of what was best for the patient. There was no place for pomposity, but a very high tone for learning, decision making, and the scope of responsibility that every physician must assume.

Attending Medical Grand Rounds was a fantastic experience. One cannot measure by any standard the heightened awareness and interest in medicine that was conveyed by these conferences. Campbell would always insist that correct diagnosis was imperative,

---

1. Arch Item: Medical Grand Rounds, *Presbyterian–St. Luke's Hospital Bulletin*, undated; Box 8, folder 6, C97-052, James A. Campbell, M.D., Papers 1924–1983, Record Group 002000, Office of the President, Rush–Presbyterian–St. Luke's Medical Center/Rush University Medical Center Archives, Chicago, Ill.

a prompt and correct decision was essential, for rarely do we get second chances. He would make up metaphors as he went along. Jim made up the Willie Sutton law: "that's where the money is." In other words, go right to the heart of the matter. Don't mess around or wander. His disapproval was quite evident when the discussion bogged down into "ruling out" this or that, or with the recitation of an exhaustive lists of differential diagnoses.

Before the meeting had ended, no matter how heated the discussions had been, Campbell would then settle himself and his audience down and carefully summarize the points that needed to be emphasized, and the message that one should take away from the conference. And at subsequent Grand Rounds, follow-up for the case discussed would be provided, thereby ensuring regular attendance.

Particularly for the students attending, the Grand Rounds experience provided a thrilling opportunity to study with those who were practicing and conducting clinical and fundamental research at its highest level. A University of Illinois medical student who had never served on any rotations as a student at Presbyterian Hospital selected it for his four years of internship and residency solely from his favorable impressions of Grand Rounds.

Medical Grand Rounds was first started by Dr. David Baldwin in 1947. When Campbell returned to Presbyterian in 1953, he made it known that he expected all members of his department to attend. By this time, the teaching philosophy of Grand Rounds was coming into its own. The idea was that anybody could contribute, the least or the greatest, and any question could be heard and responded to. The patient was the prime focus. Organized in this way, Grand Rounds excelled as a learning experience. At about that time, the well-established premier medical education discipline for the time, the Clinical Pathological Conference (known as the CPC), was beginning to run its course. In this venue, the case was presented, discussion followed, and then later the autopsy findings were disclosed. "Maybe on the next case, you could do more for the patient" was the message. But now much of the air of mystery had diminished because medicine could do so much more for the patient. Technology was exploding, and medicine was making great strides in all areas of diagnosis and treatment. The message from Medical Grand Rounds was, "maybe you could do more right here for this patient, right now."

At Grand Rounds Campbell had no patience with the timid and the overly deliberative. He demanded quick and correct decisions right now, based on what was presented. But Campbell could just as easily mold an audience in an entirely different way. Here he was also very good at communicating. He could set the tone of his message by his initial remarks. If he intended to set the presentation to a high level of sober thought he might begin in the following way.

> The great macro-historian, Arnold Toynbee, tells us that what is happening around us is rarely well understood until it becomes well ensconced in the past. Were he here today, he would probably compare us to the man who uses a microscope to examine a river flowing to the ocean. We are so close to our subject that minor activities mask the general movement of the water. He might also tell us that we have established our laboratory too close to the mouth of the river. As a result, even if we set aside our microscope for the moment, we are likely to be confused by the ebb and flow of tidal forces on the river – it seems to move backwards about as often as it does forward.[2]

Or he might communicate the same sense from one of his personal collections of aphorisms, for example, "Everything has been thought of before, the difficulty is to think of it again" (Goethe). Or, occasionally, he might start out with a spicier tone, recalling the story, without revealing the source, of an eminent physician who examines a rather dissolute man. He has an enlarged liver and a positive serology (VDRL). "No more wine, no more women," the doctor would advise, "but sir, you can sing."

2. James A. Campbell, M.D., and Richard G. DuFour, "Rush–Presbyterian–St. Luke's Medical Center: The Future of the American Hospital in the 1980's: The Organization of Resources," October 8, 1976.

Campbell's intellectual traits more often tended toward the didactic, thoughtful, and deliberate professorial posture. When he was asked why he went to college and became a doctor, Jim related his experiences working eighty labor-intensive hours per week for the California Packing Corporation in Rochelle. He found college and medical school to be a lead pipe cinch because it didn't take too much time, he worked less, had a good time, and got credit for reading, which he loved to do anyway.[3] In this sense he really appreciated the relatively luxurious life of the scholar, using his mind, not his back. His exposure to the learned atmosphere at Harvard stayed with him and he often quoted John Adams, who said, "I must study politics and war that my sons may have liberty to study mathematics and philosophy. My sons ought to study mathematics, philosophy, geography, natural history, naval architecture, navigation, commerce and agriculture in order to give their children a right to study painting, poetry, music and architecture."

Jim felt at ease and was comfortable in the academic world. He was listed in *Who's Who in American Colleges and Universities* when he was at Knox College. Later, at Harvard in his senior year, he was elected to the National Medical Honor Society, Alpha Omega Alpha. "Pretty good, for a transfer student," his good friend from Harvard, Bob Glaser, would say.[4]

Alpha Omega Alpha (AOA) was started in Chicago in 1902 by William Root to promote the ideal of excellence in American medical education and to protest the connotation of the name medical student with boorishness, immorality, and low educational ideals. There was drinking, sexual irregularities, cheating, and general dishonesty among these uncouth and rowdy students. The public did not hold the medical profession in very high esteem. Medical students were in general not well-bred. It was said that if one wanted a degree from Harvard and couldn't matriculate in Harvard College,

3. Jack Starr Interview and Bruce Rattenbury Commentary, Fall 1973 and 1991; folder 22, Box 4, C97-052, James A. Campbell, M.D., Papers 1924–1983, Record Group 002000, Office of the President, Rush–Presbyterian–St. Luke's Medical Center/Rush University Medical Center Archives, Chicago, Ill.
4. Personal communication, Dr. Robert Glaser, June 20, 1999.

he should apply to the medical school, where requirements were not so high.

AOA's first chapter was established at the University of Illinois, and the second chapter, the Beta chapter, started at Rush. AOA has identified with the highest ideals in medical education since its inception. The Rush chapter was active until the union of Rush and the University of Chicago was dissolved in 1942, but a new chapter was formed at Rush when the school was reopened. Today AOA is very active at Rush. No more than a certain percentage of the senior graduating class may be elected to membership, and many of the Rush faculty are members, having been elected either as students or later as faculty.

Jim Campbell was elected AOA's third secretary-treasurer in 1960, shortly after the Presbyterian–St. Luke's merger took place. Dr. Root had served for thirty-two years in that position and was succeeded by Dr. Josiah Moore, who went on to serve for twenty-eight years more. Campbell then served in that office until he was elevated to the presidency of AOA in 1978. Here again, Campbell had placed himself at the forefront of thinking in medical education, preparing himself, in yet another way, for the challenge of restoring life to the Rush dream.

When the AOA national headquarters was moved to Chicago, the national standing of the merged hospitals was significantly enhanced. To graduate AOA from medical school is a mark of distinction, excellence, and personal and professional integrity. Campbell and Dr. Bob Glaser worked together to foster the growth of the organization. AOA sponsored visiting professorships to underprivileged medical schools and developed the organization's quarterly publication, *The Pharos*. Membership rose from 27,000 to 50,000 and the number of chapters from 85 to 109 during Campbell's term of service. Campbell played a major part in expanding the society's role from a solely honorary one to a dynamic intellectual force influencing the nation's medical schools.[5]

5. Robert J. Glaser, M.D., James Allan Campbell: In memoriam, *Pharos* 47 (no. 1, 1984): 23

Campbell's most notable article in *The Pharos*, "Five Smooth Stones," was a reprint of his address to the honors convocation during the graduation at the University of Colorado School of Medicine in 1960.[6] He compared the struggles of David and Goliath in the first book of Samuel in the Bible. Goliath the giant is human illness, and David attacks with his five smooth stones to slay Goliath. These five smooth stones, Campbell's objectives of medical education, are:

1. Development of ability for independent learning

2. Understanding and use of the scientific method

3. Comprehension of a significant outline of sciences referable to human biology

4. Grounding in the discipline of clinical examination

5. An acquaintance with the phenomenon of disease

Then Campbell went on to point out that David slew Goliath with the first stone. He didn't need a second chance. The doctor too seldom gets a second chance and should be well versed in whatever of the five disciplines he may be called on to apply, with the skill of David. "For there would be rejoicing in the land."

Campbell repeated this presentation so often, and with such passion back at the medical center, that it was thought that he borrowed much of its content from his father's book, *Sermons of a Country Preacher.* He was given several different mementos and reminders of "five smooth stones." And as new groups of doctors in training came to the medical center for orientation, this inspirational message would be delivered once again.

Campbell maintained a close relationship with his alma mater, Knox College. He served as a trustee for thirty-two years and was exposed to the insights and challenges of academic life in a period of enormous change in American education. This experience fur-

6. James A. Campbell, M.D., "The Prepared Mind," presented at the Honors Convocation, Knox College, Galesburg, Ill., May 7, 1954.

ther broadened his background to be the prime mover in the development of a major educational institution, the future Rush University Medical Center. An honorary degree of Doctor of Science from Knox College was conferred on Campbell in 1965. Campbell was also awarded an honorary degree from Lake Forest College in 1969.

As the guest speaker for the Honors Convocation at Knox in 1954, Campbell delivered his most notable address, "The Prepared Mind."[7] It was an exhortation to the honor students to avoid the pitfalls of being merely practical, thus overlooking the larger picture with its important implications. He cited the example of Sir Edward Perry and his party going straight to the pole in one of their Arctic explorations, traveling at a rate of ten miles per day; but the ice over which they were traveling was drifting straight toward the equator at twelve miles a day. And yet no man among them would have known he was traveling two miles a day straight backward unless he had lifted his eyes to the stars from the track he was plodding. It is not only going backwards that the plain, practical workman is liable to if he will not look up and around, but also that he may go forward to ends little dreamed of.

He again quotes from Louis Pasteur, "Chance favors the Prepared Mind." He salutes the honor students who diligently apply themselves by study to develop the prepared mind because good luck and fortune as well as the appropriate key often fall to those people who have striven with great success to have minds prepared for the accident of information and knowledge that may be just around each corner. Had the man not known what the stars were saying to him, had his mind not been prepared from the study and knowledge of astronomy, even though he wisely dreamed and lifted his eyes above the plodding track, he would not have been able to tell whither they were drifting. Campbell urges his audience on to have a prepared mind, to have all the knowledge possible, even that in the fine print and the footnotes, and not to hesitate to look to the stars and set their course accordingly.

7. Ibid.

As time went on, Jim Campbell was identified as an authority in matters of health care systems and medical center development and organization. More empiricism and less scientific rigor were characteristic mindsets in these areas. One of his later presentations was published in the *Harvard Business Review* in 1981, "Outlook for Hospitals: Systems Are the Solution." Jim became less enthusiastic about the importance of research. Although it was an essential component in the mission of the medical center, and Rush had to be in the forefront of medical advances, research was not terribly cost effective, and, indeed, it was very expensive.

This later perception of Campbell is quite opposite to the reality that Campbell was a consistent, serious, and highly respected contributor to the medical scientific literature for many years. His first publication appeared in 1943 in the *Journal of Laboratory and Clinical Investigation*, "Immunologic and Toxic Properties of Casein Digestion as Prepared for Parenteral Administration." The basis of this report came from his work at the University of Chicago. He next appeared in 1946 as the senior author in the paper, "The Intravenous Glucose Tolerance Test in Liver Disease," published in the *New England Journal of Medicine*. The basis for this work was his experience at Harvard Thorndike Laboratory of Boston City Hospital.

Next came three publications from his experiences at the Edgewood arsenal that appeared in the military literature. The harm of nerve gas was the principal topic of these presentations. Jim was deeply disturbed about the moral implications of chemical warfare.

Seven publications bearing his name reporting studies related to congenital heart disease were published in 1948 and 1949 from his experiences at the John Hopkins cardiac catheterization laboratory and were co-authored with Drs. Richard Bing, Jack Handelsman, and Harold Griswell.

Jim's most productive writing years followed when he moved to Chicago in the 1950s and 1960s. He was senior author on several of the nineteen papers that bear his name.[8] He and Graettinger

8. The co-authors of these papers were Drs. Louis Selverstone, Robert Grissom, Daniel Donovan, Donald L. Fisher, Oglesby Paul, John Graettinger, and Joseph Muenster.

authored the monograph "Application of Cardiac Function Tests" for the Medical Clinics of North America in 1955.

Earlier he had presented his first paper in Chicago, "Catheterization of the Coronary Veins: A Technique for the Study of Cardiac Metabolism" at the Clinical Section of the Chicago Heart Association joint meeting held by the University of Illinois and Presbyterian Hospital on February 18, 1949. Campbell's studies in cardiac physiology were considered well ahead of anyone else's in Chicago at the time.

Campbell's writing interests then took on a different focus, that of medical education, particularly graduate medical education. "The Role of Research in Graduate Medical Education," which appeared in the *Journal of the American Medical Association* in 1959, and "The Internship: Origins, Evolution, and Confusion," which appeared in the *Journal of the American Medical Association* in 1964, were the most noteworthy. The latter paper, which dealt with the inconsistencies for establishing rotating internships and straight internships, clearly had a critical tone. In his introduction he again uses one of his favorite aphorisms, "Those who will not learn from history will surely repeat it." At that time Presbyterian Hospital was taking the lead in offering straight internships in Chicago. The rotating internship, a very selected short exposure to almost all specialties and services for the internship year, had become obsolete. A more suitable program, the straight internship into one of medicine's major branches such as medicine, surgery, pediatrics, and pathology had become a realistic necessity as medical advances rapidly accelerated, and residency training became a more likely step to follow after the individual had completed his internship.

Along with Dr. John Graettinger, Campbell became an influential figure in the National Internship Matching Program, an organized effort to allow senior medical students and training hospitals to determine in advance selection preference for the coming academic year, which usually began on July 1. Each would list their order of preference and agree to abide by this commitment when the results of the match were announced on matching day, which was usually in late winter or early spring, A greater degree of fairness for everyone concerned resulted from the Matching Program. A structure was developed to help deal with the ever increasing complexities of graduate medical education as the need for even more training evolved for extended residencies, fellowships, and the like. Campbell himself became a national director of the Intern Matching Program and later president of its Board of Directors from 1971 to 1974.

Dr. Harold Paul, an early trainee of the Campbell era, had intended to intern at a nearby hospital in the medical center but changed his mind and selected Presbyterian because his first choice of hospital had flagrantly broken the rules of the match and Presbyterian did not.

Campbell was active in the American Medical Association (AMA) and American Association of Medical Colleges (AAMC) and served on a number of national committees on graduate medical education for both organizations. He also served on the councils of hospitals and mental health for the AMA.

He served on the advisory committees for the establishment of two new medical schools, Mt. Sinai Medical School in New York City and Milton Hershey Medical School in Hershey, Pennsylvania. Campbell was now an authority in medical education and the organization of medical schools. even though he himself was not directly connected to a medical school of his own.

After a hiatus of a number of years, Campbell's name began to reappear as an author, but now on the subjects of health care delivery, new concepts in cost containment, and organization of systems to deal with these increasingly complex issues.

Campbell's most important publication came in 1968, "Report on Education in the Health Fields for the State of Illinois." Often referred to as the "Green Book," the two-volume study prepared in conjunction with two of Campbell's associates, Dr. Randolph Tucker and Ms. Irene Turner,[9] provided the rationale for expansion of medical education for the entire state. At that time, a shortage existed for

9. State of Illinois, Board of Higher Education, "Education in the Health Fields for the State of Illinois," June 1968.

physicians, nurses, and those in allied health sciences, and the recommendations of Campbell Report, as the book was commonly
referred to, ultimately enabled Rush Medical College to reopen and
provided the rational basis for the development of Rush University
for the Health Sciences. The report significantly improved the availability of health care for many citizens within the state. It called for
expansion of education for all the health fields to be done in an orderly, practical, and at the same time, cost-effective manner. It was hailed
for its creativity and farsightedness and was received enthusiastically
by both the academic community and the medical profession within
the state.

Rush Medical College, 1899, Harrison and Wood streets, Chicago. (Rush University Medical Center Archives, Chicago, Ill.)

Student and yearbook editor, James Campbell, left, with bottles of beer. (1944 yearbook *Aesculapiad,* Harvard Medical School, p. 105)

Twin seals of Rush Medical College and the University of Chicago at entrance to the medical school on East 58th Street on the University of Chicago campus.

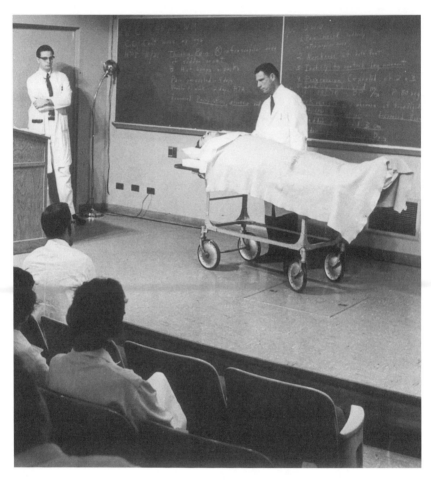

Dr. James Campbell (center) at Grand Rounds emphasizing bedside
teaching and interview of patients. (Undated; Rush University Medical
Center Archives, Chicago, Ill.)

Dr. William Castle, of Harvard, visiting Presbyterian Hospital Medical Grand Rounds. Pictured left to right: Drs. E. J. Beattie, Jr., Frederick Deinhardt, Castle, Campbell, Richard Capps, Jean Deinhardt, and Francis Straus. (1969, Rush University Medical Center Archives, Chicago, Ill.)

West Side adjacent to Medical Center on fire at time of Dr. Martin Luther King's assassination. (April 1968, *Chicago Tribune*)

Dr. James Campbell making "rounds," walking through the hospital basement. (1979, Rush University Medical Center Archives, Chicago, Ill.)

Dr. Campbell, the builder, at work in his office on the 13th floor of the Professional Building, with construction crane in the background. (1981, Rush University Medical Center Archives, Chicago, Ill.)

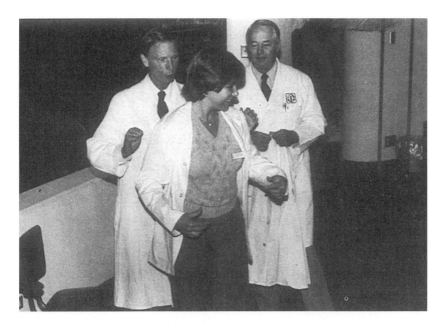

Dr. Campbell, left, and Dean Henry Russe, right, initiating freshman medical student into the medical community with the "white coat" ceremony.

Campbell with Mrs. Adlai Stevenson IV, Mrs. Calvin Trowbridge, president of the Woman's Board, and Mayor Richard J. Daley, at groundbreaking of the Academic Center. (November 1973, Rush University Medical Center Archives, Chicago, Ill.)

President Gerald Ford, Dr. Campbell, and Trustee George Young, at celebration to complete the Campaign for the Future of Success. (May 1982, Rush University Medical Center Archives, Chicago, Ill.)

Statue of Benjamin Rush, "America's Greatest Physician," Bureau of Medicine and Surgery, 2300 E Street NW, Washington, D.C.

9

Politician and Community Leader

The day-to-day job of implementing all that Campbell hoped to do both as chairman of Medicine and later as president of the medical center very often was far removed from writing scientific articles, conducting Grand Rounds, carrying out educational surveys for the state, and the like. As the time in his career approached for his most important achievement, the creation of Rush–Presbyterian–St. Luke's Medical Center, Jim Campbell would have to put aside much of what he had done before and move on to new challenges with their ensuing opportunities and problems.

Among other things, he had to develop a political constituency of individuals to support his efforts to move forward into new territory. Getting people he could rely on to help get the job done, to help him in dealing with problems as they arose, and to support his ideas when opposition developed was not an easy job.

There are several constituencies within the medical center: entrepreneurial solo and group practice physicians, salaried and non-salaried physicians, graduate school faculty, nurses, hospital administrators and employees, house staff, trustees, community leaders, regulators, the elected political community, and third-party payers. Each group has its own language and ways and, while being dealt with differently, has to be kept engaged in the mission of the institution. In this complex environment, Jim was ideal both as a leader and communicator. He was admired by many and yet frankly mistrusted by many others as well. He often proposed radical approaches and he enjoyed bucking people. But through it all, he expressed himself in simple terms and communicated a vision that engaged most everyone, even those who were not in his camp.

Campbell could rely on the young doctors he had trained who were now members of the staff. Although Jim could be tough on his former proteges, they were still his "boys"; and he was, in their eyes, a father figure. Likewise, the doctors from the outside that he recruited, Graettinger, Trobaugh, and others could generally be counted on for backing and conversely Jim was usually there for these people when they were under criticism and taking some heat. While Ted Schwartz was at Duke, he had hired a technician in his department whose husband was suspected of having been an avowed Communist. The FBI got involved and demanded that Ted give the middle initial of the name of the suspect, which Ted would not do. So the FBI went to Campbell and started beating up on him a little bit. Finally Jim yelled out through his open office door so that everybody on the entire floor could hear him, "Ted, are you a Communist? Here is some god damn fool from the FBI who wants to know if you are a Communist or not." The FBI agents were so startled by this that they were never heard from again. Ted Schwartz could not help but develop a sense of loyalty and respect for Jim.

On another occasion, Schwartz substituted for Jim as moderator of Medical Grand Rounds. The case presented was that of a diabetic, and the patient's problem with sexual dysfunction was discussed. Although a review of this type of medical problem was unusual in that era, it certainly was not inappropriate. One of the senior attending doctors felt otherwise and later came to Campbell's office to complain that this sort of discussion of a delicate nature, erections, and the like in front of nurses, was out of order. Jim was not averse to hearing the criticism, but it upset him when someone would go behind someone else's back to deliver the critical comment without confronting the individual directly. So Jim again yelled out through his open door in a booming voice so that everyone again could hear, "Hey, Ted, here is someone who thinks your presentation at Grand Rounds last week was out of line." The doctor who brought the matter up was devastated. And Schwartz could not help but appreciate the loyal and forthright manner in which Campbell handled the matter. Campbell may well have agreed with the criticism, but he made it clear to everyone (and there were many) who witnessed this event that sneaking around behind peoples' back was not encouraged.

So in speaking to Campbell, it was clear that you had to be quite careful about what you discussed and how you said it. If you went to him with a problem, he would listen carefully to every word. You had his total and undivided attention. Campbell would then say, "What do you plan to do about this?" If your response was, "I don't know," he became angry, his face and the back of his neck turned red and his distress was so marked that he appeared to be on the verge of throwing you bodily right out of his office. On the other hand, if your response had been, "Here are my options and alternative solutions that I have come up with, Dr. Campbell. Which one should I choose?" then Campbell would go over each choice and invariably bring you to the right answer. And in the discussion, he made you think all the time, and his tone then would be reasonable and reassuring when the meeting had concluded.

During discussions of this kind, Campbell might bring up another matter, a new idea that he made you feel like you were the first to know although he was merely testing out reactions to the idea. Many felt they were truly Jim's confidants, when, in fact, Jim was just testing the waters. They were thinking, "I'm one of Jim's main confidants; what he's telling me, he has told to no one else." Visitors left his office sensing that they had the inside scoop on a new development right from the top and in the process had been of help to the great man. In no time, feedback from all of this came right back to Campbell. And if reaction was favorable, he might move ahead; if not, he might back off until another time to try again. There was no failure here because Campbell just put things aside. He might move in small steps and listen to the echoes, making course corrections and thereby avoiding disasters. There was always a deliberate thought process, even when he changed course. Campbell was planning and looking ahead at all times. And when the right time came to move, if someone happened to be standing in his way, he or she would be pushed aside and Campbell would move forward.

Once in a great while Campbell would actually let his hair down and confide in one of his close associates. Then he would check up on this later to see if the trust had indeed been valued and not violated. Jim expected loyalty in return from those he brought in from the outside and then brought along and advanced. One physician from a new section in Medicine that Jim put together when he reorganized the department had received an offer from another medical center not long after he had relocated to Chicago at Presbyterian. He confronted Jim with this offer, with the expectation of obtaining a counteroffer. Jim essentially told him, "Good bye and good luck." That terminated the discussion and the individual soon left. Campbell's demands for loyalty were quite effectively communicated in this way.

Jim took politics and political support very seriously. After moving on to a promotion in another part of the country, another staff member and a good friend of Jim's was asked to withhold his resignation from the staff for as long as possible as an upcoming medical staff vote might be close, and his vote might be needed.

Jim's only serious political setback took place when the appointment for a chairman of a major department was announced before it had been approved by all the various layers of committees that are necessary to comply with the by-laws. The search committee had made its recommendation unanimously, and subsequent approval was expected to be automatic. But the fact that the decision was announced before final approval of all these committees had been cleared brought immediate criticism. Although the premature announcement may have been a clerical mistake, opposition from within the department involved immediately developed, and a campaign against the recommendation of the search committee was organized. All sorts of groundless charges were made in the corridors: the candidate couldn't operate; he was a researcher, not a clinician;

and he didn't have proper specialty board certification. The atmosphere in the staff doctors' lounge was nasty. When this came to Campbell's attention, he immediately organized a campaign to have the vote approved by the staff. A majority 70 percent was required for passage. Word of this spread throughout the institution quickly. There are no secrets in hospitals in matters such as this.

Here was the chance for Campbell's political enemies to get even with him. The issue was not really about the candidate as much as it was Campbell's power. The accusation was brought forward that he violated medical staff regulations by rushing through this appointment prematurely. He was becoming a dictator. On the day of the staff vote, members showed up who hadn't appeared for years, and enough votes were cast against the appointment, 31 percent, to block approval; 69 percent had approved. Campbell was furious and threatened to resign. Word was passed along the line to Campbell's friends at Harvard and Stanford that their protégé had suffered a major defeat.

But then Campbell settled down. A by-law staff committee was appointed, and the rules for approval were changed. And subsequently the appointment sailed through without any difficulty. The vote was nearly unanimous The new chairman went on to become one of the medical center's brightest stars.

Jim used political methods because he had to. There was never any sense that he was compromising. Whatever he decided to do was entirely correct and on the highest moral grounds. Jim had interviewed one of his future protégés and bright stars in administration before he was hired. The young man, a child of the early seventies, immediately confronted Campbell about the abuses of authority and power. Although Campbell did not suffer fools very well, he allowed this individual to state his case. As the discussion continued, Jim would take a thought usually of a highly confrontational nature, revise it, and redirect the discussion. The idea that power and control could be used for beneficial purposes had never occurred to the young man. Power didn't always involve abuses. So Jim had refocused this individual's attitude and forced him to try to rise to Jim's ideal, which was first, foremost, and always, the good of the patient.

Jim kept his ear to the ground to keep tabs on everything that was going on at the medical center, where thousands of people worked every day. He could relate to people whom he trusted to keep him informed, people at all levels all the way from the trustees to those in housekeeping. He projected the sense that "Here I am, Jim Campbell, just a nice guy who happens to be president." He often made notes on a card he carried around in his pocket or inside the lapel of his white coat as he made his way through the hospital corridors at any time of the day or even the evening. Casual in one sense, intense in another, Jim was keeping his hand on the pulse of what was going on and he was also relaying the message to everyone that they, too, had to be alert and on their toes.

But still, Campbell had a certain contempt for the political process. One Friday afternoon about 4 P.M., the medical center was informed that a state regulatory agency planned on the following Monday to inspect one of the institution's principal research programs for alleged environmental irregularities. The project was one of the institution's high-priority investigational programs heavily funded by the NIH. There was unique work being done on a program that had been moving forward for several years. Eventually, no irregularities were found. The state, as it turned out, had completely misread the nature of the complaint regarding the project. It was clear in reading the allegations that this was indeed the case. But it was late on a Friday afternoon and this inspection had to be stopped before Monday to avoid potentially costly and time-consuming delays. Everybody was leaving work in Springfield. Jim contacted one of Chicago's leading attorneys, an expert in the field of government regulations and also a benefactor and friend of the medical center, and said, "Take care of this."

To intervene in the workings of a government agency in the last few minutes of the work week to stop a scheduled inspection for the following Monday morning was no small undertaking. Many state government offices in Springfield late on Friday were, for all practical purposes, empty. Frantic telephone calls were made to find someone in authority with whom to discuss the matter. Finally, late on Friday night a determination was made that the process might be postponed if a white paper could be prepared for the governor to read over the weekend. Then and only then, by his authority, could the inspection be put on hold. Preparation of the white paper required all of Saturday and part of Sunday, and the governor was given it late Sunday night to read. The Monday inspection was postponed, and eventually the matter was resolved. The attorney who had worked all this out called Campbell at home on Sunday night to report the good news, thrilled to have been able to accomplish this nearly impossible assignment. He was hoping to get in the good graces of the boss, perhaps even to be complimented. Jim's reaction to all of this was: "Don't you think I have better things to do than write a god-dam white paper over the weekend?" What he really seemed to be saying was, "It is self-evident that we are doing God's work here. Why do I have to fool around with these bureaucrats and politicians?" The attorney was devastated. On occasion, this could be vintage Jim.

Sometimes Campbell could not bend to realities, and when this element of his makeup got out of hand, he had a good deal of trouble getting along with people. It was evident that he was a superior human being, head and shoulders above everybody else. As his friend and noted attorney Oscar D'Angelo described this aspect of his temperament, "His holy grail was excellence. Seeking the truth and the pure answer was his mission. The enemy of excellence was not the bad, but the good enough."[1] As his father, the Reverend Frank Campbell would say, "I can live with it," means no standards. When Campbell wanted something done, he didn't understand the word no. So as a result, he could create and multiply problems for himself trying to get his ideas and programs across. Things were always black and white in his mind, though maybe not in anyone else's.

Campbell was not known for his great admiration of the public system of care for the poor and indigent at Cook County Hospital, the medical center's next door neighbor, immediately to the west. He believed that this system perpetuated two classes of

1. Personal interview, Oscar D'Angelo, January 22, 1999.

patients, one at the private hospital and the other at the public hospital. He believed the best chance to eliminate what he characterized as "poor care for poor people" was to bring the poor and indigent into the mainstream of private medical care and eliminate the political component of existing systems such as Cook County Hospital and other similar municipal institutions throughout the county. Campbell's choice of words, "poor care for poor people," justifiably offended the many dedicated people who looked after patients in public institutions. But Campbell was referring to the system itself, not the individuals. Dr. Mark Lepper also believed that the care of the poor should be enfolded into the private hospital system. Both believed there was no future for public medicine because it would never be adequately funded. They believed in one standard of care and envisioned the private hospital system as the provider for everyone. And time, thus far, has proven both of them prophetic, for the two-tier system still exists.

In the 1960s, the federal government's Office of Economic Opportunity, then under the direction of R. Sargent Shriver, was looking into what could be done for people's health care to try to break the cycle of poverty. Huge gaps in the care of the poor were clearly evident. Mark Lepper, Campbell's executive vice president for Academic and Professional Affairs, was asked to come up with a program to address this huge challenge; however, Lepper was heavily committed and could not accept the assignment although he agreed to be a consultant. He referred the matter to his associate, Dr. Joyce Lashof, who was in England at the time with her husband, who was on sabbatical at Oxford. Lashof agreed to take on the project and in 1965 the Mile Square Health Center was organized to serve the indigent poor in the area immediately north and west of the hospital, a square mile of Chicago's deepest poverty populated by about 20,000 people, 98 percent of whom were black. One-third lived in a high-rise housing project and the remainder lived in some of the oldest slum buildings in the city, one of which housed the Black Panthers.

Lashof worked with local community leaders to help set the center up. People in this area would no longer have to be shunted off to Cook County Hospital for care. The care of the poor was moved into the mainstream. People's medical charts were flagged for annual checkups. Now they would be less likely to show up in the emergency room sick. A clinic was established and staffed by Presbyterian doctors and other medical center personnel. And the clinic building's mortgage was guaranteed by the Medical Center. Patients would be admitted to the hospital like any other patient. House calls by ob-gyne and medical technicians under the supervision of private attending physicians were arranged. Fetal death rates were drastically reduced.

The salutary effect of the Mile Square Program on the community was vividly exemplified during the calamitous days following the assassination of Dr. Martin Luther King in 1968. Children of the juvenile mental health program of Mile Square were playing basketball in the Mile Square parking lot, apparently oblivious to the burning buildings and looting two or three blocks away.[2]

The federally funded program was the second in the entire nation to become operational. In this way too, the medical center was effectively dealing with a local community need, not ignoring or turning its back on it. Local community leaders never forgot that. In a sense, the social contract between an admiring and generous nation with the medical profession was being fulfilled. Those left behind, the poor, were not being forgotten. The institution's reputation as an organization devoted to the overall good of the public was immeasurably raised as a result of this. There was a perception here that the medical profession and other health care professionals weren't merely sitting on their increasingly prosperous hands but were addressing wider needs and concerns for the community.

Irene Turner helped organize the Mile Square effort. She had been actively involved in the civil rights movement for the poor on the West Side. With little formal education, this energetic dynamo rose to be a sociologist and a medical technologist, and finally she taught in the medical school. She worked with Lashof and Campbell

2. Experiences with the Mile Square Neighborhood Health Center or a Chicago West Side Story, October 29, 1971, Folder 16, Box 4, C97-052, James A. Campbell, M.D., Papers 1924–1983, Record Group 002000, Office of the President, Rush–Presbyterian–St. Luke's Medical Center/Rush University Medical Center Archives, Chicago, Ill.

to establish upgrades for the clinics in the program. She knew who was influential in the community and who could make all of this happen. She cited Campbell's leadership and sensitivity to the concerns of the poor on the West Side and his insistence that these issues be seriously addressed to be major factors in the success of Mile Square. None of this could have been accomplished without Campbell's support."[3]

Campbell's dream of one standard of care for all patients was coming closer to a reality. The OEO federal program called for the establishment of 24 such centers throughout the entire Chicago metropolitan area but only one other community organized, so the program's long-term objectives could not be achieved.

In the development of the Mile Square system, at least within a small defined geographic area in which large amounts of highly professional resources were utilized, Campbell showed that the indigent could be incorporated into the mainstream of private medical care. This was a monumental accomplishment. Whether anyone else besides Campbell could have made it work is doubtful. But the success of Mile Square was applied to only a relatively small group of individuals, a community of 20,000, and the vast majority of the poor and indigent were not provided with this opportunity. Cook County Hospital has continued to serve this vast constituency all the way up to the present time. In many ways the complexities of the problems of health care for the indigent and the working poor without health insurance whose numbers run in the range of forty million today are even bigger now than they were in the Campbell era.

During this time Campbell's outspoken views on Cook County Hospital created a good deal of resentment from its many loyal supporters. The claim was made that he tried to have it closed. In the early seventies, the house staff at Cook County, in an effort to improve their benefits and working conditions, essentially closed the

3. Summary transcript of interview with Ms. Irene Turner by Jim Bowman, June 6, 1986, in preparation for *Good Medicine: The First 150 Years of Rush–Presbyterian–St. Luke's Medical Center.*

hospital to the community by admitting large numbers of patients from the emergency room so that there was no further room for anyone else. Patients denied admission to County Hospital had to be taken care of elsewhere. Campbell reacted immediately by devising the Campbell plan, which called for all hospitals in the Chicago area to accept a share of the indigent sick and thus, in a sense, obviate the need for a county hospital. Private hospital censuses were such that they could accommodate these additional patients. The Chicago Hospital Council was presented with this plan and endorsed it.

County Hospital supporters were enraged by the implied threat of the proposal that the hospital would be closed. The house staff dispute was settled and admissions through the emergency room resumed. The Campbell plan was never enacted, but the strong relationship that Rush Medical College and Presbyterian Hospital once had with Cook County Hospital in the first forty years of the twentieth century had become decidedly unfriendly.

The inability to develop a solid relationship with Cook County Hospital has to be considered something of a shortcoming in Campbell's otherwise brilliant administrative accomplishments. And in some ways, it was a failure of communication on his part. Campbell's opponents looked upon him as an arrogant patrician who wanted nothing to do with his neighbor next door and its constituency of indigent patients. He was portrayed as the champion of the establishment and the comfortable. And yet Campbell's record of moving toward a single standard of care for all patients, rich and poor alike, was most exemplary. The archaic Central Free Dispensary, where the indigent patient sat on wooden benches waiting for hours to see a physician, had been abolished, and all "clinic" patients were treated in modern state-of-the-art facilities.

Campbell took a lot of heat from the more conservative constituencies at the hospital for supporting these initiatives, many of which were formulated by Irene Turner. But he did it anyway. He would say, "Yes, Irene is a radical, but she is our radical." And Turner insisted that Campbell never wanted to close County. Turner, too, had been exposed to the ideal of the Boston City hospital system as had Campbell and understood Campbell's aspirations for a single standard of care.

Campbell's commitment of the medical center to the entire community, as well as to its large patient base, was again exemplified in a different way. In 1968, he volunteered the Presbyterian–St. Luke's emergency room services to all the victims of the explosive conflicts at the Democratic National Convention held in the nearby downtown area of Chicago.

At one time Campbell and Ruth Rothstein, then chief of Cook County Hospital, served together on several medical center committees that frequently dealt with the subjects of organization and delivery of health care. Rothstein was also a close friend of Irene Turner. One of Campbell's favorite expressions was "the systems are the solution." Rothstein said, "no, the solution is the systems." By that time Campbell was a recognized national authority on health care and did not like to be challenged in public, particularly in an area where he was considered to be quite knowledgeable. Nevertheless, Rothstein stood her ground and subsequently a very cool relationship developed between these two strong-minded giants in Chicago medicine.

But later, the two got together when Rothstein supported Campbell's grand plan for the construction of the state-of-the-art Atrium complex. Rothstein had reservations about cost overruns and construction delays but waived these considerations when Campbell approached her for her support. Campbell finally began to realize that he had to have the support of his neighbors. The vast project went on to completion. Rothstein was featured as an honored speaker at the dedication ceremonies. And later on, under the leadership of Campbell's successor, Dr. Leo Henikoff, the two neighboring hospitals reestablished a strong affiliated relationship.

Within the Near West Side community Campbell earned very high marks for political leadership in the late sixties during the time of riots that followed the assassination of Dr. Martin Luther King. Violence and chaos were evident everywhere. Snipers targeting cars passing below were operating on the overpasses that crossed the Eisenhower Expressway on the north boundary of the hospital.

Through an effective, but still not well understood system, hospital employees were told to turn on their headlights when entering or leaving the medical center so they could be recognized and not targeted. Much of Chicago's West Side was on fire, and the hospital was right in the middle of it all. When viewed from a helicopter, smoke obscured the outlines of many of the hospital's buildings. Federal troops marched down Harrison Street in clear view from Campbell's office, which was then on the first floor of the Jelke Building. He was a sitting duck for a sniper with his floor-to-ceiling window facing the street. There was fear that the entire medical center might have to be enclosed by barbed wire or even relocated far away from the area.

But Campbell and the trustees did not buy into this. There would be no barbed wire. The decision had been made some time back. Presbyterian–St. Luke's was staying and what's more, planning for expansion. Efforts were organized to step up the active support of the local West Side community in which the Mile Square project was already active. The hospital would reach out to engage and involve the entire community in its operations.

Television personality Werner Saunders was there at the time. He supervised the Archie Moore Gymnasium for the Better Boys Foundation at 15th and Pulaski. During the riots he acted as a go-between for the all-white band of reporters and the many gangs and other angry constituencies on the West Side. His impressive voice was heard on sound bites on the television evening news. Later Channel 7 hired Saunders and the rest of his celebrity rise is history. "Pres.–St. Luke's was never viewed as enemy territory by the gangs. They were left alone."[4] After the riots, Jim Campbell served on the Lawndale Peoples' Planning and Action Conference, which was instrumental in rebuilding the poverty-stricken and explosive Lawndale area.

Danny Davis, then a West Side activist for health care, later alderman, and eventually the United States Congressman for the 7th District and Campbell worked together to create an atmosphere of community cooperation. Congressman Davis's image of Campbell

4. Personal communication, Werner Saunders, November 22, 1999.

wearing his white doctor's coat to all the meetings was a reminder of what all the activity was about, and that was the patient. Davis recalled, "Those were heady days; there was an aura of excitement which was invigorating, as the possibilities for improved health care were being seriously addressed. Campbell was intensely interested in everything that was going on on the West Side. After the planning meetings with other leaders in the medical center, Campbell would have Davis and his good friend Hats Adams come back to his office, where they would discuss further what they hoped to do with the community. Campbell was constantly seeking new insights."[5]

Steps were taken to form a department of community relations at the Medical center, and Reginald (Hats) Adams was recruited to lead this effort. Community relations became involved in all of the medical center's building and expansion programs. Jim and Hats would look out over the Eisenhower Expressway north and see Reo's saloon at the corner of Van Buren and Paulina. Campbell hoped one day to change all this. Eventually this became the location for the new Anchor Building, a major improvement for the community. Jim's and Hat's motto was "We should act, not react."

Hats and Jim became good friends. "Dr. Campbell's enthusiastic attendance at new employee orientation was terrific," Hats recalls. "He never missed attending." Jim would speak first, Hats second, and then someone from security third. Jim would then ask the group, "Who is the most important person in this place?" There might be a pause as the audience hesitated to reply. He would then say, "Of course, it's the patient who is the most important person in this place. The patient comes first." And new employees never forgot this.

Jim might run into Hats in the corridors and say, "Come on, Hats, walk with me and let's make rounds." Very often this could be on the afternoon or even the evening shift. Before they were finished, they might have toured the whole medical center, from the basement to the top floor, 13 Kellogg. Campbell seemed to know all the employees by name. "Hello, Cora," "Hello, Bob," he would say. Everybody was important to Dr. Campbell.

5. Personal communication, Congressman Danny Davis, January 24, 2001.

The door was always open to Jim's office, whatever the problem might be. He always had time to listen and was accessible to the entire employee team. You could talk to him and disagree with him. He would spend hours trying to convince you and win you over to his side. Hats recalls, "Jim was a fighter. Once he made up his mind, that was it." And usually you came around to his way of thinking as well.

When he was interviewed by Campbell about taking the job, Hats said, "What about me, I do not wear a tie." Campbell said that it would be perfectly all right. Hats later commented on Campbell's ties, which were not terribly attractive. "By any standard, you wear the worst ties of any man in the world," Adams would say. Campbell would reply that someone famous had given it to him. Perhaps this might have been so, maybe twenty years before.

Campbell's dress code would never qualify him to be considered among Chicago's best-dressed men. His white coat was frayed at the cuffs. His plaid trousers were faded. He might have worn the same pair of shoes for almost thirty years except that we know that he and Hats one day ventured to Chernin's discount shoe store on Roosevelt Road to purchase another pair of the same plain brown shoes he had always worn.

10

In the Ascendancy

After Jim and Elda returned from Albany, they lived at 232 East Walton Place on Chicago's Near North Side near the Drake Hotel. Living on the Gold Coast was expensive and beyond what one ordinarily could afford from the income that Jim would receive engaging in academic and administrative medicine. Elda's independent income helped make up the difference. Jim and Elda enjoyed living in the city, and although they didn't stay very long before moving to the suburbs, they returned later when their children had grown up. Many of Elda's good friends lived close by, including those who belonged to the exclusive Casino Club just a block away from where the Campbells lived.

Jim and Elda entertained at home, particularly with Jim's old friends from Harvard and doctors from local and national medical organizations who happened to be in town. For the most part, the Campbells did not interact socially with members of the medical staff of Presbyterian–St. Luke's or their spouses. Their personal and social contacts were with the elite of Chicago's business community, many of whom were also members of the hospital's Board of Trustees. George and Mary Young, Sargent and Eunice Schriver, and Marshall Field IV and his wife Kay were among this group. These Young Turks of Streeterville, as they were called, Jim, George, Marshall, and Sargent, all lived close by on the Near North Side and their friendship was bonded by their intellectual approach to life and their political ways of thinking, which were usually liberal. Marshall Field IV, then the publisher of the *Chicago Sun-Times* and head of Field Enterprises, appointed Young to be chairman of Field Enterprises and publisher of World Book. Although the Shrivers eventually moved back East, Jim kept in touch and became a trustee for one of the Kennedy charitable foundations in Boston and later on, was considered for a position in the Kennedy-Johnson administration.

Jim and Marshall IV became best friends. When they weren't discussing the opportunities and the challenges that the merger of the two hospitals presented, they spent a great deal of time playing chess together, and the cerebral Marshall was among the few who could beat Jim at the game. Jim was also Marshall's doctor, and the Field and Campbell families spent a good deal of time together, particularly after Jim and Elda moved up to Lake Forest. The Marshall Field family had been interested in both hospitals for several generations, spanning the time frame of almost a century. Upon his death in 1906, Marshall Field I had bequeathed equal amounts to two hospitals in Chicago, Presbyterian and St. Luke's.[1] Marshall IV was also publisher of the *Chicago Sun-Times*, the paper Marshall Field III had started during the Second World War. The Field family expanded their media interest when it acquired WFLD, the first UHF channel in Chicago. In 1969, Marshall Field V succeeded his father as publisher of the *Sun-Times* and the newspaper for the first time was able in its Sunday City edition to exceed the circulation of its rival, the *Chicago Tribune*. As a young man Marshall V worked with Campbell and later served as chairman of the board.[2]

In the early fifties, Marshall IV decided to build a country house on a large parcel of property in Lake Forest close to Interstate

---

1. John Tibbett, *The Marshall Fields: A Study in Wealth* (New York: E. P. Dutton, 1947).

2. Marshall V spent his early years in the East and first became acquainted with Campbell in 1968. During that time Marshall was also serving in the National Guard at the Democratic National Convention in Chicago, while his friend Jamie Campbell was covering the story for the *Sun-Times*. Marshall V moved to the Chicago area and has lived

294 across from Lake Forest Academy. This property had been the Ogden estate. The estate of two-time presidential candidate and governor of Illinois, Adlai Stevenson, was close by. A portion of this property, about 25 acres with its own lake, was not included in Marshall's plans, and he made this available to the Campbells, who were also looking for property at the time. So the Fields and Campbells both built homes and became next door neighbors.

Marshall and Jim became interested in sheep breeding and built barns on their property to house the animals, the Willow Lakes Barn on Field's farm and the Frisbee Barn on Campbell's property. Eighty to a hundred sheep was the usual number under management at a time, but at one time that number rose to 300.

Field and Campbell traveled to country fairs all over the Midwest to show their Hampshire sheep, and eventually they won several prizes at these shows, including the prestigious International Livestock Exposition held in Chicago. Jim had now learned to fly an airplane, so he, Marshall, and another friend, Bob Sessions, would go on from one show to another on these barnstorming tours. And once in a while Jim and Marshall would fly to the Field home in Jupiter, Florida, for some relaxation and fishing.

Size and leanness of these sheep, as well as the thickness of their wool coat, were the criteria that won awards. Jim had figured out a way to increase the weight in these animals by altering their breeding habits. He had the barns air conditioned so that breeding occurred in the summer rather than the fall, when the weather was cooler, the time that breeding normally took place. Lambs would usually be born in the early spring and achieve a certain weight and leanness in the summer when the fairs were held. Campbell's technique ensured that the lambs were born three months earlier and thus would be twice normal size when the fairs were held the next

there ever since. The Field family private secretary of over sixty years, Doris Schnur, has related that many of the family's doctors were affiliated with Rush–Presbyterian–St. Luke's. The Field children were born there. Obstetrician and gynecologist Dr. John Long, also a close personal friend to Marshall V and his wife Jamie, delivered Marshall VI in 1966, and later the three Field girls, Jamie Carolyn, Stephanie, and Abigail

summer. Campbell and Field walked away with all the prizes for
their entries, which came from the Willowbee Farms, the name of
the friends' combined farms. The Field and Campbell homes were
filled with trophies. In 1964, the Willowbee Farms was host for the
meeting of the National Hampshire Sheep Association, which
attracted hundreds of visitors. Willowbee Farm's certified ram champion stud, Walnut, was in such demand that the farm actually made
money for a while.

Jamie Campbell was the oldest of the children, followed by
Bruce and then Douglas, who was just a baby. They all grew up in
Lake Forest, played little league games and hockey and even did
chores around the farm. The boys became members of 4H, not the
usual activity for children of the North Shore. In spite of his very
busy schedule, Campbell was ever present at their schools' athletic
events. Jim would take the boys down to the hospital when he had
to go in on the weekends, and he was very proud to show them
around to his friends there.

During this time in 1963, on the occasion of the twentieth
anniversary of his graduation from Harvard, Jim wrote back to his
classmates about what he was doing. Things seemed to be going
pretty well for Campbell at that time, both personally and professionally. "The children and the hospital have grown. I have aged.
The influx of more and younger graduates of HMS [Harvard
Medical School] has been exciting indeed. Research buildings and
research personnel are coming into their proper growth, and some
early spade work seems to have been worthwhile." He then adds at
the end a job description for his work, framing it in the form of a laboratory report, "administration four plus, teaching two plus, and
practice trace."[3] Campbell, the former editor of the *Aesculapiad*, was
at it again.

Elda and Jim were busy socially in Lake Forest. They became
good friends with the A. B. Dicks and the Ed McCormick Blairs as
well. Ed Blair thought very highly of Jim. He admired his brilliance

3. Harvard Medical School Class of 1943-B (1943–1963), *Twentieth Reunion Report*,
edited by John C. Nemiah, M.D.

and liked his personal ways and mannerisms, which were almost shy and retiring in contrast to Elda's more outgoing and gregarious social graces. Campbell was comfortable in these social circumstances, but he would have been just as happy reading a book at home. The Youngs, the Fields, the Dicks, the Blairs, and the Campbells spent a good deal of time together socially. All of these people were influential on the board at the medical center, so Campbell had the unusual opportunity as well as the exceptional challenge to relate to them as both a friend and a professional and business colleague, to whom Jim was ultimately accountable.

Jim was also personal physician to many of these individuals on the board as well. When Marshall became ill and didn't respond to treatment, Jim would fly with him all over the country to consult with leading doctors and medical specialists. He was devastated when Marshall died at the early age of 49 of a heart condition. He was not in town when it happened and always felt that, if he had been there, he might have made a difference.

After the merger, the hospitals continued to grow and expand so that by 1964, the year that Jim Campbell assumed full responsibility for overseeing and directing the institution as its first president, the medical center was a vastly different one in complexity, size, and scope than either parent organization of the 1950s. The Kidston Building, the McCormick Center for Nursing residences, the Jelke Research Building were among the new additions to the undertaking. Throughout the world the development of scientific and technical advances was continuing at a rapid pace and being incorporated into the scientific armamentarium at the medical center.

No one, however, was really in charge to oversee this increasingly vast undertaking in its entirety. To have a few trustees, an administrator, and a Presbyterian or Episcopal clergyman meet every week or so to attend to the entire operation of the medical center wasn't going to be enough anymore. If there was a budgetary problem, an increase in room rates might have to be considered, and it would then usually go to the medical staff where it was approved ordinarily by voice vote. The field of hospital administration was in its infancy. Blue Cross and Blue Shield were becoming the major underwriter for hospital insurance, and out of this arose the concept of coverage in a two-bed room for the insured. But there were many patients who had no insurance and whose cost had to be covered in some way or other.

Increasingly specialized care for patients required training hospital personnel in new and complicated techniques and involved the use of expensive equipment. Finding space for these new initiatives was another problem. As each new program was introduced a way had to be found to pay for it. Physicians, nurses, and other hospital personnel had no real training in monitoring finances. The hospital was required to raise capital on the open financial market. Hospital costs started to spiral on a skyrocketing path that continued on in an almost totally unrestrained manner for the better part of three decades. So it was said by Dr. John H. Knowles, the general director of Massachusetts General Hospital, that if a device or machine was good, the hospital must have it regardless of the cost. The first principle and the principal goal is to improve service in the care of the sick and the prevention of disease. Any savings of money would be a secondary gain.[4]

Medicine and its allied sciences were now characterized by economists as an undertaking in the process of transformation from a group of isolated independent cottage industries to a vast business. The term "health care industry" was born, and eventually this industry would consume between 10 and 15 percent of the U.S. gross national product. As boards of trustees of hospitals all over the country met to approve hospital budgets, they were startled by the rising costs and expanding programs. Trustees did not see such things in their own businesses. Presbyterian–St. Luke's vision of its mission to be a world-class medical center was translated into being there first or among the first with each new evolving technology. Of course, everyone wanted these new advances, but where in the world would the money come from to pay for it all. In addition to all this was the

4. Kenneth M. Ludmerer, *Time to Heal: American Medical Education from the Turn of the Century to the Era of Managed Care* (New York: Oxford University Press, 1999), p. 166.

dream and ambition of Campbell to build an even bigger empire and in the process resurrect the Rush Medical School. And the institution started taking steps and making commitments pointing in this direction. Financial commitments for educational and research programs were undertaken well beyond those that a first-rate hospital would ordinarily consider. And very few of these efforts would ever pay for themselves or could be considered profitable. Dr. Joseph Muenster put it well in describing this time of the early 1960s by saying that the hospital was not a medical school at the time, but was becoming organized like one.[5]

The Board of Trustees recognized clearly that a huge commitment by the hospital to the community and the nation had been made in creating the merger. Gone were the days when the hospital wouldn't have to be concerned about staying in the black. Costs had quadrupled within a decade. The board was quick to note that doctors and administrators were not grounded in sound business practices. They had no experience or training in this area. A person would have to be found who could lead the medical center. Board Chairman John Bent and Trustees Ralph Bard, Edward Blair, George Young, and A. B. Dick III studied this problem in some depth. All these people were highly respected members of the Chicago business community. An outside management consultant firm conducted a two-year study and recommended a broad program for advancement.[6] It strongly advocated finding a full-time executive who could lead by initiative and by example. Such an individual must be able to lift up the sights of those around him to the task ahead. The remainder of the report supported the idea that a first-rate nationally regarded metropolitan medical center could be developed, a need existed, and all the tools were in place for this to happen. The

5. Summary transcript of interview with Joseph Muenster, M.D., by Jim Bowman, June 10, 1986, in preparation for *Good Medicine: The First 150 Years of Rush–Presbyterian–St. Luke's Medical Center.*

6. Development Program for Presbyterian–St. Luke's by Booz, Allen and Hamilton, 1960, Presbyterian–St. Luke's Hospital, Record Group #41000, Presbyterian–St. Luke's Hospital, C96-001, Box 00032, File 0007, Rush–Presbyterian–St. Luke's Medical Center/ Rush University Medical Center Archives, Chicago, Ill.

board would have to lead the way, which would not be easy. There should be a continuation of development of both full-time and private voluntary staff, the free clinics should be restructured toward developing better financial support for the eventual objective of being self-supporting, and the overall organizational structure should be strengthened for better planning and community development.

At the time of the merger, the chief administrative officer for the hospital was Dr. Karl Klicka, a physician with virtually no business background. Klicka was eventually succeeded by Mr. Gavin Pitt, who had been recruited from Johns Hopkins. Again, the board did not see the administrative and business credentials they felt were required to direct this immense undertaking. The retiring executive vice president of Commonwealth Edison, Chicago businessman Mr. Herbert Sedgwick was then appointed as a temporary chief executive officer. Sedgwick did a very good job in applying sound business principles to hospital financial activities. Budgets were established, and hospital occupancy rates set to determine what was needed to keep the hospital in the black. Sedgwick's contributions were significant but short-lived, as he was at retirement age.

So the question of who would lead the medical center over the long term remained unanswered. The job description for such an individual had yet to be written. In the early sixties, very few hospitals even conducted audited financial reports. It wasn't until after Medicare was enacted in 1965 that the rigorous disciplines of accounting began being practiced by even the major hospitals. A search committee headed by George Young was appointed and met for over eighteen months before making a decision.[7] The first issue to be decided was whether the candidate should be primarily an administrator, a financial person, or a physician. The answer to this question simply was not known. With few exceptions, such as the Cleveland

7. Other Trustees on the committee included John Bent, Philip Clarke, William Collins, A. B. Dick III, Anthony Michel, Sedgwick, John Simpson, and Hall Taylor. An advisory medical staff committee to the trustees included, in addition to Campbell, Dr. Ted Beattie, Drs. Ormond C. Julian, Thomas Coogan, Richard Capps, and Stanton Freidberg.

Clinic, physicians did not engage in this sort of work. Norman Brady, the administrative officer for the merged hospitals who had come from St. Luke's, was considered for the position. Chairman of Surgery Dr. Ted Beattie, who had demonstrated exceptional organizational and leadership skills in that position, was also considered, as were a number of individuals from outside the medical center.

Jim Campbell was the leading candidate. In the eyes of many, he had been the de facto "boss" for some time. Since his return in 1953 from Albany, he had reversed the fortunes of the Department of Medicine and established it as one of the premier places to train in the nation. His influence extended well beyond his own department, as other areas felt the pressure to compete and come up to the standards that Jim was setting. As much as anyone else, he was responsible for the success of the merger. And he did it operating mostly behind the scenes. Many doctors were never aware of this. The trustees placed great importance on his proven skills in diplomacy during the merger.

After the merger Campbell began to develop a definite financial sense about things, something his previous medical training did not provide for. He was willing to learn in this area as he listened to the trustees and heeded their advice. His financial competence became evident as he learned to understand financial language and to effectively communicate with the board. Even the hard-nosed businessmen of the board, who were not easily impressed in this area, took note of this. He had a sense of what you had to pay for things. He paid attention to financial things that most physicians who were medical leaders did not. Twenty years later this sort of skill among physicians was not so rare, but in the early 1960s it was almost unheard of.

But the appointment did not come quickly. Campbell started to look for other opportunities. He was not patient. As his son Jamie described his father, "Dad was always in a hurry." Interest in Campbell was expressed by at least three other major medical centers, in New York City at Mount Sinai, in Seattle at the University of Washington, and in Tuscon at the University of Arizona, where positions for medical center leadership were being developed. Jim's interest in the New

York opportunity was serious. He had wanted to return to the East when he finished his cardiology training but was persuaded by Howard Armstrong to come to Chicago. He had many friends in New York, and his wife Elda liked New York as well.[8]

Eventually, Jim was offered the job and accepted. The search committee was aware that Jim was not well liked by some of the doctors. He was not collegial and didn't "stroke" the doctors as much as he could have. He wasn't one of the boys. The committee recognized that this was a real shortcoming, that it wasn't just some prima donna physicians griping. His approach at times could be too harsh and unyielding. His sense of being able to take on any task or challenge, and to do so exceedingly well, actually frightened people. It is possible that the eighteen months that the committee took to make its decision reflected to some extent that reservation. But Jim eventually got the nod. The committee was impressed that Campbell never allowed himself to get into a rut, and he always had new and creative ideas to approach new problems as they presented themselves.

The board also took into account that Campbell was active in many professional organizations covering a wide spectrum of activities related to medical administration, organization, and training. In addition to his strong leadership role in the National Intern Matching Program, Campbell was active on the Internship Review Committee of the AMA and the National Board of Medical Examiners and was the chairman of the Institute on Clinical Teaching of the Association of American Medical Colleges. He was secretary-treasurer of the Alpha Omega Alpha Medical Honor Society and was on the Board of Trustees of Knox College. Campbell also served on the Advisory Committees for the establishment of two new medical schools in New York and Pennsylvania. High regard among his peers was self-evident, an important quality to look for in an individual considered for the office of the presidency.

8. Jack Starr interview and Bruce Rattenbury commentary, fall 1973 and 1991, folder 22, Box 4, C97-052, James A. Campbell, M.D., Papers 1924–1983, Record Group 002000, Office of the President, Rush–Presbyterian–St. Luke's Medical Center/Rush University Medical Center Archives, Chicago, Ill.

And Campbell grew from the long period of uncertainty that preceded his appointment as the Medical Center's first president. He began to develop a much broader outlook and to recognize more than ever the importance of all constituencies in the medical center. His driving vision was even more evident to all. He became quite mindful of his need to further develop, refine, and hone his management, diplomatic, and sensitivity skills. Most of all he had to begin to recognize the need to strive to establish a balance of power among all the constituencies in the medical center. For example, he began to recognize the vital importance of Surgery, which to some extent had previously been his whipping boy. He became a staunch ally of Nursing and eventually engaged the institution in a major reorganization of nursing that had important national implications.

The appointment was announced at the staff meeting in October 1964. A few of the doctors grumbled and mocked the efforts of the search committee, saying, "Have you ever heard such baloney in all your life?" Or "The whole thing was rigged from the beginning because of Campbell's relationship with the board." Many of these critics eventually came around as they began to realize the importance of having someone in charge who was capable and flexible in dealing with the massive changes in health care that lay ahead.

The appointment was big news. Campbell, as the first physician to be a president and chief executive officer of a medical center, was now a national figure. Congratulations were received from all over the country. Jim's father, Frank, was grateful that he had lived to see the great success of his son. Campbell also received a note of personal congratulations from the entire Junior Class at the University of Illinois Medical School.[9]

In his first address to the medical staff, Campbell announced that racial discrimination for hospital admissions and racial segregation of patients would no longer be permitted. Taking such a stand

9. Correspondence regarding appointment as medical center president, October–December 1964, Folder 11, Box 2, C97-052, James A. Campbell, M.D., Papers 1924–1983, Record Group 002000, Office of the President, Rush–Presbyterian–St. Luke's Medical Center/Rush University Medical Center Archives, Chicago, Ill.

now would go unnoticed, but for the time, it was unusual. Campbell also supported the policy of not restricting the appointment of Jewish physicians to the medical staff of the hospital. At one time, only one Jewish physician had carried on an active practice at Presbyterian Hospital.

Campbell moved quickly to define the authority of his new office. Norman Brady had been responsible for operations or the day-to-day running of the hospital. It had been assumed that Campbell would develop policy, oversee public relations and fundraising, and deal with the board. He was expected to leave the actual operations to Brady. Campbell's role was assumed to be "Mister Outside" and Brady's "Mister Inside." Mr. Donald Oder, of accounting firm of Arthur Andersen, who was then serving as a consultant on corporate organization to the medical center informed Campbell that this was the way big corporate organizations were organized. But Campbell felt differently, even after carefully considering the advice of Oder, whom he highly respected. In his mind he was already very much involved in day-to-day operations. People had been already bypassing Brady for him. He insisted on being in charge of day-to-day operations and prevailed. Symbolically, his office with its floor-to-ceiling windows was located on the ground floor of the Jelke Building on Harrison street, where he could keep track of everybody as they came and went.

Campbell and Oder then organized a management structure for the medical center that was totally new for the field of health care. And once organized, it has remained unchanged right up to the present time. Many institutions emulated this Rush organizational structure as the health care field grew and expanded and became one of the country's largest industries. It called for the creation of four positions under the Office of the President, executive vice presidents for administration, finance, public relations and development, and academic and professional affairs. Norman Brady was made executive vice president for administrative affairs, and Richard Slotow was appointed vice president for public relations and fundraising. Oder left Arthur Andersen to become vice president for finance. And Dr.

Mark Lepper was appointed vice president for Academic and Professional Affairs.

Recruiting Lepper would go down as one of Campbell's most significant accomplishments. The first that Oder, a close Campbell confidant, knew of it was the day that Lepper was appointed. The negotiations had been carried out in complete secrecy between Campbell and Lepper.

The Lepper appointment was significant for several reasons. First of all, by creating the Office of Academic and Professional Affairs, Campbell wedded patient care and teaching together. One needed and depended on the other. Although such a relationship might seem self-evident now, for the time it was not. Academic affairs were isolated in many medical centers and often in conflict with ideas related to patient care. All these issues as well as those of research had to be interrelated. The patient would come first.

Second, this office would provide the framework for the future development of a medical school and subsequently a fully developed academic medical center, which did indeed occur just a few years later. The appointment of Lepper was a signal to everyone that something was in the wind. It was part of Campbell's hidden agenda, strongly sensed but not yet well understood within the medical center family. As well as things were going, the sights were being set on higher goals.

Finally, the exceptional talents of Lepper were enlisted for the huge tasks ahead.

11

The Rebirth of Rush

By the beginning of the 1960s, medicine's landmark discoveries of the 1940s and the 1950s were now incorporated into established practices. Effective treatment for infections, first sulfa, then penicillin, and then many other antibiotics, and the discovery of cortisone, the first of the steroids, resulted in dramatic improvements in outcomes for many severe and chronic illnesses. The expectations of even further scientific breakthroughs attracted the attention and admiration of the entire nation. Government proposals for support for all kinds of medical programs enjoyed wide general backing. The interest of the public in a healthier nation captured the imagination of many Americans and was a unifying force in our national life. Great financial resources, both public and private, were being expended to train doctors, build hospitals, and advance medical research.

Medicine was among the most, if not the most, admired of all careers in American life. Physicians enjoyed great respect. A Gallup poll found that they outranked Supreme Court justices in popular esteem.[1] American medical schools and hospitals had become the

1. John C. Burnham, "American Medicine's Golden Age: What Happened to It?" (1) *Science* 215 (March 19, 1982) (4539): 147–49.

best in the world, and American physicians the best prepared in the world. Confidence in medicine was very high and the image of doctors had become decidedly heroic. Doctors were widely perceived as working on behalf of the public interest and also as advisors and counselors who knew their patients and families well. Few people resented medical incomes. Though greed was hardly absent, a spirit of charity pervaded the profession, as manifested by the enormous amount of free care physicians provided.[2]

To become a doctor was the dream of many, and those who elected to undertake the rigorous demands that the study of medicine required were held in high esteem by their peers. To be among the most highly respected members of one's own community, to devote one's life to something truly worthwhile, and at the same time enjoy a fairly comfortable living were the common aspirations of those entering medicine. The enactment of the GI Bill of Rights in 1945 had enabled many who otherwise would not have been able to afford it to go to college for the three or four years of pre-medical studies and the four years of medical school required for the M.D. degree. The GI Bill also widened considerably the characterization of young Americans entering medicine. In earlier times, the medical student very often came from prosperous circumstances or from a physician's family. Now the very brightest, the hardest working, and most idealistic from all segments of American life were provided with the opportunity to enter the profession. It was not uncommon for older military dischargees to embark on a career in medicine. Having experienced first hand the tragedies of war, these individuals were among the most highly motivated and most mature in contributing to the advancement of medicine's highest ideals. The world might well be a better place from their labors, they hoped. So the best and the brightest in America were aspiring to medicine as a career. This era of expand-

2. Kenneth M. Ludmerer, *Time to Heal: American Medical Education from the Turn of the Century to the Era of Managed Care* (New York: Oxford University Press, 1999), p. 122.

ed opportunities did not extend to women, however. Women in general were not encouraged to enter medicine and only a handful were admitted into medical school.

The life and career of Mark Lepper could serve as an example for what America might expect from its doctors. Mark's background was modest. Both parents worked for the government all their lives. From this Mark gained a knowledge, a respect, and a fascination for government service. He was educated at the George Washington University Medical School in Washington, D.C., and remained there for several years after he completed his training. Working as a consultant for Walter Reed Hospital, he undertook a detailed study of severe epidemics of streptococcus infections that were occurring in military installations throughout the world. He worked and practiced with Dr. Harry Dowling, who was becoming a pioneering expert in the study of infectious diseases long before the field developed its own discernible identity.

Mark and his wife Joyce moved to Chicago in 1950 to join Dr. Dowling in the Department of Medicine at the University of Illinois Medical School located on the West Side. Dowling had been appointed chairman of the Department of Preventive Medicine. Mark and Harry conducted a number of studies of infectious diseases that earned them worldwide professional recognition. Lepper was also medical superintendent of the Municipal Contagious Disease Hospital in Chicago, located at Twenty-sixth and California and he and his wife Joyce lived in an apartment right there on the premises. At MCD Lepper conducted epidemiological studies on tuberculosis, whooping cough (pertussis), rheumatic fever, and polio, and in 1952 moved up to Dowling's job when Dowling was appointed chairman of Medicine.

Mark's idealism and personal integrity were of the very highest type. He always attempted to comply with both the spirit and the letter of the law. He had been turned down for military service because of evidence of tuberculosis on a chest X-ray. Subsequently, the infection was cleared with treatment. The military procurement office was not aware of this, and so Mark presented himself and his new evidence of good health to a military induction center and was drafted. How many would have done such a thing?[3]

Lepper was gifted with an extraordinary medical mind with the ability to grasp and understand in depth an immense number of subjects related to medicine. Not only could he remember in enormous detail all the important medical papers, books, proceedings of meetings, and the like that he ever read, but he was able to communicate this information to his colleagues in a truly inspirational way. This generated a sense of infectious enthusiasm that encouraged and motivated people to move forward with their own ideas and initiatives. He started a Sunday Journal Club in his home, where the material from current journals was reported by a preassigned participant and discussed. From these discussions, Lepper was able to correlate basic science cell biology concepts with potential clinical applications, and from these sessions hypotheses were generated that would eventually be tested in clinical and epidemiological studies. Mark's reputation as a medical scholar spread and physicians from all over the Chicago metropolitan area attended these Sunday sessions.

Mark's fundamental commitment to humanity was expressed in so many ways. He enjoyed working with young people. He always gave of his time to their concerns and problems and encouraged them to reach as high as they could in improving themselves and the profession. Then he would share their successes with them as if the whole thing were their idea. He pushed students and faculty ahead of himself when it came time for promotions and was very pleased when they came through. A man of towering intellect, he was always pleased to redirect his colleagues' thinking when he enlightened or corrected them always in a humble and modest manner, being careful never to be overbearing. He helped people grow a great deal, both personally and professionally, from these encounters. Dr. Edward Lichter, the recipient of the Henry P. Russe Citation for

3. A Celebration in Honor of Mark H. Lepper, M.D., Monday, June 14, 1982, Room 500, Rush–Presbyterian–St. Luke's Medical Center, Chicago, Illinois. File 9, Box 11, C97-052, James A. Campbell, M.D., Papers 1924–1983; Record Group 002000, Office of the President; Rush–Presbyterian–St. Luke's Medical Center/Rush University Medical Center Archives, Chicago, Ill

Compassion in Medicine for the year 2000, cited Lepper as the "brightest person in the city in health care, clearly and without question, and so regarded by his peers. But he would be the last person to tell you that. He was so very modest."[4] At medical grand rounds, the temptation to impress others with his knowledge was not Mark's way. He was never in any way a "smart aleck."[5]

Lepper's focus of attention began to change from conducting clinical studies such as those on the utilization of new antibiotic agents for infections to designing, effecting, and structuring health systems management programs. Serious community problems such as the delivery of health care for the poor and the limited opportunity for training in medicine for minorities were studied. The development of an illness could be influenced by social factors such as access, health education, and demographic trends. And once engaged, Mark attacked these community problems with a ferocious tenacity. He worked with the sisters of Marillac on the West Side to help the homeless. Lepper would then take such a study group a step further and discover that the incidence of hypertension in these homeless people was higher than expected.

In 1952, Lepper, Dowling, and a few others from around the country interested in infections and epidemiology met to establish the specialty of Preventive Medicine. In many ways, however, Mark was a generalist at heart. He criticized the tendency of his specialty-conscious colleagues to belittle the general practitioner. The primary care giver must be the most talented and knowledgeable of all in health care delivery. Mark was an excellent clinician as well as an

4. Personal communication, Dr. Edward Lichter, May 4, 2000.

5. Lepper trained some of the country's leading doctors. Dr. Adrian Ostfeld later went on to become chief of Preventive Medicine at Yale, Dr. Jeremiah Stamler chief of Preventive Medicine at Northwestern, Dr. Jack Remington chief of Infectious Diseases at Stanford, and Dr. Marvin Turck chief of Infectious Disease at the University of Washington in Seattle. He worked with Dr. Hyman Zimmerman to develop a strong Department of Medicine at the West Side Veterans Administration Hospital and conducted several major studies on alcoholism with Zimmerman. Dr. James Schoenberger was recruited by Mark from a busy private practice to study a number of preventive aspects of heart disease. Schoenberger later went on to become the president of the American Heart Association. Others included Dr. Edward Lichter, Dr. Nickolas Cotsonas, and infectious disease expert Dr. Stuart Levin.

investigator. He taught well at the bedside, and the house staff would not hesitate to call him in the middle of the night to discuss a problem. Mark might even come in to see the patient, even if it wasn't his turn to be on the call rotation. Mark insisted on broad experience in training and would often talk of the ideal of the "good doctor." He would say, "the best way to be a good doctor is to see a bad doctor in practice." Going back to his student days, Lepper related, whenever he saw a doctor doing something wrong, especially when he treated a patient or nurse or student poorly, he would say to himself, "I'll never do that."[6]

Mark then proceeded to formulate several creative ideas in medical education, first while at the University of Illinois with Drs. George Miller and William Grove, and later on when he moved over to Presbyterian–St. Luke's to become vice president for Professional and Academic Affairs.

Prior to 1964, Mark had little more than a passing acquaintance with Jim Campbell. Lepper's Fellowship for Infectious Diseases at the University of Illinois started to include a rotation at Presbyterian–St. Luke's, and here again he made a very strong impression on the doctors there with his encyclopedic medical knowledge.[7] Lepper was a candidate to fill the position that Campbell had just vacated. But Campbell had something entirely different in mind for Mark in his grand plan for the medical center. As Mark revealed in a personal interview many years later, he was told by Jim, "Mark, you don't want to be head of Medicine here, I have something else in mind. Just wait a while, maybe a year or so. I want you to come over here and run the place. If you come over here, all I want from you is your ideas. I will pick your brain and sell your ideas. I want you to know that ahead of time."[8] Now that he was president of the hospital, Campbell was focusing more clearly on the idea of reestablishing a new and entirely different hospital, and Mark would be the key person for this under-

6. Personal communication, Prof. Edward Eckenfels, November 23, 1998.

7. Personal communication, Dr. William Phelan, May 14, 1998

8. Sheldon Garber interview with Mark H. Lepper, October 5, 1992, File 3, Box 20, C97-096, Sheldon Garber Papers, 1964–1996, R6 003000, Office of Philanthropy and Communications, Rush–Presbyterian–St. Luke's Medical Center Archives.

taking. The man Jim needed most to make his plans succeed was Mark. Mark added a new dimension of credibility to Presbyterian–St. Luke's and its plans, both within and beyond the confines of the institution. A person of such stature would be necessary to lead a talented medical staff into new and uncharted waters. All of Chicago medicine took notice.

Although Mark and Jim were temperamentally quite different, they got along well together. Many had wondered just how Campbell was able to recruit Lepper over from the University of Illinois, where by that time he had become one of the most highly regarded faculty members within the entire university. Mark was known to be quite liberal in his political views, and Campbell by this time was more inclined to moderate or conservative views. Mark knew almost everything about research, Jim not nearly as much, but he understood how important research was to the overall scheme of things. There were things in place in the Campbell program that were unique, which were of great interest to Mark. There was the prospect of opening a new medical school, proposals for the development of several social initiatives such as the Mile Square Program, new ideas about health care delivery such as the Anchor HMO, and proposals for the study of the state's health manpower needs. The University of Illinois was embarking on a program of expansion in medical education that was often stymied by the uncertainties of state legislative political considerations. Not so at Presbyterian–St. Luke's Hospital, where it was clear that Jim Campbell was the man in charge. He had a clear vision of where he was going, and there was no one in the institution to obstruct these plans. And Campbell knew how to get things done. Mark appreciated this. Put another way, Mark was always on the side of the angels. But very often it took a man of Jim's pragmatic and visionary style of leadership to make these dreams of Mark's come true.

Lepper marveled at Campbell's ability to recruit top people from the business community in Chicago to serve on the hospital board and effectively engage these trustees in his mission. Jim would take a proposal of Lepper's that was considered quite radical and somehow secure the enthusiasm and support of the conservative fiscally oriented board. How did he do it? He would take a proposal, revise it, revise it again, and then pump Mark and his associates for further ideas, modifications, and changes. He would then go back to Mark and his associates, and pump them again, to come up with a package that the board could accept. As a result, the institution, which was often identified with big money conservative interests, was often in the lead on social initiatives and social changes.[9]

When Mark Lepper and Jim Campbell entered medicine in the late thirties and early forties, very few were turned down when they applied to medical school. If one had the necessary college grades and financial resources to see their way through the long period of training, they could do it. Medical schools often did not even require a personal interview. There was no such thing as Medical College Admittance Testing (MCAT) scores at that time.

But then, in the late 1940s, public pressure began to develop to train more physicians to meet the needs of the country. America was becoming more health conscious as people began to consider access to medical care more of a basic right than was heretofore the case. The existing schools could not meet this expectation. Swelling college enrollment from the GI Bill also placed great pressure from college undergraduates for places in medical school, which became very difficult to secure. In addition to this, many communities, particularly in rural settings, were seriously underserved medically.

By the end of the 1950s, an explosive growth in the country's population resulted in a national shortage of doctors. The origins of this shortage dated back to the 1920s and early 1930s, when the number of physicians in training had been curtailed as a result of the Flexner report. "A few well trained doctors would be better than more mediocre or poorly trained doctors," so the thinking went. Excellence was stressed. And in terms of numbers, the country was fairly well served by doctors up through the Second World War. But then new physician production began to fall behind. In 1959, the Bane study projected a serious shortfall of nearly 40,000 doctors for

9. Ibid.

the country by the year 1975.[10] The report went on to recommend that the annual production of physician graduates of 7,500 be raised to 11,000.

In responding to this shortage, medical educators rightfully insisted to Congress that standards could not be lowered for training. To shorten the period of training by accelerating the curriculum, as was done during the Second World War, was totally unacceptable. Quality simply could not be compromised. The training now required more time because of the explosion of medical information and technology. Increased physician production was to be achieved by expanding class size and establishing new schools. Congress acted in 1963 by providing funds, some direct and some matching, to all medical schools considering expansion, and to new schools in an even more liberal fashion. Federal loan money was made available for needy students. In one way or another, large subsidies were provided for both the construction of new facilities and for medical school operating expenses.

During this time of the late 1950s and into the mid 1960s, the trustees of Rush Medical College,[11] led by Dr. Frank B. Kelly, Sr., and Dr. Frederick dePeyster, continued to operate the school on paper by having regular meetings, appointing Rush professors at the University of Illinois, and carrying on various other formalities, such as keeping the legal requirements for incorporation up to date. DePeyster, as a more recent Rush graduate, quietly and effectively maintained alumni interest and kept pressure on for some sort of Rush revival. Rush also owned the Rawson and Senn buildings, which they had leased to Presbyterian Hospital, and the Rush Library. The very modest financial assets of Rush did support the appointment of a Rush professor in virology, research scientist Dr. Frederick Deinhardt, who along with his wife, Dr. Jean Deinhardt, developed a vaccine for mumps.

10. Ludmerer, *Time to Heal,* pp. 211–12
11. Additional Rush trustees included Drs. R. K. Gilchrist, Bertram Nelson, Willard Wood, and Fred Preist.

But on a day-to-day basis, the Rush presence at the newly merged Presbyterian–St. Luke's Hospital was barely evident. Nationally the number of active Rush alumni, at about 3000, although still a significant number, was declining each year. The trustees' hopes for reactivating Rush had been discouraged in 1963, when officials of the American Medical Association[12] told them that it would take thirty million dollars to start another medical school and another thirty million to operate it for ten years. No such money was readily available. The University of Illinois was no longer appointing Presbyterian Hospital staff members as Rush professors within the university faculty, as they had originally agreed to do.

After he became president, the Rush trustees approached Campbell. Kelly's group was told that the time was not yet ripe for such an undertaking. When that might be remained to be determined, and, although Campbell had a plan he was starting to formulate, he kept these thoughts entirely to himself. Dr. Kelly, however, was very important to Campbell. As an outstanding teacher and highly respected clinician, Kelly was the embodiment of the Rush tradition. He had received the Golden Apple award from the University of Illinois medical students as an outstanding teacher. He had kept in contact with the University of Chicago, making every effort to keep all lines of communications open with Rush's former affiliate. The venerable Rush traditions enjoyed a high level of credibility because of Kelly.[13]

Campbell had laid the groundwork by raising the level of academic credibility of the medical center by establishing the office of Executive Vice President for Professional and Academic Affairs and recruiting Mark Lepper to fill that position. The implications of this

12. Interview of Frederick A. dePeyster, M.D., by Stuart Campbell, Ph.D., March 28, 1994, Oral History Collection, Rush–Presbyterian–St. Luke's Medical Center Archives, Chicago, Ill.

13. In the spring and summer, 2001, an exhibit featuring the activities of Rush Medical College of the University of Chicago in 1926 was displayed in the Exhibition Gallery in the Department of Special Collections at the Regenstein Library of the University of Chicago. Kelly was one of the Rush physicians cited in the presentation.

were well understood by the medical community both in Chicago and throughout the nation. As Harvard professor Dr. Julius Richmond, a friend of both Campbell's and Lepper's, pointed out, "Mark was an academic giant. He was well known and highly respected throughout the country in educational circles. In fact, he was almost unique. Lepper had the most creative mind he had ever encountered.[14]

At the merged hospitals, the basic sciences of pathology, bio-chemistry, and microbiology needed for a new school were established departments with scientific credentials. In the 1950s and 1960s, 128 University of Illinois medical students, a large number indeed, received all of their clinical training in their third and fourth years at the hospital. The hospital was providing more than an adequate patient base for clinical training, which was top notch. Credible research was also being conducted. So a major portion of the strong professional component necessary for the development of the medical school was largely in place.

The real problem was money. And where could it be found? The federal government had stepped into the process by offering generous amounts of money for both construction and general maintenance of schools willing to expand, but the aid would be in the form of a matching grant, not primarily seed money. Two dollars would be granted for each dollar expended by the school. The cost of building and expanding schools was in the millions, so in order for federal assistance to be forthcoming, the school had to come up with a great deal of its own money to start the process. If, for example, it required an annual budget of six million dollars to operate a school, the federal government would provide four million, but the school had to come up with the first two million.

In the mid 1960s, Governor Otto Kerner began to look into the problem of shortage of medical manpower within the state. The severity had been underscored in an article that appeared in the *New England Journal of Medicine* by Dr. Ward Darley, in which he point-

14. Personal communication, Julius Richmond, M.D., January 14, 2000.

ed out that a serious shortage of medical manpower for all categories of health professionals existed for the entire country.[15] Darley and Jim Campbell had worked together when they were national directors for the Intern Matching Program. Darley was dean of the University of Colorado School of Medicine and executive director of the highly influential Association of American Medical Colleges (AAMC).

The chairman of the State Board of Higher Education, Chicagoan Ben Heinemann, selected Campbell to conduct a study of the health manpower needs for the state. Campbell's credentials in medical education by this time were well established nationally, both as a proponent for improving medical training and for general medical reform. Heinemann, a prominent civic and business leader, worked closely with Campbell through the entire subsequent historic undertaking and was most impressed with his insistence on excellence. "Campbell was tops," Heinemann recalled.[16]

The study group was charged by the State Board to conduct a comprehensive assessment in the health professions of medicine, dentistry, and related fields. It was to include proper geographic locations for, the probable cost of, and the necessary ancillary facilities, such as hospitals and nursing schools, required for the establishment of such programs. The board also encouraged the study group to depart when desired from traditional thinking about methods of meeting the needs in health-related fields and encouraged innovation in formulating concepts of how best to provide the needed professional and technical manpower for Illinois and, indeed, the entire nation.

Campbell pointed out that a survey of education in the health fields necessitated consideration not only of the educational system but also of the health care delivery system in which and for which health care personnel are to be prepared. These considerations

15. Ward Darley, M.D., and Anne R. Somers, "Medicine, Money, and Manpower: The Challenge to Professional Education," *New England Journal of Medicine* 276 (June 22, 1967): 1414–23.

16. Personal communication, Mr. Ben Heinemann, March 14, 2001.

account for the inordinate complexity of education in this field. The interlocking of areas of practice and areas of training make health education quite different from engineering, legal, and other professional educational systems.

Campbell established a number of committees to oversee the study, but the day-to-day working group was composed entirely of Presbyterian–St. Luke's professionals.[17] A "think tank" of sorts was set up in Campbell's large office on the ground floor at the east end of the Jelke Building. And the team assembled was composed of Campbell, Mark Lepper, Dr. Joyce Lashof, Dr. Randy Tucker, and Ms. Irene Turner.

Randy Tucker was working in the Endocrine Laboratory of Dr. Ted Schwartz, collecting data for diabetes research. Randy had interned at St. Luke's Hospital, then spent time training in his home town of Cincinnati, and had returned to Chicago to work with Schwartz. He had never formally been introduced to Campbell until, one day, he was called into Campbell's office and asked if he would like to do the State of Illinois Manpower Study. Campbell had never directly spoken to Tucker before, even though Tucker had been around for some time. That was it. Schwartz had spoken to Campbell about Tucker's amazing talents with statistics. Tucker was very bright and could also read eight hundred words per minute. Tucker worked closely with Campbell and the others in the group, often exchanging information several times each day, and his data collection formed a major part for the entire report.

That Campbell did not know all the answers in this new endeavor was quite evident to Tucker, but Campbell would listen to the very bright people with whom he had surrounded himself. He would often disagree, but he would listen. In this group of four col-

17. A General Advisory Committee of thirty state leaders in health care was formed as was a Medical Deans Committee consisting of the five deans of the established active schools within the state. Other appointed committees included a National Research Advisory Committee, a Health Education Committee, and an overall National Advisory Committee. Drs. Robert Glaser, Mark Lepper, Julius Richmond, Hans Popper, Joyce Lashof, Ward Darley, and Robert Wissler served on several of the committees, all well known to Campbell. Glaser was dean of the Medical School at Stanford, and Wissler the chairman of the Department of Pathology at the University of Chicago and fellow classmate of Campbell's there.

leagues were individuals who were considerably more liberal politically than he was, but Jim listened and learned from these people.[18]
Dr. Lashof gave Campbell a paperback copy of a liberal-oriented
book, *American Medicine and the Public Interest,* by Rosemary Stevens,
which he referred to often and carried around in his back pocket.
The book contained the outline of several new proposals in the field
of health care.

Later on, when an Office of Research Affairs was developed
to perform internal reviews of all institutional research, Tucker was
again approached by Campbell. "Take care of the grants," Campbell
said. That was all he said. Before that, Mark Lepper had to bring
home colossal amounts of paperwork and documents each evening
for review. But the growth of research activity extended beyond even
Lepper's ability to manage. Tucker went on to oversee the institution's research efforts for several years.

Another member of the "think tank" team, Dr. Joyce Lashof,
strictly speaking was recruited by Lepper. Joyce moved to Chicago
after her residency at Yale and took an assignment in infectious disease and student health at the University of Chicago. She was unable
to get more than a year's commitment for her job there. Being a
female physician at that time carried many disadvantages. Mark
Lepper then recruited her to the University of Illinois, and she
moved over with Mark to Presbyterian–St. Luke's in 1965. Campbell
engaged her to reorganize the obsolete and rundown free clinics by
modernizing the facilities and providing much better up-to-date care
for these patients. Campbell's standard of one class of care for all
patients moved closer to a reality as a result of this.

Joyce eventually became chairman of the Department of
Public Health when Rush reopened. She established the policy of
mandatory Pap smears for all hospitalized women for cervical cancer screening, the first regulation of its kind for the state. Her career
changed course when she moved on with Lepper to Springfield
when he was appointed the director for Public Health for the state.
Joyce eventually went to Washington and became associate secretary

18. Personal communication, Dr. Randy Tucker, November 25, 1998.

of the Department of Health, Education, and Welfare in the Carter administration and continued on in the Reagan and Bush administrations. Later she was appointed dean of the School of Public Health at the University of California at Berkeley. Lashof described Jim Campbell as "a most extraordinary individual, combining the talents of a great teacher and a dynamic visionary leader."[19]

The report, *Education in the Health Fields for the State of Illinois*, which took two years to complete, began by interviewing representative groups of consumers of health care about how they obtained their health care services and by surveying parallel samples of physicians, dentists, pharmacists, and hospital administrators, as well as health departments and influential citizens throughout the state. Alumni of five medical schools in Illinois from the classes of 1952 through 1960 were asked about the fields of medical work in which they were engaged, why they had left or stayed in the state, and what might entice them to return if they had left. Data from the U.S. Public Health Service, the U.S. Department of Health, Education and Welfare, and other sources such as the Illinois Study Commission on Nursing were evaluated. The study group also looked at the major health care establishments in the state and reviewed the curricula of the state's medical schools, both by correspondence and personal visits.

The study called for an immediate expansion of all fields in health education within the state, with the objective of doubling health manpower by the year 1980. It found a serious shortage of personnel in all health care fields and noted that the State of Illinois was woefully behind in the production of physicians. The state ranked fourth in the nation in per capita income and fifth in population, but eighteenth in its ratio of physicians to population. Alumni of Illinois medical schools from 1952 to 1960 located practices outside rather than inside the state by a ratio greater than 2 to 1.

The study also recommended that the number of medical school graduates annually be doubled from 400 to 800. New medical school curricula were to be established, including the incorporation

19. Personal communication, Dr. Joyce Lashof, November 2, 1999.

of the first year medical school into the college curriculum and, by doing so, accelerating premedical and medical education. Special attention was to be given to the development of family practice programs for the training of primary care physicians. This recommendation over the ensuing years would be the most difficult to implement. However, the University of Illinois College of Medicine at Rockford, which was established as a result of the recommendations of the Campbell report did comply in training physicians for primary care. Through its Rural Health Initiative it effectively addressed the problem of the underserved rural population by incorporating rural family physicians into student training programs, as well as by selecting students for the school.[20]

The Campbell study also urged that state legislation be enacted to support these findings. The report repeatedly stressed that expansion could be done largely with existing physical facilities and, thus, was quite cost-effective. The state enacted legislation to carry out these recommendations and, in doing so, made a major commitment to support graduate medical education and allied health programs in private as well as public institutions.

Financial aid from the state would come in three ways. First, by subsidy for capital and one-time costs for expansion and planning of existing medical school facilities; second, by direct assistance for operations established by a formula that looked at the number of new students each school took on; and finally by a smaller student stabilization grant.

All schools in the state benefited. The University of Illinois went on to double their enrollment and establish new schools at several downstate university locations. The other schools, Loyola, Northwestern, Chicago, and the University of Chicago all increased the size of their classes. For the University of Chicago, this was a departure from their long-standing policy of educating smaller numbers of students, which was an issue when they broke up with Rush

20. Stanley W. Olsen, M.D., *A Generation of New Physicians: A History of the University of Illinois College of Medicine at Rockford, 1971–2001.* Copyright 2001, University of Illinois College of Medicine at Rockford, Rockford, Illinois.

twenty-five years before. They increased the size of each class from 72 to 104.[21] Except for the University of Illinois, the major beneficiary would be the Medical Center. The formulas for state aid were based on grants for expanding existing classes with new students in established schools. For Rush, all of their projected classes of new students would be eligible for assistance, since Rush had kept its charter alive. All their students would be "new students."

Now with this state subsidy, the baseline support could be established for federal matching grants, which would at least double the funding. A major portion of the expansion of buildings and programs involving the reestablishment of Rush, including the $25 million Academic Facility, the flagship structure housing the new educational enterprise, would be paid for largely from government sources. Fifteen million dollars came from federal and state sources, and ten million from borrowing. And yet this funding for expansion of production of doctors as exemplified by Rush, cost taxpayers considerably less than it would have if an entirely new school had been started.

Philanthropic support for further growth came from the establishment of endowed chairs. Campbell had initiated this program, the first of its kind for a hospital in the United States, in 1963. The Jean Schweppe Armour Endowed Chair of Neurology was established by Trustee A. Watson Armour III. The chair was a memorial to his wife in tribute to her leadership as a medical center volunteer and member of the Woman's Board. Armour was also a friend of Campbell's. The Armour Chair was held by Dr. Maynard Cohen, Rush's chairman of the Department of Neurology.

A chair could be named for a donor, in honor of an individual, in honor of a deceased person, in support of a specific program or department, or in honor of a particular physician. During Campbell's tenure as president, 29 chairs were created. Rush's ability to recruit many of the best individuals in the medical world has been significantly strengthened through the development of this program.

21. C. W. Vermeulen, M.D., "For the Greatest Good for the Largest Number: A History of the Medical Center, University of Chicago, 1927–1977," Vice President for Public affairs, the University of Chicago, 1977, p. 118.

Yet there were still other obstacles to be overcome and steps to be taken before Rush could start up again. By this time Campbell had become the preeminent spokesman for medical education in Chicago. All the other medical schools in the city were aware of the potential reentry of Rush. They knew that the Rush trustees never allowed their charter to lapse and Rush could return to the medical education scene. The fact that Campbell headed the state manpower study, rather than a representative of an existing active medical school with students, did not go unnoticed. With the Rush name, the new school would be formidable competition, particularly with Campbell in charge. Lepper was also there as well as a very strong medical staff. Dr. Ted Beattie, the former chief of Surgery at Presbyterian–St. Luke's, who later became chief of Surgery and CEO at the Sloan-Kettering Memorial Cancer Hospital in New York, was astonished by Campbell's ability to work through all these intense rivalries and adversities of this time.[22]

Next came the formal surrendering of the 1837 Rush Medical College Charter to Presbyterian–St. Luke's Hospital that occurred in November 1967. Eventually the entire complex would be renamed Rush–Presbyterian–St. Luke's Medical Center and in September 2003, it was again renamed Rush University Medical Center. The Rush trustees handed the charter over to the hospital trustees with the understanding that the medical center would make every effort to reestablish the college within five years. The Rush board had been approached by at least one other medical center in the Chicago area to obtain the charter and reactivate the school. But for Kelly and the others, their loyalty would remain with Presbyterian–St. Luke's. The Rush trustees must be given great credit for keeping the Rush tradition alive for twenty-five years. Their efforts had been looked upon with a good deal of skepticism and considered by many impossible to carry through.[23]

22. Personal communication, Dr. Edward J. Beattie, February 14, 1998.
23. Record Group 023000, 94-037 Rush Medical College Trustee Meeting, May 19, 1957, Rush–Presbyterian–St. Luke's Medical Center/Rush University Medical Center Archives, Chicago, Ill.

In considering the proposal for the startup of Rush, the board appointed an Academic Committee to look into the matter.[24] The board was quite aware of the high costs of operating a school. The endowment-rich University of Notre Dame had recently considered starting its own medical school but decided against it because of cost. But the plan for state aid that the Campbell report had worked through appeared to be adequate to cover all the anticipated expenditures.

A very difficult issue to consider was the long-standing affiliate relationship with the University of Illinois. The board was aware that a teaching hospital and a medical school are not one and the same thing. So, as Presbyterian–St. Luke's Hospital and the University of Illinois School of Medicine were separate and distinct entities with different missions, a new mission would have to be assumed if Rush started up again, with all the implications that this involved. A medical school with university roots is directed primarily toward the future, and its chief task is to educate doctors for sounder methods of practice for tomorrow. In contrast, the teaching hospital develops from a service tradition that defines its main responsibility as caring for patients in the immediate present. Teaching and research, in the last analysis, belong to the medical school and the care of the patient to the hospital. The hospital's objective is to care for sick people, the medical school's to produce good doctors.

Conflicts within such a newly structured organization would develop just as they had when Presbyterian–St. Luke's and the University of Illinois were both affiliated and independent.

24. The committee included Edward McCormick Blair, John Bent, Edward Blettner, A. B. Dick III, Elliot Donnelley, and Arthur Wood and was chaired by George Young. A national advisory educational committee was also formed, composed of Dr. Ward Darley; Dean Robert Glaser, of Stanford Medical School; Dean Robert Ebert, of Harvard Medical School; Dr. Julius Richmond, of State University of New York at Syracuse; Dr. Hans Popper, of Mt. Sinai Medical School in New York; and Dr. Paul Werley, of the University of Southern California School of Medicine. Many of those on the committee were associates of Campbell's on the national medical education scene. The Ebert and Glaser connection went all the way back to medical school.

Traditionally, strains have existed between even the closest of affiliated hospitals and schools.[25]

In the early years of the relationship between Presbyterian and the University of Illinois, the two institutions' affiliation was adversely affected by the disruption caused by World War II and the unfavorable notoriety surrounding controversy over Dr. Andrew C. Ivy and Krebiozen. By the early 1950s, however, the Departments of Surgery and Medicine at the university under the leadership of Dr. Warren Cole and of Dr. Harry Dowling had developed strong training programs, which strengthened the affiliation.

At about the time that Dowling arrived at the university, Campbell had returned from Albany to Presbyterian, to establish a new excellence for the Department of Medicine. Although the university could rightfully claim many excellent faculty members in Medicine, the Campbell program was also very formidable, and a competition developed between the two programs. Campbell could claim that his university-affiliated programs in some areas in Medicine were stronger at Presbyterian. There was a sense that the university had a tendency to remain somewhat aloof. They were the university, and Presbyterian Hospital and Presbyterian–St. Luke's Hospital were hospitals and nothing more. Campbell and Dowling were of different temperaments and attitudes. Their views on social issues and private medical practice were different. Campbell was energized by the increased vigor resulting from the merger of Presbyterian and St. Luke's. All sorts of issues regarding finances developed. Campbell was developing an entrepreneurial spirit as he learned quickly about finances. The university was excessively bogged down in bureaucracy. Individual doctors who were active at both institutions noted that it was much less complicated and hassle free to get resources such as space and support salaries at Presbyterian than at the university because of this. Campbell seemed to be so much more flexible in dealing with these issues.

But the staff of Presbyterian–St. Luke's benefited from this affiliation. Without the university connection over the years, there would

25. Ludmerer, *Time to Heal,* pp. 170–73.

have been problems in professional recruiting. All hospital appointments had to be approved by the university, and these appointments were rarely if ever questioned by the university. But when Presbyterian requested a Rush professor designation, this often would be stricken from the application. The appointments had to be renewed annually and were designated by the University as nontenured.

There was virtually no acrimony between the two institutions in Surgery. Effective cooperative training programs had been developed between the two. But when Dr. Cole retired in 1965, his successor recruited a new full-time surgical staff that would not be active at the merged hospitals as it had been before when many of the surgeons from the university conducted their private practices at Presbyterian–St. Luke's Hospital. In some of the surgical specialties, affiliations for training did continue. What was lost, however, was the cohesive influence of Cole, which was highly beneficial to the affiliation.

The retirement of University of Illinois Dean Granville Bennett affected the relationship in a similar way. Dean Bennett, who had known Campbell when he was a member of the faculty at Harvard, was a cohesive and moderating force in the relationship. Bennett was succeeded by Dr. William Grove, who had been active in Dr. Cole's department and was an advocate for certain reforms in medical education. Drs. Grove and Campbell did not get along too well and often clashed. The loss of Dr. Mark Lepper as well as others at the university to Presbyterian–St. Luke's were significant. A sense of mistrust and keen competition between the two institutions was evident to many. And the twenty-five-year affiliation agreement between the two institutions would be terminating soon and would have to be renegotiated.

Rush could have been started up again and remained within the University of Illinois. The university was embarking on a major program of expansion that the Campbell Report had mandated. The university would go on to more than double its enrollment and expand to several other sites within the state. Rush could have been one of those sites, thus bypassing many of the costs of construction and recruitment that starting a new school from the beginning would entail.

The Medical Center had been compensated very poorly for training substantial numbers of University of Illinois medical students and this grievance went uncorrected over many years. For this reason Campbell insisted that an autonomous totally financially independent school, Rush Medical College of the University of Illinois, be established. It would have direct access to Urbana, bypassing the existing university medical school administrative structure in Chicago altogether.

Perhaps if a better and smoother relationship between the hospital and the university had developed over the years since the arrangement started in 1941, there would have been a better sense of collegiality and teamwork between the two. But such was not the case. As the years passed and Rush remained inactive, the university tended to dismiss Rush as a meaningless paper entity. George Young reported to the trustees that many years of negotiations for a better relationship between the two institutions had gone on without any real success.[26] However, if Rush were to accept a proposal for union on the university's terms, although it might well lose much of its independence, its financial security in the future would be more certain, since it would then be state supported.

Campbell also saw many new opportunities for improving medical education in a new setting. There were several archaic practices in the existing medical schools such as repeating science courses that had already been taught in the premedical curriculum that might be remedied. Existing medical school curricula paid virtually no attention to important future health concerns such as environmental issues, health personnel management, genetics, and other areas. Existing schools' curricula were also placing too great stress on specialty recruitment as a major part of their agenda. The underprivileged had been inadequately supported by the existing system of medical education, which Campbell felt he could do something

26. George Young, Special Meetings of the Trustees, Sept. 3, 1969, folder 9, Box 17, C97-052, James A. Campbell, M.D., Papers 1924–1983, Record Group 002000, Office of the President, Rush–Presbyterian–St. Luke's Medical Center/Rush University Medical Center Archives, Chicago, Ill.

about. Integrated with a strong clinical program, a new medical center could lead the way for innovative medical delivery systems that clearly would be needed in the future. And approval for these programs would not have to go through the tedious approval process of state government.

The Rush alumni were very supportive of reestablishing the school even without having a university affiliation. When the University of Chicago decided not to continue the operation of the school in 1942, Rush was totally vulnerable. And being a university-affiliated hospital, as the arrangement with the University of Illinois was in fact, was not the same as having your own school. Conferring an M.D. degree from a college might create some problems, but Campbell would eventually deal with this by establishing Rush University.

The termination of the twenty-nine-year agreement between the University of Illinois and Presbyterian–St. Luke's Hospital was formalized in 1970.[27] And Rush started its first class in the fall of the following year. The university was unable or unwilling to meet the demands of Campbell and the trustees, which essentially called for almost complete autonomy, self-determination, and financial independence. But for all practical purposes, after the medical staff and the Board of Trustees met in separate sessions on the same day, September 3, 1969, the decision had been made. The trustees were satisfied that a sound financial plan for establishing the school had been provided. A shortage of doctors existed. The Campbell plan was widely and enthusiastically accepted throughout the state. Darley's national advisory committee enthusiastically recommended the move. Basic academic management was already in place and Campbell's innovative ideas were viewed very favorably. "Go it alone," they said. Now a very substantial national contribution by the institution could be developed.

27. Arch Item: Letter from Lyle H. Lanier to James A. Campbell, M.D., February 17, 1970; folder 19, Box 17, C97-052, James A. Campbell, M.D., Papers 1924–1983, Record Group 002000, Office of the President, Rush–Presbyterian–St. Luke's Medical Center/Rush University Medical Center Archives, Chicago, Ill.

Later in the day at the medical staff meeting, the pros and cons for maintaining an affiliation with the university or establishing its own school were discussed at length.[28] The university was in its own process of reorganization, trying to deal with its own proposed expansion, which had been mandated by the Campbell report. It didn't appear that the Presbyterian–St. Luke's Hospital system was being given the highest priority in the proposed new arrangement. Campbell again reiterated that the clinical expertise and patient base of the institution could be a sound basis for starting the school. Patient care would remain the top priority. Research was to have a significant place, but the mainstream would be medical practice. It would be an academic medical center with this as the top priority, not a "Research and Education Hospital," as the University of Illinois Hospital was called. Although there might never be enough money to do the planning for programmatic spending, the new institution ought to be able to provide quality education in first-class facilities without undue risk. Affiliation with little or no remuneration had caused problems in the past with the University of Chicago as well. A majority of major government and private supported funding was earmarked for medical centers whose medical school and hospital were virtually one and the same thing. The Rush posture for significant philanthropic support had always seemed to be weakened by their university affiliation, first with the University of Chicago and then the University of Illinois, for different reasons but having the same result. Now could be the time to move to this highest level of medical excellence. The staff endorsed the proposal unanimously.

"Without undue risk" may have been Campbell's public pronouncement in the move to go it alone, but in his own mind he had to be apprehensive and wonder how all this would work. There was risk, indeed. The Rush name was still there, but the great glories of the Rush tradition, when it had been the absolute leader in the field, were now in the distant past. Campbell had no illusions that the

28. Summary of tape of combined staff meeting and trustee meeting of Presbyterian–St. Luke's Medical Center (undated) by Jim Bowman in preparation of *Good Medicine: The First 150 Years of Rush–Presbyterian–St. Luke's Medical Center.*.

good old days could be brought back. The Rush name had not been identified with the advances of medicine's golden age for almost three decades. All sorts of good schools and hospitals had been developed in the meantime. No school could now occupy that lofty position again in the same way that Rush once had. And all of this huge new commitment would take a great deal of additional resources over the long run, both financial and otherwise, which no one had any way of quantifying. Mark Lepper, Chief Financial Officer Donald Oder, and the trustees all shared in this apprehension. But Campbell had ideas on how to reestablish Rush in a new and important way, and indeed he was able to carry out these new ideas very effectively.

The University of Illinois went on to expand its schools and double its enrollment at great financial expense and the expenditure of other important resources to start up other schools throughout the state, some essentially almost from scratch, when they could have had an almost ready-made operation if they had been able to deal more successfully with Campbell and Rush. And Rush did well and, indeed, became a very successful operation.

Some of the faculty who were involved at both institutions felt that an opportunity was lost when each went its own way. They were next-door neighbors and could have done a lot of things together at considerable savings in cost. Yet, the relationship between the two had always been tenuous and awkward. Campbell is blamed for some of this, and the University of Illinois's bureaucratic inflexible mindset was another factor. Campbell's driving ambition to "build an empire" was sensed in a hostile way in his dealings with the university. He wasn't collegial. During the time of the critical negotiations in the late sixties particularly, Campbell and university officials didn't seem to get along very well at all. Still Campbell had many on the University of Illinois faculty who admired his effectiveness in getting things done, even if it meant making waves and enemies.[29] Campbell had been a hero to many of

---

29. Personal Communication, Dr. Truman Anderson, May 12, 1999.

the student body at the university when he was chairman of the Department of Medicine in the preceding decade.

On the other hand, President David Dodd Henry, of the University of Illinois in Urbana, during his entire tenure had never visited either Presbyterian Hospital or Presbyterian–St. Luke's Hospital, important University of Illinois constituencies. The university would have demanded not only complete financial control of the entire educational operation from Rush, but also the surrender of all its endowments.[30] And finally, of course, the political realities of government funding are such that ongoing state support by taxpayers' money for a private educational institution would be difficult to effect over the long run.

So, like a phoenix, Rush Medical College, would arise from the ashes, on the site of Presbyterian–St. Luke's Hospital, to start life again in a new and exciting era.

30. Robert D. Ray, M.D., Ph.D., "Department of Orthopedics, the University of Illinois, 1956–1983, and Presbyterian–St. Luke's Hospital 1956–1971" (unpublished), p. 30.

12

The New Commitment

Once the decision to reopen Rush was made, it became apparent that a whole new wave of creative energy had been generated. A sense that "this has to work" permeated everyone's thinking as many sensed they were now part of a cause bigger than themselves, an ethic that transcended many other considerations.[1] Campbell's style of leadership and his fast and furious pace were infectious. People got caught up in the excitement and the challenge such that Rush became a fun place to come to work. Campbell had engaged virtually everyone in this new venture.

Reopening Rush was a remarkable accomplishment. It brought Campbell praise and approbation, even from those who were not among his admirers. Students and young doctors were quick to take note of his idealistic, visionary, and, at the same time, highly pragmatic concepts of medical education. Spirits were elevated by the vision he projected for the entire institution. He was saying in one way or another to each and every one of his constituencies, "we are something very special." The message of this "hidden agen-

1. Personal communication, Prof. Edward Eckenfels, November 25, 1998.

da" was widely sensed and was instrumental in molding professional attitudes, values, and temperaments throughout the institution.

The transformation of Rush Medical College to the Rush University for the Health Sciences occurred almost overnight.[2] The Rush name was applied to programs involving model institutions for care and academic function, and the acronym RUSH for Rush University System for Health Sciences was used to summarize it. A university structure grew up rather quickly. The medical college opened in September 1971, accepting 61 students for the first-year class from over a thousand applicants; 31 were accepted for the third-year class, including some transfer students from the University of Illinois; and 6 students were accepted for Ph.D. programs.

The traditional criteria for admission were broadened so that recognized competence in courses other than science became acceptable. Representatives from the public at large were placed on the school admissions committee to further broaden the selection process, as the committee struggled to sort out the most qualified from among the very large number who applied. More women were accepted; this marked the beginning of a national trend that accelerated in subsequent years.

To address the existing physician shortage, some of the students were placed in an accelerated program leading to an M.D. degree in three full years. Another program combined the last year of college with the first year of medical school on the campus of one of Rush's newly formed network of affiliated Midwestern colleges that included Knox, Grinnell, Beloit, Coe, Cornell, Mount Vernon, Macalester, Monmouth, Ripon, and the Illinois Institute of Technology. In this way, expenditures were reduced by utilizing existing facilities and qualified faculty on the liberal arts college campuses to teach the first year's basic medical science. Affiliated programs within this network were also extended to the other newly created colleges within Rush University.

In 1972 the College of Nursing and in 1975 the College of Health Sciences were initiated, and in 1981 the Graduate College

2. Personal communication, Dr. Jack Trufant, October 12, 1998.

became Rush University's fourth college. The development of the Graduate College underscored Rush's commitment to research. By the mid 1980s, Rush University offered 30 degrees at three levels, baccalaureate, master's, and doctor's in the university's four colleges and had conferred over 3600 degrees. The enrollment for each year was about 1150, with 350 graduates.

By the next decade, specialized or programmatic accreditation through Rush University was also available for nurse anesthesia, clinical pastoral education, dietetic internship, health systems management, medical technology, occupational therapy, perfusion therapy, and speech-language pathology, and audiology.[3]

Rush University would be the framework to insure excellence that had been developed through the long-standing Rush Medical College tradition, which dated back almost 150 years but now applied to the exploding field of health sciences. The foundation of the university would be its grounding in a high-quality patient care milieu. A university structure was needed for accreditation and to meet guidelines for state approval and recognition by the outside world as a degree-granting institution. Hospitals could not give degrees and universities could not care for patients.

Mark Lepper was not the original choice to be the Rush Medical College's first dean. He was already heavily committed as executive vice president for Professional and Academic Affairs for the entire medical center. The search committee had selected nationally recognized medical educator and former Chicagoan, Dr. Julius Richmond, for the position. Richmond had been the first director of the national Head Start program, had served in the Surgeon General's Office, and was an influential leader in the National Academy of Sciences in Washington. He had expressed great interest in overseeing Rush's rebirth and participating in reestablishing the Rush traditions. An offer was sent to Richmond for the position of dean in January 1970, but the letter somehow got lost in the mail. Richmond in the meantime had received an offer from Harvard, which he

3. A Self-Study Report of Rush University, Chicago, Illinois, December 1997, Rush University, Rush–Presbyterian–St. Luke's Medical Center, Chicago, Illinois, p. 4.

accepted. Rush would be starting in September 1971 without its top-most position filled and time was growing short, so Lepper agreed to take on the additional responsibility and served for three years.

Lepper was now both vice president for Professional and Academic Affairs and Dean of Rush Medical College. Serving under Lepper would be four associate vice presidents and associate deans, all of whom were recruited from within the institution. Dr. William Hejna was associate dean and associate vice president for Surgical Sciences and Services, Dr. Robert Carton, associate dean and vice president for Medical Sciences and Services, Dr. Max Rafelson, associate dean and associate vice president for Behavioral Sciences and Services, and Dr. John Graettinger, associate dean and associate vice president for Student and Faculty Affairs. All four brought wide experience to the responsibilities of these new offices. Hejna had highly developed organizational skills and in addition was an outstanding practicing orthopedic surgeon. He was among the first to perform artificial hip replacements. Carton, an outstanding teacher who was originally active at Presbyterian Hospital, returned from the University of Illinois, where he had served as the director of Pulmonary Medicine. Rafelson was chairman of the Department of Biochemistry at Presbyterian–St. Luke's Hospital and prior to that time had been at the University of Illinois working on the integration of laboratory techniques with clinical applications. Graettinger had been recruited originally from Harvard by Campbell and had served as chairman of the Department of Medicine, succeeding Campbell.

This organizational configuration integrated the concerns of patient care, education, and research into a unified structure different from the fragmented or disjointed ones that existed in many medical centers where advocates of these interests often competed with each other. Rush was designed as a small university medical school within a large hospital, not a small hospital within a large university. The hospital and patient care would come first, no matter what happened to the university. Several advantages accrued from this. For example, health professionals were educated in a patient care rather than a research setting. Education would serve patient care, and research served education. If, for some reason, a university were to close, the university hospital would close. At Rush, however, the university could close, but the hospital would survive. The primacy of patient care was unashamedly stressed. The educated health care professional at Rush was first of all grounded in care of the patient. Rush would not be an institution where only special diseases were seen, and often in a research setting. Campbell and Lepper believed that the wrong message was given in such circumstances. Faculty appointments would not discriminate against practitioners, as was often the case at other medical centers.

Campbell insisted that the establishment of an academic medical center must be structured to include a fourth pillar of support, management, to guarantee accountability and efficiency. This was to be added to the three traditional pillars of support, education, patient care, and research on which most academic health centers were organized. To that end a master's degree in health systems management at Rush was developed. Here again, Campbell's vision was exceptional because he foresaw how the field of health care would evolve in the coming decades.

Individuals from the outside were recruited as Campbell continued to assemble his new management team. Dr. Henry Russe had received all of his training at the University of Chicago, rising through the ranks to be appointed chief of staff. His credentials were such that he could have been appointed dean at any number of university hospitals. Russe had taken notice of Presbyterian–St. Luke's and then Rush and was impressed with their strong clinical programs and their ability to develop new initiatives, such as producing closed circuit television programs for national medical meetings that were being held in Chicago. High technology and leading edge advances abounded everywhere. Russe and his colleagues at the University of Chicago were startled when they learned that plans for higher education for the state came from Campbell's institution and not their own.

Russe joined Rush as an associate vice president in Medical Sciences and Services and was later appointed dean. By 1986, Rush students were being selected for the best postgraduate training programs at Harvard, Yale, and Hopkins. But Russe found Rush to be an institution that was doing a great deal more. Rush was extremely well managed. Its flexibility allowed people to make things happen, all the way from the development of alternative health care systems to the maturation of the medical college. Diversified patient care programs were being formulated and issues of access to health were being carefully scrutinized.

Russe, a very kind and gentle man, was highly respected both as an educator and a physician. He was elected for six terms as president of the Institute of Medicine of Chicago.[4]

Others recruited from the University of Chicago included Drs. Paul Carson, Frederick Malkinson, and Andrew Thomson. Carson brought his malaria research program to Rush and became chairman of the Department of Pharmacology. Malkinson was recruited to head the Department of Dermatology. Thomson, an internist with a special interest in liver disease, came a little earlier when he was recruited for the Dr. Richard Capps practice. Thomson eventually was elected president of the medical staff and served on the Board of Trustees for several years, quite an unusual thing for a physician. Thomson was exceptionally effective in developing philanthropic support for Rush. Thomson and Campbell had a run-in shortly after Thomson joined the staff, in which Thomson held his ground, something that did not happen often. Campbell frightened many, but Thomson was not one of them. Andy was very proud of this.

Among the bright new people who joined the Campbell team was Dr. Stuart Levin, who came over from the University of Illinois with Mark Lepper and was later elevated to chairman of the Department of Internal Medicine, the position that Campbell once held. Campbell's successor, Dr. Leo Henikoff, first joined the staff as an intern in Pediatrics in 1963. He had been voted the outstanding teacher by the University of Illinois students in 1966. Henikoff then

4. In honor of Russe in 1993, the Board of Governors of the Institute of Medicine of Chicago and the Board of Trustees of Rush–Presbyterian–St. Luke's Medical Center established the Henry P. Russe, M.D., Citation for Exemplary Compassion in Health Care. Since its inception, this prestigious recognition has honored fourteen individuals from the Chicago health care community who have made exceptional contributions to their own chosen field of specialization in health care and in doing so have influenced a wider community beyond their own areas of expertise. In addition the citation can only be awarded when these achievements are carried out in a singularly compassionate manner.

worked with Drs. John Graettinger and George Flanagan in the Office of Curriculum for the new school before he moved on to develop and formalize the admissions process. The first class in 1971 was one that Henikoff and his associates were very excited about. Those selected were sort of "educational entrepreneurs" as they threw their lot in with the new Rush, after having been accepted at other schools. Leo was appointed assistant dean while at the same time serving as chairman of the Admissions Committee, practicing pediatric cardiology, supervising a clerkship in pediatrics, and running a small laboratory for the new school. Campbell seemed to be able to engage his brightest protégés and pushed them close to the limits of their capabilities.

Dr. William Hejna, orthopedic surgeon and associate dean for Surgery, was instrumental in developing affiliatians with feeder colleges and later succeeded Mark Lepper as dean. (Dr. Penfield Faber, one of the nation's leading chest surgeons, then replaced Hejna as associate dean of Surgery and vice president for Surgical Sciences and Services.) Lepper took on the responsibility of director of Health Planning for the State of Illinois. Later Leo Henikoff succeeded Hejna as acting dean, and Dr. Robert Blacklow, of Harvard, was appointed permanent dean in 1978. Dr. Henry Russe succeeded Blacklow in that position in 1981.

Dr. John Trufant was appointed dean of both the Graduate College and the College of Health Sciences and Dr. Luther Christman, dean of the College of Nursing to complete Campbell's new organizational structure consisting of four colleges within the university.

In 1973 the 99th commencement of Rush Medical College took place, and in 1975 the first commencement of Rush University was held. The 98th graduation of Rush Medical College had taken place on June 13, 1942, at Rockefeller Memorial Chapel on the campus of the University of Chicago. One of the last students that day to be awarded an M.D. degree by President of the University Robert M. Hutchins was John Tobin.

After having served his internship at Presbyterian Hospital, Dr. John Tobin received further training at Cook County Hospital and the Mayo Clinic. Well known in Chicago medicine as an outstanding teacher, he became chairman of the Department of Cardiology at the relocated Loyola University Stritch School of Medicine in Maywood and later became dean. Tobin's father was a Rush graduate in 1901 and a member of the 1901 Rush football team. He worked with Dr. Nicholas Senn in the Department of Surgery and became a Senn Fellow, as did later Rush notables Dr. Dallas Phemister and Dr. Francis Straus. Two of John's brothers were also Rush graduates. And in 1977, John's daughter Mary Kay graduated from Rush and is now on the Rush faculty in the Department of Medicine and in the Department Immunology and Microbiology. Thus, continuity of an important Chicago medical educational institutional tradition extending over a century was clearly reestablished when Rush was reborn.

Vera Markovin was another Rush graduate that day in 1942. She was among five women in the class. Two-thirds of the class had received their undergraduate training from schools other than the University of Chicago in various locations throughout the country. For many, their first exposure to the university on the Midway was on that day, graduation day. Many were enthusiastic about the plans for the new affiliation with the University of Illinois, and many of the graduates were aware of the very paltry funding that the university had provided for Rush. They also sensed that Hutchins viewed those in intellectual sciences to be superior to doctors, lawyers, and engineers.

Dr. Vera Markovin went on to serve a four-year residency in Surgery at Cook County Hospital and was, therefore, among the first women to be fully trained in Surgery. Dr. Markovin, however, described herself as a "War Profiteer" since the only reason she received this much sought-after residency was because all the men were off to war. And after the war, no further women were received into the program for many years. Dr. Markovin later became a pioneer in developing the specialty of emergency room medicine.

Issac Micheal joined the 13th General Presbyterian Army Unit after his internship at Presbyterian Hospital. Dr. Micheal returned from the service, went into general practice, and later took a residency in internal medicine at Mayo Clinic, then returned to Indianapolis to practice.

George Handy returned to Presbyterian Hospital for his residency in internal medicine after the war and later established a practice in Arizona. During his training, Dr. Handy worked with the newly arrived wizard cardiologist from Harvard, James Campbell.

Each year on the second Saturday of June, the entire Rush community came together, to observe the institution's most solemn hour. In the early years, ceremonies were held at Orchestra Hall, but later moved to Medinah Temple in order gain a better view. With the graduates filling the entire main floor, the faculty filling the stage, and families, friends, guests, and other visitors filling the galleries, a sense of special intimacy was created. Even in those rebellious times, all the graduates attended. Very often more than one, and sometimes several family members who were there that day had supported the graduates through their long years of education.

Dr. Robert Glaser, who was then the dean at Stanford Medical School was the first commencement speaker in 1973 for the reactivated school. Glaser was impressed with the sense of history that had been brought to the occasion by Campbell. Rush had been brought back into the family of medical schools with a sense of significant academic character and class. The great attention to detail was effectively worked out and planned by Dr. John Graettinger, the university marshall, and, as marshall, Graettinger would lead the academic procession of faculty and graduates into the auditorium.

Clearly, the 1973 ceremony had many emotional overtones for Campbell and the entire Rush family. Campbell was just leaving the University of Chicago in 1942 when the last Rush graduation was held, and so to have finally reestablished the Rush traditions was an exceptional achievement. Everyone could rightfully be proud on this occasion, but for Campbell, it was a personal triumph. "His dynamism was the key and his vision made him an example of the true scholar-physician," Dr. John Trufant recalls. "He took risks, saw what could be. His example was clear to all of us."

The faculty, trustees, and honorees, regaled in colorful caps and gowns of their respective schools, filed on to the stage in proper order and rank. The graduates followed and were seated in the first set of reserved rows in the audience. Campbell then called the gathered group together. This was followed by an invocation from one of the clergy affiliated with the medical center. Next came the conferring of honorary degree of Doctor of Humane Letters and a presentation address by the honored awardee. The first address was delivered by Dr. Robert Glaser, the second in 1974 by Dr. Robert Ebert, and in 1975 the third by Dr. John Knowles. All three were nationally known figures in medicine and added to the prestige and dignity of the occasion. Ebert was dean of the medical school at Harvard, and Knowles had served as the general director of Massachusetts General Hospital in Boston before becoming director of the Rockefeller Institute in New York. For Ebert, this occasion had considerable personal meaning because his father, Dr. Michael Higgins Ebert, had been a Rush professor of dermatology several decades before. All three speakers, Glaser, Ebert, and Knowles shared strong Harvard roots with Campbell.

Then each class was presented to Campbell and the chairman of the Board of Trustees for the conferring of the degree from each dean of his college within the university: Medicine, Nursing, Health Science, and the Graduate College. When the degree was conferred, the candidate shook hands with both Campbell and the chairman of the board.

Following this, a second high point for the occasion was reached as Campbell delivered a farewell presentation to the graduates. His 1974 address reads as follows.

> Congratulations to you. You are a very special class. Of course, you are a centennial class, as has been repeatedly emphasized, and thereby achieve the distinction of all such coincidental occasions.
>
> In addition, however, you have in your membership the first persons who were ever admitted as first year students to the new Rush. Also many of you hold diplomas as the first graduates of the grueling and intense three year curriculum: several of you represent the first Rush graduates to receive house officer appointments in new programs and in some very old hospitals.

You are the first class to have a Marshall who has led you into these exercises behind the magnificent and first mace and specter presented to Rush by Dr. Economou last night thereby establishing instant tradition for the second century of graduates – graduates not only of medicine, but of other health curricula as well.

Many of you were subjected to my Five Smooth Stones on entering and I will not hurl Five Rough Rocks of admonition at you on this commencement day. My statements to you on this occasion are only those of affection, trust, and expectation.

We like you, we think you are enormously talented and dedicated, we expect your talents to be directed to the "benefit of mankind" remembering that "to whom much is given, of him shall much be required."

An example of how this new privilege of physicianship is viewed by many has been expressed beautifully by Robert Louis Stevenson in the late nineteenth century. "There are men and classes of men that stand above the common herd: the soldier, the sailor, and the shepherd not infrequently; the artist rarely, rarer still, the clergyman, the physician almost the rule. He is the flower (such as it is) of our civilization. Generosity he has, such as is possible to those who practice the art, never to those who drive a trade; discretion, tested by a hundred secrets; tact, tried in a thousand embarrassments; and what are more important, Herculean cheerfulness and courage."

We feel you are capable of measuring up to this expectation of physicianship in the finest tradition of Herrick, Bevan, and all the Eberts.

You are capable as intellectual and scholarly persons; you have demonstrated compassion in many of your recent clinical experiences even at a junior level. You have expressed social awareness by positive deeds. Your decision to take an oath by which you guide your professional lives indicates a commitment of maturity and dedication – this also marks you as a special class of this or any other medical college. I consider this moment of opportunity one of my greatest honors and I accept it with deep gratitude and respect.

Maimonides (1135–1204), born in Cordoba, Spain, first studied medicine at 32 in Cairo, where he took refuge from persecution. He became rabbi of Cairo, physician to the Sultan of Egypt and author of theological and medical treatises. His influence as an Aristotelian on Albertus Magnus and St. Thomas Aquinas was great, and his religious commentaries are studied by modern scholars of all faiths as the most important Jewish post-biblical writings of their kind.

You have elected to take this oath, which is in the form of a prayer and a supplication for help in a life of service in medicine.

Will the class please rise.

Will you all turn to face your families and friends.

I will now read this ancient plea.

> Almighty god, you have created the human body with infinite wisdom. You have chosen me to watch over the life and health of your creatures. I am now about to apply myself to the duties of my profession. Support me in these great labors that they may benefit mankind.
>
> Inspire me with love for art and for your creatures. Do not allow thirst for profit, ambition for renown and admiration, to interfere with my profession, for these are the enemies of truth and can lead me astray.
>
> Preserve the strength of my body and soul that they ever be ready to help and support rich and poor, good and bad, enemy as well as friend. In the sufferer let me

see only the human being. Enlighten my mind that it recognize what presents itself and that it may comprehend what is absent or hidden. Let it not fail to see what is visible and permit it the power to see what cannot be seen, for delicate and indefinite are the bounds of great art of caring for the lives and health of your creatures. Let me never be absent-minded. May no strange thoughts divert my attention at the bedside of the sick, or disturb my mind in its silent labors.

Grant that my patients have confidence in me and my art. When those who are wiser than I wish to instruct me, let my soul gratefully follow their guidance; for vast is the extent of our art. Imbue my soul with gentleness and calmness.

Let me be contented in everything except in the great science of my profession. Never allow me the thought that I have attained to sufficient knowledge, but vouchsafe to me the strength and the ambition ever to extend my knowledge. For art is great, but the mind of man is ever expanding.

Almighty god! You have chosen me to watch over the life and death of your creatures. Support me in this great task so that it may benefit mankind, for without your help not even the least thing will succeed.

Will you now raise your right hands and, if you invoke the essence of this ancient plea for guidance and support in your medical careers which have opened today, say "I do."

Please turn around and may we all stand with this splendid class for the closing benediction.[5]

---

5. James A. Campbell, M.D., Commencement Address, June 6, 1974, Box 5, Folder 7, C97-052, James A. Campbell, M.D., Papers 1924–1983, Record Group 002000, Office of the President, Rush–Presbyterian–St. Luke's Medical Center/Rush University Medical Center Archives, Chicago, Ill.

Before Campbell closed, he asked individual members of each graduate's family to rise to be recognized. The parents, fathers and mothers, would be recognized first. Then wives and husbands. Then followed the grandparents, children, aunts, uncles, nephews, and nieces. Infants were held up. Each group was enthusiastically greeted. Many remember the Rush graduation to be among the finest they had ever attended.

Campbell would then add one final word. He would tell the story about his grandmother: "When I was very little, as I was leaving the house my grandmother would always say, 'Be careful crossing the street.' Later on when I was older, I would visit and she would always say again when I left, 'Be careful crossing the street.' Finally, one day I asked my mother, 'why does grandmother always say to me when I am leaving, "Be careful crossing the street"?' My mother then answered, 'It's because she loves you.'"

Jim stood quietly before the audience, and there was silence. And then he said to the graduates, "Be careful crossing the street."

Campbell had connected with everyone. There was scarcely a dry eye in the audience or even for that matter among the faculty and trustees. His stage presence and timing were outstanding. Even for those attending who did not know Campbell, it was clear that here was an individual who rarely expressed this kind of emotion. This subtle expression of affection, therefore, was even more moving.

13

Everybody's Leader

Campbell continued to sustain his vigilant focus on care for the individual patient even as the scope of medical center operations expanded and he became more heavily involved in administrative, financial, and organizational matters. The relentless commitment of the teaching hospital to quality, both in the professional care rendered to patients and in their academic missions, had to be upheld. Success was not to be determined by the size of the institution, the number of patients seen, or the condition of financial ledgers, but by professional standards and scientific work.[1] For Campbell, the patient was the only thing that mattered. If arguments occurred and feathers were ruffled, it was of no concern to him. Only the patient counted. The place would be nothing without patients. Later on in this phase of his career, he might express it a little differently when he became chief executive officer for the corporation. "We never had to create value for our shareholders, it was always what was best for the patient. Do well by the patients, we'll do well by the corporation."[2]

1. Kenneth M. Ludmerer, *Time to Heal: American Medical Education from the Turn of the Century to the Era of Managed Care* (New York: Oxford University Press, 1999), p. 169.
2. Personal communication, Dr. Wayne Lerner, July 3, 1998.

Campbell's stern, authoritative façade could convey a sense of antagonism when he was dealing with physicians. But this was clearly not the case. Campbell had the highest respect for the medical profession, and he always considered himself, first and foremost, a physician. He understood the uncertainty that was fundamental to medical education and practice. He knew that it was a myth that students and later practitioners could attain knowledge of medicine and disease behavior that allowed them to act with certainty in every situation. Doctors had to deal with major dilemmas every day. The well-trained, experienced physician or surgeon, even though far removed from the beginning trainee, still had to deal with uncertainty. Whether in the office, on the hospital floors, or in the operating room, clinical problems rarely presented themselves in an idealized textbook fashion. Different individuals presenting with the same illness often reacted quite differently. The physician had to try to make sense out of all this. The experienced surgeon had to be alert to react to any unexpected development during an operation. This would be particularly so as he was often referred the more difficult and complicated cases. For the surgeon in particular, there were no second chances.

Training for uncertainly is fundamental to medical education and medical practice, and confronting this challenge demands the development of rigorous scientific and disciplined attitudes to reduce and minimize the chances for error.[3] The doctor must be thinking at all times and he must have an inquisitive spirit. He must spend enough time to listen to and observe the patient and to look at how the patient responds to stress. No two patients are alike. The commitment must be all consuming. No one has all the answers, and this would be particularly so when it comes to the evaluation and treatment of human illness. Ongoing peer review each and every day with one's colleagues must become a way of life. The most brilliant of doctors would be regularly humbled by the unpredictability of human illness.

3. Ludmerer, *Time to Heal,* p. 69.

What was newest and best for the patient yesterday and today might become obsolete tomorrow. One had to be committed to keep up with all new developments. Not just this year or next year, but throughout one's entire professional career.

Even physicians with heavy administrative responsibilities were required to look after patients. Campbell felt that everyone's perspective had to be balanced by maintaining ongoing contact with patients in the "trenches and battlefields of human illness."

Campbell stayed in contact with patients indirectly, by addressing all the complaints that funneled into the medical center from a patient or a patient's family regarding their care, no matter what it might involve. Not everything goes well or smoothly in a hospital, and over a period of time, each real or perceived deficiency or shortcoming that the hospital might have was brought to his attention. Emotional reactions centering on human illness can often be extreme. Patients and their families are not always easy to deal with. Like any other physician, Campbell had to respond to their concerns in a highly professional, dignified, responsible, and appropriate way. However as president, Campbell was also the recipient of many letters and calls from patients and families expressing gratitude and appreciation for the very high quality of care they had received.

Earlier in his career, Jim took a rather dim view of the fee-for-service system for physician reimbursement. It was highly immoral to take money from a patient. But his views gradually changed over a period of years, and the medical center for the most part continued the fee-for-service system. At the same time, however, flexibility for physician compensation was worked out in a number of different ways. A physician might receive a part-time salary from the institution for administration, research, and teaching, and the remainder of his income could then be derived from practice fees. The physician might receive all his compensation from private medical fees and none from institutional sources. For a few doctors, an arrangement was developed for a defined limited income from fees. The remaining revenue from professional fees would revert to the institution. This insured that the doctor under such an arrangement would not spend too much time in practice at the expense of other commitments to the medical center.

As president Jim recognized the critical importance of surgery to the growth and welfare of the medical center. He came to admire the great work that these professionals were carrying out every day, and he was most admiring of surgeons' enterprising spirit. Some thought that Jim might even have aspired to be a surgeon. He was adept and dexterous with his hands. In his early career in cardiology, Campbell became skilled in passing a catheter through the brachial vein at the elbow all the way up into the right atrial chamber of the heart.

Campbell encouraged competition among doctors and doctors' groups. In so doing he felt that the patient would be the beneficiary. As doctors both individually and in groups grew in activity and became stronger, Jim tried to encourage the growth of competing entities. The patient, through his referring doctor, benefited when there was a choice available. There was the usual concern when a new doctor was appointed to the staff that this might affect the activity and volume of the existing practices. It almost never did. Jim monitored the activity of practices on a regular basis. He knew who was doing the work, and how much work they were doing. The very heavy operating room schedule of the medical center was carefully watched. Campbell would take note each day of the number of units of blood that were being typed and cross-matched for use as a monitor of what was going on. "For a CEO of a major academic medical center to be keeping an eye on this was most unusual," Dr. Bob Glaser pointed out. "Jim related well to practicing physicians; most medical center leaders do not. Most now are not even physicians."[4]

Campbell maintained a flexible policy regarding compensation for physicians. In the case of hospital-based physicians who were not involved directly in patient care such as pathologists, biochemists, and microbiologists, a group practice for the whole department was the rule. And, in a startling turn of events in the seventies, he vigorously supported the development of the first major health

4. Personal communication, Dr. Robert Glaser, June 18, 1999.

maintenance organization (HMO) in Chicago, Anchor, which was looked upon by many as a major competitor for the well-entrenched fee-for-service system at the medical center.

In 1949 and 1950, Dr. Earnest Irons, the former dean of Rush Medical College and an active practicing internist at Presbyterian Hospital, served as president of the American Medical Association. Irons was a strong advocate for maintaining and developing the medical practice system of providing private care by physicians or groups of physicians through the fee-for-service mechanism and private employee-sponsored health insurance. Federal government intervention into the process of providing health care, which had been proposed, beginning in 1945, by the Truman administration, was strongly opposed. And as the medical center grew and developed in the fifties and sixties through the merger of the two hospitals, it clearly prospered under this arrangement.

But as Campbell and Mark Lepper embarked on the development of the Rush University Systems for Health, it became clear that an alternate system or systems for both the delivery and the financing of health care needed to be developed. Private medical care might still be the dominant way, but other systems had to be explored which could deal with the evolution in the growth of health care in its complexity, its costs, and its implementation.

In 1970, union officials representing about one thousand medical center employees (dietary, housekeeping, laundry, maintenance, nurses aides, and transport) sought to gain better health benefits than those that were being provided by their existing health coverage programs. The union officials seemed intent on running the health benefit program themselves, including the finances. Mr. Nat Kramer was assigned to look into what could be done to respond to these union demands. Campbell had recruited Kramer from the Mine Workers Union in West Virginia to reorganize the outpatient clinics, which were then providing a large amount of free care for indigent patients. Kramer came up with the idea of a prepaid comprehensive scheme that provided better coverage at lower costs for these individuals. Union health officials had no choice but to go along with the idea. Financial control remained with the hospital. It was the beginning of the first major HMO in the Chicago area and the transformation of employee group insurance health program into the Rush Anchor System. Soon outside groups such as Board of Education employees were enrolled, so that, within six months, the number under enrollment had grown to over 5000. With this number of patients, Anchor could now go out and recruit physicians, both for primary care and specialty care, which in itself would make this scheme more attractive for additional subscribers. All the physicians involved were Rush staff members, and many were retained on the usual fee-for-service system.

At about that time, the Nixon administration and Congress were putting together the HMO act, which enabled anyone to establish and market an HMO, provided that they could meet federally regulated guidelines. Rush was among the first in Chicago to meet these guidelines and thus was able to recruit even more enrollees. In time, Anchor enrollment rose to well over 100,000 and was the dominant prepaid health insurance system in the entire Chicago Metropolitan Area for well over a decade. The program as originally set up with better coverage at lower costs was attractive to large employers. These employers encouraged the growth of Anchor by setting up incentive mechanisms with their employees to select Anchor over the more expensive traditional group health insurance such as Blue Cross–Blue Shield and others. And Anchor offices convenient to subscribers all over the Chicago metropolitan area were opened.

Campbell vigorously supported the Kramer plan, even though he knew he would be subjected to severe criticism from medical staff advocates of the private fee-for-service system who would claim it was in direct competition with, and would ultimately result in the end of, traditional private practice. Campbell never envisioned this outcome, and here again he was entirely correct. In some ways, Campbell understood the intricacies of the private practice system better than the "docs," even though he himself was not in practice. Here again, he differed from many leaders in other medical centers and many practicing physicians as well in seeing the increasingly complex factors that were evolving to deal with issues such as access and distribution as well as cost. Being at the hospital at all times of

the day and night kept him in touch with these realities. He anticipated that many HMO subscribers would be individuals who had
not previously had a private physician. Most subscribers of private
health insurance would not buy into this system. In a sense, the number of individuals now eligible for private medical care would
increase. Rush and Rush physicians' "market share" of patients
would increase, and that is the way it turned out. Hospital activity
increased at a greater rate, as did the work of physicians who elected to participate in the program. Campbell had offered the opportunity to participate to every physician on the staff at Rush. Some did
and some did not.

The large number of educational programs to which the institution was becoming increasingly committed were provided with
more clinical material to strengthen these efforts. And the patients
served, many of whom had no previous private medical care of any
sort, were receiving care from a nucleus of salaried primary care
physicians, all of whom had had extensive experience in private
practice previously. And the specialty care that Anchor provided was
exactly the same as an individual would receive in a private fee-for-
service practice system. It was a win-win situation for the medical
center, and Rush became a Chicago leader in the development of
innovative health care systems far ahead of the competition. The
Anchor program addressed in a serious way the issue of rising health
care costs and at the same time broadened the number of individuals who could receive better health care. And it was a step further in
the Campbell dream of setting up a single standard of medical care
for everyone.

The Anchor plan was just the beginning. As time passed, issues
of cost, the development of other alternative health care systems, the
evolution of ambulatory and outpatient care, and many other factors
would challenge not only Rush but all health care providers to deal
with these increasingly complex issues. Campbell believed that the
public should be offered a choice, whether it be private fee-for-service, an HMO, or, as would later be developed, a preferred provider
organization (PPO). Even today, solutions to these matters are not
completely settled. But for the time of the 1970s and early 1980s,

Rush and Campbell were quite right. Campbell never hesitated to support Kramer and Anchor in spite of much criticism and grumbling. Campbell once again was the visionary who saw what could be, did not hesitate, and moved to make it happen. And through it all Rush maintained the traditional private fee-for-service medical care system for most of the individuals and public that it served.

Jim took great pride in wearing his white coat. In this way he projected the image of looking like and acting like a doctor very effectively. As his career progressed and Campbell became more closely identified with managers and administrators, these new associates were very impressed. Here was this individual wearing a white coat, and they had difficulty keeping up with him and with his budget projections and the like. Campbell could be quite tough when he questioned his associates. Yet, through it all, the message was clear: The patient came first. This style of leadership motivated these managers and administrators to very high levels of performance.

How Campbell impressed the doctors was another matter. They all knew he was not seeing patients. And Campbell knew, of course, that they knew. Urologist Dr. Jim Valenta had a hearty laugh and along with it a great sense of humor. He had a way of laughing at you as well as with you. One day he confronted Campbell as he was sitting down in the doctors' cafeteria in the old hospital to have lunch. Valenta sensed that Campbell was in a good mood and said to him, "Hey, Jim, what do you do around here anyway?" Jim replied, in a rather sheepish way, "Nothing really."

But Campbell insisted that all the doctors wear white coats, something that was not done when he first took over as chairman of Medicine in 1954. At that time all the private attending practitioners wore business suits as they made rounds in the hospital seeing patients. The Brooks Brothers crowd had no use for the butcher aprons as they called the white coats that the hired hands, those salaried doctors Campbell had recruited from the East, were wearing. Campbell was attempting to establish a policy of physician parity and this would be translated into the notion that every patient was at parity. No one would be second rate. Nonsensical as it might seem now, there was great resistance to all of this, but Campbell eventually prevailed.

After Rush was reactivated in the early 1970s, many of its students had tendencies as rebellious as students in most other educational institutions of that time. Students on their clinical rotations would appear on the hospital floors wearing baseball caps and carrying their lunches. Patients, their families, nurses, doctors, and many others were understandably quite upset and concerned. How was this defiant group going to be brought into line? So Campbell instituted the white coat ceremony. Each student was given a white coat when he was assigned to clinical floors, with much pomp and ritual. Campbell pointed out to the students the symbolism of wearing a white coat and its importance in the eyes of the patient. As the students donned their new coats, he would remind them that patients would tell them things they wouldn't tell their spouses or children. They must accept this responsibility with great humility. Subsequently the students proudly appeared on the floors wearing their new white coats without their previous objectionable trappings. What Campbell related to the students was entirely true, but at the same time the students never realized that the master had done them in.

Rush faculty member Dr. Norma Waggoner, who later became the dean of students at the University of Chicago (Pritzker) Medical School, pointed out that the white coat ceremony was later adopted by many other schools. Campbell also developed a feeder system with several Midwestern colleges serving as affiliates to educate future Rush students.[5]

Campbell used his address to the semi-annual medical staff meetings in May and November to communicate to the doctors all that was going on to make the medical center bigger and better. Without ever coming out and saying so, Campbell communicated to the doctors a sense that they were the finest in the country. Many of the doctors would leave these meetings charged up and resolved to excel and do even more. A sense of excitement and innovation mov-

5. Personal interview, Dr. Norma Waggoner, January 26, 1999.

ing forward was expressed in Campbell's presentations. The medical
center was alive with activity, as the wrecking ball worked day and
night to make way for new construction projects. Many of the new
projects were not the usual type, for example, constructing a building over the existing Chicago Transit Authority elevated train tracks
or closing a public street (Paulina) to accommodate the construction
of the new hospital Atrium Building.

Jim Campbell projected by his confident demeanor the sense
that it made no difference that the medical center was not in the best
location. Campbell had a vision and the institution would persevere
to fulfill it regardless. There were still some old, seemingly antiquated facilities, but Johns Hopkins had buildings well over one hundred
years old that were still essential elements for their operations.
What's more, there was no need to apologize as long as the medical
center remained top notch, always bearing in mind that the patient
comes first. Campbell stayed with this large view and conveyed this
sense to those around him. One of these individuals was a prominent
and influential hospital trustee, considered by his peers to be among
the most respected and capable attorneys in the country. He needed
to be hospitalized for surgery and, apparently through an administrative oversight, was assigned to a two-bed semiprivate room in an
older section of the hospital. The trustee was also a member of the
executive committee of the board and a close friend of Campbell's.
When Campbell learned of this, he immediately attempted to relocate his friend to a private room in a newer section. The trustee was
totally unperturbed and insisted on remaining where he had been
assigned. He had bought into Campbell's belief of one standard of
care for all patients. And this individual, of course, did well.

No matter how Campbell might dismiss the importance of
location of the hospital, location did make a difference. Crime, poverty, ghettos, tax-base erosion, and flight of the middle classes to the
suburbs were staggering problems both in Chicago and throughout
the nation in the older metropolitan urban areas. Security for
employees was another concern as was recruitment of staff. The riots
following the assassination of Dr. Martin Luther King in 1968
occurred in close, almost immediate, proximity to the hospital. But in

his public stance at least, these things never seemed to get Campbell down. He was always positive and upbeat, and, most amazingly, the institution lost little of its following among its affluent patient clientele during these times. Campbell's very presence every day seemed to convey the message that things would work out, which indeed over the long run they did. Absolutely nothing would keep the medical center from growing and developing.

During these difficult times of the late 1960s, Campbell determined that something should be done to attract nurses. After the merger, the diploma nursing program had been closed and nursing education at Rush was at a low ebb; nursing education generally throughout the country was in a state of disarray. It seemed that nurses were being trained for everything except nursing and nursing duties were being delegated to the least qualified members of the nursing staff. Dr. Luther Christman, a nationally known nurse educator, and his associate Dr. Sue Thomas Hegyvary were recruited to revive nursing education at Rush, and this transformation would eventually result in Rush becoming the first school in Chicago to offer a doctor's degree in Nursing Science. Bringing nursing back to the bedside was a welcome change, and very much appreciated by patients. Eventually the "Rush Model for Nursing" was advanced, which gained national attention and greatly enhanced the recruitment of nurses for the medical center. The combination of education and practice in the Nursing College was similar to the program of Rush Medical College. The John and Helen Kellogg National Center for Excellence in Nursing was established. Nursing's professional status was upgraded and was so recognized by appointment of a dean of nursing who had equal professional status with the dean of the medical college. Upgrading professional status was something Campbell was not reluctant to undertake, even though it was feared that the concept of equal status with doctors could be interpreted as being quite threatening. This did not turn out to be the case at all, as Campbell envisioned it would not. Everyone benefited from this. Nursing was now keeping up with and indeed staying ahead of medicine's rapid advances. Christman and Hegyvary developed one of the leading nursing programs in the country and both recognized the

importance of the support that Campbell provided in this effort. He
insisted that the changes in nursing be supported. The spirit that he
brought to their effort was the same spirit that he brought to the
entire institution. Professional people of all sorts came to Rush and
were infused with Campbell's "Type-A behavior."[6] Campbell encouraged all the other professional components within the medical center
in the same direction. He would add, however, "I can offer you professional equity within the corporation, but you have to earn parity."

Leaders of Campbell's stature often spent a significant amount
of their time traveling and consequently were away for considerable
amounts of time from their work. Getting involved in national organizations was something Campbell could have done, but chose not to.
This was not Campbell's leadership style. As it was, Campbell did
serve on a number of national organizations' governing boards and
did project a national image for the institution. And, of course,
Campbell's Harvard credentials were well known. But ongoing
heavy outside commitments would take up more of his time than he
was willing to give and would take away from his primary commitment to the medical center. He never took more than one week off
at a time for vacation. If he had to leave town for the day, he would
usually return that same day, and often stop by his office on the way
home. This vigilant spirit and the example he set thereby was considered by many to be his greatest strength.

And so it went. Campbell picked up trash from the corridor
floor. If the head guy did this, then maybe everyone else would have
to follow. One had to take pride in the place. Campbell usually ate
lunch in the cafeteria and later Room 600, so as to mingle with everyone. As he chatted with the employees, he would try to understand
all their issues and often in the same settings relate to the broader
issues as well. He was regarded as a friend to many. He was willing
to work with the "troops" and avoided the trap of isolation that many
leaders fall prey to. And there was no patronizing sense about any of

6. Summary transcript of interview with Dr. Sue Hegyvary by Jim Bowman, June 12,
1986, in preparation for *Good Medicine: The First 150 Years of Rush–Presbyterian–St. Luke's
Medical Center.*

this. It was Campbell's belief that each and every person working at the medical center was of consequence. No one was unimportant.

When Campbell walked down the halls of the hospital, he knew many people by name. Seemingly obscure people felt a sense of belonging. "Here," they were thinking, "is a genius who never acted like a genius." They were proud to be a part of the team. He would sort of half smile and in doing so he was communicating to them the idea that they were doing a good job. And yet his resolute walk caused many to start to step aside almost automatically, but then Campbell would signal by his deferential body language that he did not expect this. The same could not be said for some doctors. Campbell fostered a sense of team spirit and being there all the time was critical during the riots of the 1960s. In these times, he softened much of the racial tension and communicated the idea that everybody was part of the team, doctors, nurses aides, those in housekeeping, orderlies, and the all the rest.

The Campbell influence was reflected in many different ways. When the new hospital addition, the Atrium Building, was opened on Memorial Day weekend in 1982, public relations was planning to have a VIP-type individual or some prominent public personage to be the first person admitted to this new section of the hospital. Plans had been made to set up special equipment to record the event and publicize it accordingly. Campbell dismissed the idea totally and then enthusiastically went ahead and greeted the first new patient to the facility who happened to be a person of no special station or privilege. Jim took the occasion to reinforce his support for the idea of a single standard of care for everyone, a message that was very well understood by all who witnessed the event, who in turn passed on the story to others.

The James A. Campbell Distinguished Service Award was established to recognize an employee who best served as an example of Campbell's dedication to the Rush mission of patient care, education, research, and community service. Campbell had exemplified this ideal of strong patient advocacy by eliminating charity wards and grouping patients according to their medical needs instead of economic status because he believed in a single high standard of care for all patients, rich and poor alike. His goal was to provide the same quality of care for the average patient in a ward or a semiprivate room that a wife of a trustee or community leader received in a VIP suite.

To single out any one exceptional employee of the Campbell era is difficult. Ruth Williams was one such individual. She started out at Rush working as a ward clerk on the Pediatric floors in 1963. She next advanced to become a licensed practical nurse (LPN) and eventually earned both a bachelor's and a master's degree in nursing. Williams established a reputation as an outstanding surgical nurse and subsequently became head nurse for the surgical floors of general surgery, thoracic surgery, and orthopedic surgery. In so doing, she was responsible for supervising, coaching, hiring, disciplining, and monitoring her staff to insure quality control. Williams was then promoted to unit director and appointed as an instructor in the College of Nursing. In recognition of the advocacy of the ideals of clinical excellence, Ruth Williams received the James A. Campbell Distinguished Service Award.

One of Campbell's favorite "watering holes" was located in the Physical Therapy Department on the fourth floor of the old Jones Building. He claimed to have a bad back, which needed occasional PT attention, but probably this was just a ruse to make a stop in the department to find out the latest gossip. In many ways the hospital community is very much like a close-knit small town, and nothing that transpires within it can be kept secret for very long. Eleanor Stupka and Leroy Irving were close friends of Campbell's. They had their finger on the pulse of the entire medical center, and Jim could rely on them to keep him informed. The stories were all out there in the "PT" department. Whether they were completely true or not was another matter.

Campbell held court in the PT coffee room and put on his show, often to a standing room only crowd. PT was also a favorite stopping off place for orthopedic resident surgeons to visit on coffee breaks or in between cases in the operating room. Campbell would await the appearance of a certain orthopedic resident who would come in, swagger, put his legs up on the table, throw his weight around, and generally make an egotistical ass out of himself. One was made to feel that they were in the presence of surgical greatness. People demanded squatters' rights to see these encounters. Campbell would wait and allow the resident to carry on in his usual way, and then he would cut him down to size. It was described as a surgeon's cut, swift and clean. He would totally undress the resident verbally. The theme of Campbell's barbs always centered around the message, "Remember, you are a doctor, taking care of sick people." But it took a few minutes for the victim to realize that Campbell had totally torn him apart. Then he quietly left the room with his tail between his legs.

When Leroy Irving and Campbell would go over to the Lakeside Field in Grant Park to watch the hospital baseball team play, bystanders would ask who the guy giving tips on coaching and strategy was. People were flabbergasted when they learned that it was the president of Rush mixing it up with the regular people. They simply couldn't believe it. Campbell received as gifts many baseball shirts, bowling shirts, basketball shirts, and jackets with lettering on the back saying, "#1 Guy" or "#1 Boss." He kept these in his presidential office and proudly displayed them to his fellow trustees and friends.

Campbell's intensity was entirely consistent. He never did anything mindlessly. He never wasted words or time. As a nurse who had worked with Campbell for many years recalled, "When Dr. Campbell would leave his office to make a stop in the hospital or do some kind of errand or keep an appointment, he always left his office an hour early. During this time he would stop and greet people but at the same time he would be checking up on things. Even though he was polite and friendly, you knew he was looking things over, and he knew you knew he was doing it. He made sure of that. He was always on a mission."

Campbell often stopped in the basement, deep in the interior of the sprawling institution. Here was another place where he would get inside news. The employees from Human Resources were there. A great deal of information about what was going on throughout the hospital was passed on in front of these seemingly harmless quiet people when they were up on the floors working. And, of course, this would all then be passed on to the big boss.

The Department of Radiation Therapy was located right in the middle of the basement far away from the elevators, so that everyone who went there, doctors, students, technicians, and patients, had the opportunity to get a full tour of this dull, drab, and unattractive part of the hospital. For the time, there was no other space available to accommodate the needs of this first-rate, rapidly expanding department. It was so far away from the garage that patients had difficulty finding it. Conferences were regularly held in the department, usually around noon, at which time lunch would also be served. The basement usually was a bit on the warm side, so many of the doctors in training caught up on their sleep and indulged in naps during these meetings. Elevator service to and from the basement was usually quite slow, so the stairways were the preferred route from the third floor to the basement.

Campbell visited the department every day for several weeks during the time that his wife Elda was receiving postoperative radiation treatments. The department was eventually relocated to the choicest spot in the entire medical center, on the first floor at the northwest corner of Harrison and Paulina, where the Woman's Board Cancer Treatment Center is located. Dedicated parking for patients was made available. Campbell very likely had something to do with this.

The expanding medical center now extended on the north from the triangle office building on the other side of the Eisenhower Expressway that also housed Anchor and on the south to the end of the Johnston R. Bowman Center at the corner of Polk and Paulina streets, a distance of several blocks. Long walks became a way of life for Campbell and for everyone else, and several short cuts were devised to try to minimize these trips. The elevators at the junction of the Jelke Building and the Academic Facility were the slowest and were best avoided if at all possible. The same was true for the Johnston R. Bowman elevators. It was almost always faster to climb the stairs going up from four, frequently up all the way to seven, than to wait for these very slow elevators. But the stairs were equipped with a safety devise that had to be tripped before opening the stairway door. In the usual rush of the day, this was often overlooked, and a very objectionable, loud, and frightening alarm would be set off. As unsettling as this disturbance could be, it became so commonplace that hardly anyone would take notice. Even patients on the floors seemed to get used to it, and carry on as they were before.

One of Campbell's favorite shortcuts was the "fire escape" where the Jelke Building and the Senn Building connected on the fifth floor overlooking Harrison Street. In 1960, when the Jelke Building was built immediately to the east of the older Senn Building, no connections were designed to join the upper floors of the two buildings, so as an afterthought a door leading from the newer building connecting the two buildings at the fifth floors to the older building's fire escape whose fifth floor was a few feet higher was devised. The fifth floors of each building housed the busy Department of Pathology and its research laboratories. The alternative time-consuming route of taking the elevators from 5 Jelke down to the second floor, crossing over to the Senn Building, and then up the antique Senn Building elevators was very time consuming and was to be avoided if at all possible. So the ancient fire escape of Senn on the fifth floor connected to a door at the west end of the Jelke Building was a busy passageway for the pathologists and a common thoroughfare for those working on the one or two floors below and above. To get across from west to east, the Senn Building door had to be opened, and the five steps of the rickety wrought iron fire escape negotiated and then the heavy door of the Jelke building opened. The footing could be wet and icy. On a dark windy day in the middle of winter, it could be a harrowing experience. If one didn't successfully complete the passage, the next stop was three floors below. But Campbell and those who used it never gave this a second thought. This unprotected connection eventually was redesigned and the hazard eliminated.

Campbell also discovered that the new elevators at the west end of the Atrium Building, going from the ninth floor to the basement were a real time saver. It was one of the medical center's best-kept secrets. You seldom had to wait for one of these elevators to arrive and they traveled at a very high rate of speed. If, for example, if you had to travel from the ninth floor of the Atruim building to the X-ray Department on the first floor in the Kellogg Building and you were familiar with the basement, all you had to do was take the elevators to the first floor, walk down a short flight of stairs to the basement, walk across the basement, and up a very short flight of stairs to 1 Kellogg and you ended up right in the center of the X-ray Department. There were four or five alternative travel paths available but they took ten to fifteen minutes longer. The trip between the Atrium Building and the X-ray Department often had to be made several times a day, so this shortcut was a big help.

In contrast to Jim's friendly, down-to-earth, nice-guy approach in dealing with those who worked out on the hospital floors, his deportment would take on another color when he dealt directly with those in management roles. His very presence commanded that you put starch in your spine. He was judging every aspect of your very being. If he sensed that you as an individual working for him and under him didn't know more than he did, he would tell you right out that he really didn't need you. You always had to be prepared when he talked to you and asked you a question. Yet he inspired those in management positions with his vision of the delivery of health care for the betterment of people. His broad concepts engaged these people to do their very best. In Campbell's monthly administrative meetings, each staff member had to submit a written report. Campbell read, questioned, and critiqued every report, sometimes in humor, but always with a serious and insightful quality. So everybody was kept on their toes, and these routine meetings evolved into a great learning experience.

A highly respected Rush-trained Chicago hospital administrator, Dr. Truman Esmond regarded Campbell as a totally unique leader, like no one else. He seemed to be able to see twenty years into the future while most people were still stumbling in the present. He could envision a path to get there and then establish the priorities necessary to accomplish his goal. He was the consummate leader, out in front, while you were trying to catch up. So even though you would be beating your brains out, you were having fun.

Campbell had some of the best advisors around, for example, Don Oder, Gale Warden, Mark Lepper, and many physicians, but Jim was the leader. He would not be directed, and he reserved the right to change his mind, even in such things as construction projects, even until the very last brick was laid. Everyone was engaged, and he knew all those on the job, who told him what was going on. His sources would inform him that some concrete was not being poured on time. At the next construction meeting, he would say, the concrete hasn't been poured yet, what's going on?

Campbell was among the first to introduce modern financial accountability into a major academic health care institution. His emphasis on this in effect took an outstanding faculty up a notch further. Hidden costs were eliminated. Department chairmen were required to develop a budget. For those times, such practices were unheard of. Campbell had the vision to see the increasing complexity of health care as it was expanding and the need for other professionals to develop the financial disciplines to deal with these new challenges. "If we need it, to hell with the costs" was no longer an acceptable mindset. New programs proposed would require an assessment of cost, budget, and the like.

But in the eyes of administrators and financial managers, Campbell was first and always a doctor, often referred to as the "super doc." Even after he became a full-time administrator, Campbell closely followed the development of new medical advances and discoveries. When his friend, Bob Sessions, was struggling in the early stages of developing cardiac pacemakers, Campbell encouraged him to continue his work even when it was met with very little enthusiasm and a good deal of skepticism from several of the institution's cardiologists. Campbell foresaw the potential in the development of this device, and here again he was entirely correct.

Campbell's philosophy of strict financial accountability in combination with his vigilance in looking for potential new scientific developments was well exemplified in Rush's procurement of the first CT scanner in Chicago. In 1972, an associate in training with Dr. Maynard Cohen, the chairman of the Department of Neurology, had just returned from a meeting in England, where it had been reported that a revolutionary form of imaging, called Computerized Axial Tomography (CAT scan), had been developed. The claims for the device seemed exaggerated and were greeted with a good deal of skepticism. The manufacturing company involved was the same one that had produced the Beatles recordings.

Cohen spoke to Dr. Michael Huckman, the new director of the section of Neuroradiology who had just been recruited from the prestigious Mallincrodt Institute in St. Louis. Huckman had not heard of this development. So he put a call in to his former chief, Dr. Juan Taveres, who had just moved from Mallincrodt to the Massachusetts General Hospital in Boston. Taveres told Huckman, "I can only tell you, get it." That is all he would say, apparently fearful of any information leak. Armed with this information, Huckman spoke to Dr. Richard Buenger, the chairman of the Department of Radiology, who relayed this information to Campbell. The message was, we have to have it. This relay of information from Cohen to Huckman to Buenger to Campbell all transpired in the same day. And the following day, a $350,000 order was placed for the purchase of the scanner. Campbell had come up with the money. In less than a year, Rush had the CT scanner installed and operational. It was the third such device installed in the United States, just a few months behind Mayo Clinic and Massachusetts General Hospital.

The technology of CT scanning, the introduction of computers into imaging, was one of medicine's major technological advances of the twentieth century. It was first introduced for study of the brain, and for the first time many sections of the brain could be imaged in a detailed manner. Its use has been extended to revolutionize virtually all diagnostic studies in medicine and many forms of treatment as well.

Rush was the only center in Chicago to have a CT scanner for more than a year, and the cost of the scanner was paid for several times over, even though it was often employed when no financial compensation could be recovered. So in such situations, Campbell was available and ready to hear all this potentially important information. After asking some very hard and penetrating questions of the doctors involved, he acted immediately. Placing the institution in the lead in the development of medical advances like the CT was highly beneficial to the morale of the entire institution and also confirmed the confidence that people in the organization had in Jim Campbell as their leader.

Others from outside also praised Campbell's leadership skills. Presbyterian Hospital alumnus Dr. Arnold Brown had known Campbell when he trained in pathology in the early Campbell years. He later relocated to the Mayo Clinic in Rochester, Minnesota, and then the University of Wisconsin at Madison and during this time became a recognized national leader in medical education. Campbell traveled to Minnesota to interview Brown for the position of dean at Rush. In Brown's opinion, "Jim Campbell would have been a leader in any environment. He could have run Madison or Rochester or most anywhere else for that matter." Dr. Bill Holmes was another Campbell admirer. Holmes moved on to several leadership positions after he left Rush. "Jim was the best." Bill had worked with Jim for many years. Campbell was the best leader he had ever worked for. He was reliable, and he meant what he said. His word was good, period.

Nevertheless, even as Campbell grew and matured, his harsh anger could still surface. When people didn't catch on or, even worse, when they let ego get the better of them, Campbell would react in a very definite and even frightening way. He came across as very judgmental. He could turn into a stoic icicle or, as one associate described him, a penetrating laser. So one always had to bear this in mind in dealing with Campbell. There was fear of precipitating one of these situations. But these dark encounters occurred less often as time went on. He became more understanding and tolerant when things didn't go as he had directed. Although still as organized and demanding as ever, Campbell acquired a much less punishing manner and more forgiving way of dealing with his staff. The high expectations remained, and mistakes were taken very seriously, but he began to develop a sense of understanding and a sense of forgiveness as he would try to turn the event into a positive learning experience.

Campbell's newer and more considerate style of leadership was exemplified by the experience of Rusty Knight, a young administrator who was assigned the overall supervision of one of the new hospital construction projects. Campbell would walk through the project once a week. He could read blueprints very well. He understood the importance of physical facilities and paid close attention to their execution. There were very few design flaws in the medical center's many construction and building programs. Campbell oversaw all of this and tried to relate every detail to the big picture.

Even though Campbell would end up knowing as much detail of an assignment as Knight did, he delegated exceedingly well, and gave Rusty a fair amount of leeway, which he and his administrator associates appreciated. "He would give you a fair amount of rope to run with although you knew he was always at the other end of it."[7]

---

7. Personal communication, Mr. Rusty Knight, April 12, 1999.

14

Fully in Charge

The dean of Chicago science writers, the *Chicago Daily News'* Arthur Snider, wrote a feature on Campbell dated November 11, 1974.[1] It had been 10 years since he assumed the presidency of Rush–Presbyterian–St. Luke's Medical Center, and Campbell's startling accomplishments of that decade were listed in some detail. The accelerated pace of development had not found favor with some who protested, "How can we move in so many directions at once? It's his guts and our blood." Modest, slender, and boyish-looking at 55, Campbell had an appearance that belied his dominant personality. While coming on strong, he could also be courtly and charismatic. It was almost impossible to follow him through a door; and at the same time he was probably the only president of a $100 million corporation who wore a long white coat at his desk. He would be on duty to make rounds all over the medical center to make as sure as he possibly could, amid the tall towers, shining equipment, and well-appointed offices, that the patients' welfare was put first. He overlooked

---

1. Arthur Snider, "Campbell Throbs as Hospital's Pulse," *Chicago Daily News,* November 21, 1974.

nothing. He would go look at anything. He was able to talk at any level. He could make the listener feel comfortable. But, if something were out of place, you would hear about it right way, for sure. Campbell had astonished associates with his management skills, even though he had no formal training in business administration. The cutting edge cardiologist turned administrator had some of his classical quotations to apply to this his newly chosen vocation. One from John Gardner, he used often: "An excellent plumber is infinitely more admirable than an incompetent philosopher. The society which scorns excellence in plumbing because plumbing is a humble activity and tolerates shoddiness in philosophy because philosophy is an exalted activity, will have neither good plumbing nor good philosophy. Neither its pipes nor its theories will hold water."[2] Developing excellence and high standards of performance at every level of medical center activity was clearly the Campbell message, and this kept the morale throughout the institution at a very high level.

The reopening of Rush, the expansion of hospital bed capacity to 850, the massive increase in the size of the budget and the value of the center's assets, acquiring further property (4.5 acres for future expansion), establishing Anchor, and the beginnings of affiliation with several outlying hospitals were listed among some of Campbell's accomplishments, with more in the planning stage to follow. Campbell's photograph in the Snider article was taken in his office, which had now moved to the top floor of the Professional Building. In it he was looking across at the massive Alden's Building at the southeast corner of Harrison and Paulina as the construction wrecking ball was being readied to demolish that structure. And there were other similar projects in preparation.

The construction of the five-story Professional Building at 1725 West Harrison Street to provide office space for physicians adjacent to the hospital had been completed in 1965. Doctors in general were not enthusiastic about having their practice offices relocated so close to the hospital, and the medical staff of Presbyterian–St. Luke's

2. John W. Gardner, *Excellence: Can We Be Equal and Excellent, Too?* (New York: Harper & Row, 1961), p. 86.

felt very much the same way. Would anybody really consider abandoning their downtown offices? How could you send a patient from LaSalle Street over to the slums on Congress? Many doctors had practice office locations in downtown Chicago, particularly on Michigan Avenue, that dated back almost to the turn of the century. They were afraid that their patients would find other physicians rather than follow them over to the medical center and that the pattern of referral from other physicians would be disrupted. Perhaps the most overriding concern was that the increasingly powerful hospitals would swallow up the doctors if they had more direct "control" over them.

Building occupancy was low in the beginning. Pharmacist Homer Manfredi would dispense only a handful of prescriptions each day from his small office at the south end of the building. Eventually the pharmacy would become the largest in Chicago. Jim Campbell would meet with Manfredi at 5:30 or 6:00 each morning to monitor the goings on of this new hospital-based outpatient pharmacy. As he watched its explosive growth, he also was able to see what trends were developing in medical practices. Being such a well-informed physician as well as a CEO made Campbell truly a unique medical leader. If the leading doctors in Chicago at Rush were doing new and different things, Campbell could anticipate needs for the medical center well in advance of others. He kept questioning Manfredi on how the patients and their physicians were reacting to this new type of service and how service to both could be improved. Practicing physicians had no idea that Campbell was watching all of this. Campbell also regularly conferred with inpatient hospital pharmacist Dr. Louis Gdalman in a similar way.

In a sense, the medical center was taking a chance in constructing the facility. The concept of hospital-based doctors' offices was quite new for the time. But as it worked out, the building became one of the largest of its kind in the world and 1725 West Harrison Street became a familiar address to many Chicagoans who visited their doctors at this facility. Orthopedic surgeon Dr. Claude Lambert was the first occupant in Suite 548. Soon other surgeons followed. Their practices were largely hospital-based, so the convenience of hospital operating rooms adjacent to their offices was an attractive feature. The advantages to all physicians of having the hospital close to their offices eventually became evident, and then the stampede began. The big internal medicine practices moved over. As Dr. Philip Jones, of the Capps, Jones, Thomson practice, recalled, "in 1970, we decided to move over. We had been at the same location downtown since 1912. We were keeping all fingers crossed. About ten percent of the patients in our practice did not follow us over. But in a rather short time, this attrition was more than made up by the many new patients we attracted."[3]

It wasn't long before a six-story addition was built, but in order to accommodate to the configuration of connecting buildings, the first floor of this building was redesignated the ground floor, and therefore all the office numbers in the building dropped by one floor. For example, Lambert's office became Suite 448. This was followed by construction of another connecting 11-story building, Professional Building 2, and later another 11-story structure, Professional Building 3. And shortage of space still continues to the present time. The Professional Buildings were not placed in the tax-exempt category of not-for-profit organizations, and thus the medical center significantly augmented the tax base of the local community when it was most needed.

Eating facilities in the West Side Medical Center district were limited to hospital cafeterias, coffee shops, and the "Greek's," a restaurant located on Harrison Street just across from Cook County Hospital. As the medical center grew and expanded, it became evident that a facility for meetings and conferences as well as an attractive space for dining were needed. Professional activities expanded even further when the medical school reopened, and with it came a large number of new visitors. An attractive facility for staff recruitment became a necessity. Room 600 (later renamed Room 500), an

3. Summary transcript of interview with Philip Jones, M.D., by Jim Bowman, June 9, 1986, in preparation for *Good Medicine: The First 150 Years of Rush–Presbyterian–St. Luke's Medical Center.*

elegant physician-faculty dining room, which could accommodate upwards of 300 people, was constructed on the sixth floor of the Professional Building.

Room 500 eventually became the center of all professional activity for the medical center, exclusive of direct patient care. Breakfast and lunch were served every day and evenings were taken up with special functions, such as receptions, dinners, and meetings of groups both inside and outside the medical center. Many local medical societies held their meetings at Room 500. Postgraduate courses and specialty certifying examinations of regional and national professional organizations also were conducted there. Very few hotels, even the large downtown ones, could accommodate these large groups and offer a central location with adjacent convenient parking. At the semiannual Rush University Medical Staff Meetings in November and May more than 300 physicians would convene for both faculty and staff meetings in the late afternoon, followed by cocktails and then dinner.

Until very recently, no other medical center in Chicago could claim such a facility. Campbell, instead of decrying what was perceived by some as a misfortune of location, developed a faculty club that was both unique and highly beneficial to the morale of the entire medical center community. Visitors and nonprofessionals within were frequently received as invited guests, as were the members of the many constituencies of the wide family of Rush University Medical Center, such as volunteers, trustees, and its many friends. Room 500 became the attractive front parlor and living room for the entire medical center family.

In 1971, a wealthy benefactor, Mrs. Lula Bowman, bequeathed money exclusively for the care of the elderly, and the Johnston R. Bowman Center, a separate 176-bed building, was constructed, virtually a hospital within a hospital solely for the care of the elderly. Campbell's design team connected JRB, as it became known, to the south end of the medical center campus, symbolizing Rush's commitment for comprehensive health care for all age groups. The medical center competed successfully for this benefaction against seven other institutions in the metropolitan area when it created this facility and its design emphasized subacute care, assisted living, and independent living.

The concept of geriatrics was in its infancy at that time. The restoration of sick elderly patients to relative self-sufficiency, emphasis on rehabilitation in more than physical terms, including patient and family counseling, and discouragement of the idea of a nursing home as an end-of-life arrangement were stressed as well as psychiatric rehabilitation. Establishing rehabilitation programs for patients released from the hospital as soon as their health allowed, always with a view toward returning them, as nearly as possible, to full social participation, is now a rather well accepted objective, but for the time it was quite new. And again Rush was in the forefront of these important advances. JRB patients, with their problems of a less acute and more chronic nature, were integrated into the training programs for Rush health care professionals at a time when exposure of trainees to the problems of the chronically infirm was unusual and was considered as a deficiency in training.

Today as one approaches the campus of Rush University Medical Center from the east, the unsightly elevated train tracks are not visible for a distance of three city blocks as they disappear at the north end of the campus where the Kellogg and Atrium Buildings join and do not emerge until the station stop at Polk Street. Once concealed, the tracks traverse a route that is within a few feet of thirty operating rooms, patient beds, hospital corridors and elevators, sophisticated laboratories, the Rush Library, and the Armour Academic Facility. The affairs of Rush University and its four colleges, classrooms, study areas, and laboratories, are conducted in the Armour Building. The sound-proofing of these structures required installation of sand within the concrete building blocks, and the placement of sound absorptive panels to cover the sealed joints.

The medical center, featuring parklike and campus amenities such as extensive open space, an enclosed outdoor running track and tennis courts, is found in the middle of a densely populated major metropolitan area. There are modern building structures like the

Armour Academic Facility, and the Atrium Hospital Complex and several other features that distinctly set it off from its surroundings.

Design for the entire medical center had to be planned within the limitations of the elevated tracks. The block long Armour Building, which was constructed on stilts above the elevated tracks, became the center structure and main thoroughfare for all the other connecting buildings on the campus at its fourth floor level. Here it became a crossroads for traffic as it connected to the Atrium hospital complex, the garage, Professional Buildings 1, 2, and 3, and to the south, the Johnston R. Bowman Center for the Elderly by way of a connecting bridge.

But the creation of this did not come easily. Land available for expansion was very difficult to acquire. The projected plans when Campbell assumed the office of the presidency in 1964 called for replacement of many parts of the 50- to 60-year-old hospital buildings, further expansion of the Professional Buildings, development of a building dedicated entirely to research, expansion of parking facilities, the redevelopment of the medical school and expansion of it into a university, and all the ongoing replacement of laboratory facilities necessary to keep up with changing technical and scientific developments.

Most of the adjacent buildings in the area, which the hospital did not own, were deteriorating and run down. Rush's neighbors to the west and south, Cook County Hospital and the University of Illinois, were solid impenetrable barriers to expansion. And, to the north, expansion was limited by the Eisenhower Expressway. Campbell found a way to get around this. During the 1970s, demands for space became extreme, particularly so for the Professional Buildings. Conditions were such that the medical center had to contract for space in locations as far away as two miles to keep up.

A triangular parcel of land adjacent to the elevated CTA track just north of the Expressway on Paulina Street. became available. This site, although across the expressway from the main campus, was considerably closer than the other distant locations then being used. The Triangle Office Building and, later, the Anchor Center would be built at this location. Campbell and his staff moved quickly to acquire this property, even in advance of the Board of Trustee's knowledge of any of this. Land clearing was started and construction begun before the legal transfer of a portion of the property had been completed. On the very same day the project was initiated, Campbell ordered his staff to prepare a list of all strictly nonprofessional people with offices in the Professional Building who would then be moved across the Expressway to the new site as quickly as possible. In this way Campbell was able to free up more space for doctor's offices.

Nevertheless, the only realistic direction for expansion was to the east. And the massive eight-story Alden's Warehouse, occupying more than one half of the square block of Paulina, Harrison, Congress, and Ashland stood in the way. There were other buildings in the other half, but Alden's was the main obstacle. The building created a huge traffic flow problem, particularly from trucks diverted from Ashland Boulevard. Local traffic, particularly during the holiday season from October to December, was a major inconvenience. Although the location of the Alden building was within the Medical Center District, it had been constructed before the district was created in the early forties and it took years of negotiations and legal efforts before the property could be acquired and the warehouse razed. The elevated CTA tracks, also to the east, would not go away, so they were bypassed by building over them. Paulina Street, also to the east, between Harrison and Congress presented an impregnable barrier to break through. The subsequent necessity to close Paulina Street in 1979 escalated into a major public controversy that would test Campbell's leadership skills very severely.

Late in the nineteenth century, many of Chicago's elite lived on South Ashland Boulevard, which was then considered Chicago's Gold Coast. Mayor Carter Harrison declared Ashland to be a boulevard between Lake Street on the north and Roosevelt Road on the south in order to reduce traffic congestion. Commercial traffic was thus prohibited in this section and diverted to Paulina Street, one block west. It was the only part of Ashland, a very long street extending from Evanston on the north to Beverly on the south, to be so designated. The original reason for this restriction had long since passed.

Once Rush acquired the Alden property, the location of Paulina Street, between Congress Parkway on the north and Harrison on the south, stood directly in the way of providing space for the medical center's much needed plans for expansion and replacement of its hospital beds. To build under Paulina Street would make construction costs entirely prohibitive. So acquiring Paulina Street and closing it to through traffic seemed to be the only solution.

Commercial traffic would be allowed on Ashland Boulevard. In addition to this, diverting eastbound traffic exiting the Expressway from Paulina to Ashland would eliminate the traffic bottleneck at Congress Parkway and Paulina, which often led to a backup of vehicles all the way back onto the Expressway. An eastbound exit farther west at Damen was proposed which would then provide an exit for those going into the more western sections of the Medical Center District.

With this in mind, Campbell and the trustees approached city officials about the feasibility of acquiring Paulina Street. As prominent attorney Oscar D'Angelo recalls, the answer to Campbell's request from the city would be a definite no. But Campbell was totally unfazed by this. City Commissioner of Streets Quigley was then consulted, and an attractive plan for the expansion of Ashland was designed, with island street dividers and other amenities so as to have the dual effect of improving the appearance of the entire neighborhood as well as relieving traffic congestion. Campbell won out, and the City Council approved the sale of the short city block of Paulina Street between Congress and Harrison to Rush. The Medical District Commission also endorsed Rush's plans for expansion.

In January 1979, Paulina Street construction barricades were installed, just at the time when one of Chicago's more severe blizzards hit the entire city with ferocious intensity. It was the beginning of a two-month period of very severe weather conditions and a time of major inconvenience for everyone. Nineteen seventy-nine was the year that the Chicago Democratic political machine was voted out of office for the first time in its history because of its alleged poor management of snow removal, which left thousands of Chicagoans stranded, unable to get anywhere or do anything.

In the media and the press, Rush was depicted as the public villain. The affluent big hospital plans severely inconvenienced its surrounding neighbors. People from the University of Illinois and Cook County Hospital were outraged. A suit was filed against Rush by the University of Illinois to have Paulina reopened, but it was dismissed. Traffic tie ups from the construction barricades became the leading story on the ten o'clock news. Candidate for mayor Jane Byrne vowed to have the barricades removed if she were elected. An unsubstantiated claim was made and highly publicized that the reduced access resulting from the street closure caused the death of a patient who was unable to get access to medical care. Rush was taken to court for alleged illegal deceptions but was found innocent.

Had the severe weather not occurred, the controversy surrounding the closure of Paulina very likely would have been minimal. The resulting traffic pattern design was a major improvement for the entire neighborhood. Campbell and the trustees took a great deal of heat from all of this, but they had everything covered to withstand the criticism. That someone could buy a city street was, in the eyes of many, the ultimate in political clout. Campbell stood his ground, however, and did not back down even an inch. He realized it would take a good long while for all this to settle down. And three years later, Jane Byrne, now the mayor, stood on the speakers' platform at the dedication ceremonies for the new Atrium Building, praising Rush for its great contributions to the city. The speakers' platform stood directly over the closed section of Paulina Street.

This sort of courageous leadership on Campbell's part inspired people throughout the institution. Rush–Presbyterian–St. Luke's Medical Center seemed to have a sense of where it was going. While people might have certain reservations about some of Campbell's new and innovative ideas, they would go along with him anyway and give him the benefit of the doubt because things always seemed to work out. And Campbell's successes never seemed to go to his head. He was on to the next big program, even before the current one was finished. He was relentless. And he never rested on his laurels. Everyone could sense this.

Campbell could never have achieved any of his successes without the active and enthusiastic support of the institution's Board of Trustees. The board was composed of many of Chicago's civic and business leaders. He was so effective in working with the board that to many observers this remarkable relationship seemed in a sense to be almost automatic. But each time a new chairman and a new Executive Committee came on board, Jim had to reengage these leaders in his mission and adjust it to the ever-changing circumstances of the exploding health care industry. He had to show first his abilities to present things in terms that the board could understand and relate to. By learning to understand the significance of a balance sheet, a budget, and the like, and with the input of Mr. Donald Oder, Campbell was always well prepared when he presented these financial reports to the board.

Mr. Donald Oder became the medical center's chief financial officer at the time Campbell became president in 1965 and remained in that position until his retirement in 1997. He was an essential key to the Campbell-Rush success story. Oder left college early to enlist in the military, served as a combat sergeant in Korea and then returned to college and received a degree in accounting from Wichita State College. Don met his wife Roberta at Wichita State, where she also studied accounting. After he joined the accounting firm of Arthur Andersen in 1958, his first assignment involved helping the medical center, then Presbyterian–St. Luke's Hospital, put together its first bond issue for borrowing, something the institution had never done before. This newly created type of financing provided capital for construction of the East Pavilion (Kellogg) Building at the time of the merger and then was used to finance other programs as well. (Later tax-exempt financing for hospitals became available when the Illinois Health Facility Act was established in 1975.)

The entire financial operation for the medical center was housed on the fifth floor of the ancient Coyne Building at the southeast corner of Paulina and Harrison. The accounting was done by the punch-card method. It was a simpler time in hospital financial affairs. Arthur Andersen had only a few hospitals as clients, and these accounts often were served at a discount at off-season times during the year. Andersen considered it part of one's civic duty. St. Luke's was a big prestigious account and received first-class service. In the early years, St. Luke's books were kept in the office of Mr. Solomon A. Smith, the president of the Northern Trust Bank, as the trustees in that era were much closer to the daily operations of both hospitals.

Oder was reassigned again to Presbyterian–St. Luke's to do a program-cost study in 1960 and 1961. The hospital had not yet acquired its first computer to bypass the laborious punch-card system. By that time financial control of the hospital had largely passed out of the hands of the clergy of the Presbyterian and Episcopal churches, as the number of seats they held on the board had been reduced at the time of the merger. It was the beginning of a more modern system of tracking expenses. Oder met with some of the department chairmen to determine what costs they were incurring. He had not yet been introduced to Campbell. This does not mean, however, that Campbell did not know who Oder was, because Campbell was watching everyone who had anything to do with the important matters of hospital business.

Oder then was assigned by Andersen to set up the finances of the Puerto Rico Medical Center in San Juan in 1964 and 1965. He had just returned to Chicago when he was again called back to the Presbyterian–St. Luke's Medical Center, as it was called at that time, to go over the books and operations with Board Chairman A. B. Dick. Dick was having some problems balancing the budget after analyzing it at home with a new device at that time, his own personal calculator. Just prior to this, the hospital controller and most of his staff had left to go to a major hospital in New York, so Oder became acting comptroller on loan from Andersen. Andersen was also looking at a management reorganization for the medical center. It was during this time that Oder met Campbell for the first time; Dick and Campbell soon recruited Oder to be the medical center's chief financial officer. The recruitment of the highly regarded Oder from Arthur Andersen was an important move for the medical center, since the hospital industry was entering into a period of massive expansion with the passage of the Medicare Act of 1965. For years afterwards, the finances of the institution were in the capable hands of Oder and his staff. The loss of Oder to the medical center was a big one for Andersen. Oder was regarded as an excellent person and an outstanding performer. He was being groomed to be the health care specialist for the firm, as it became evident that this field would grow in importance. Among Don's talents was his highly legible, extremely rapid handwriting, which actually was very readable print. He would get quite upset if he ever made a mistake in his handwriting style, although he rarely did. A caricature of Don as the typical accountant personality would be highly inaccurate as he possessed very effective people skills.

The financial resources of the institution in the 1960s were very modest. There was a minimal operational cash reserve. Budgets were very tight. And there was real concern as to whether the next payroll could be met or not. There was no such thing as allowances for coffee or perks of any type. To finance a typewriter was a major expenditure. Campbell was very tight-fisted. In one instance, payment for the procurement of marmoset monkeys for Dr. Freidrich Deinhardt's research project was delayed, thus jeopardizing Deinhardt's relationship with important suppliers. The intense Deinhardt became extremely irate over this, and Campbell and Oder eventually did approve the expenditure. Whenever the hospital wanted to raise room rates, particularly in the days before Medicare, the medical staff often expressed their disapproval in no uncertain terms. When Rush separated from the University of Chicago in 1942, several of its endowment funds were returned, but they were of very modest dollar amounts. And many of the funds were earmarked for specific purposes, so there was very little help from this source for operational reserves.

While Herbert Sedgwick was overseeing finance, that is, before Oder arrived on the scene, the hospital did begin to depreciate its buildings. Before that, the hospital's attitude was simply that the buildings had been paid for, usually by donations, and that was the end of it. But even after a depreciation schedule had been set up, it was over the life of the building which could be for as long as forty years; so funding depreciation in this manner was not realistic since it did not cover true replacement costs or account for inflation. An accumulation of cash for the development of reserves from a schedule of this sort was also very slow. Then funding depreciation became considered a legitimate expense for nonprofit organizations and later was permitted by the federal government when the Medicare Act of 1965 came into being. This enabled Oder to change the depreciation schedule to a more realistic accelerated form, so that by 1969, when the reactivation of Rush Medical College came under consideration, a cash reserve of over $8 million had been built up.

So when the Campbell Study was reported in 1968, and the financial basis for restarting the school became possible because of both state and federal capitation and capital grants based on the number of new students which existing schools would be willing to enroll (in the case of Rush, this would include all students), then the financing could proceed. It was not possible to carry out the construction of a new academic facility in time for the proposed reopening in 1971, so the Schweppe-Sprague Building was renovated, two floors were added to the Jelke Building, and six floors were added to the professional building to meet this deadline. This interim arrangement provided for the necessary classrooms, laboratories, administrative offices, and the like, which a new school required. The A. Watson Armour III and Sarah Wood Armour Academic Center of Rush University, known as the Academic Facility, was eventually completed in 1975, and the entire financing of Rush University was managed with relatively modest additional fundraising.

Throughout the entire Campbell era, there was never the slightest sign of any financial scandal or irregularity of any sort, thanks to Oder and his staff's careful supervision When the federal government entered the picture, there were innumerable regulations and outside reviews and audits, and Rush was always in full financial compliance. Margaret Taylor, in fund accounting, demanded absolute and full compliance to the spirit as well as the letter of the law. Miss Taylor served the medical center faithfully throughout her entire working career. Margaret started at St. Luke's in 1937 and retired in 1983. She was doing expenditures and budgeting for St. Luke's at the time of the merger and fit right in with the growing operation. She became known as the institution's watchdog for the NIH. One of the top officers for the corporation attempted to get the cost of a coffeemaker written off to a fund. Margaret stopped this effort in its tracks.

In the 1970s, when the College of Health Sciences was being set up, Oder joined the faculty as an associate professor to teach health systems management. On his own initiative, Don returned to school to prepare for this, taking two years, at one day each week and no time off for summers, to earn a master's degree in business administration from the University of Chicago. Don felt this was the appropriate thing to do because his students would be earning graduate degrees. Sister Sheila Lyne, the highly respected CEO of Mercy Hospital, and formerly commissioner of health for the city of Chicago, was a fellow student with Don at the University of Chicago. Don was very helpful to Sister Sheila while she struggled to gain knowledge of accounting. Don seemed to know everything. He was considered to be in a class all by himself as a leader in the Chicago hospital community and Don served as chairman of the Illinois Hospital Association for many years.

Oder's decision to seek an advanced degree was not unusual in the Campbell era. Any employee could have a major portion of their tuition paid for by the medical center if they were able to maintain a certain average, and the employee could have their entire tuition covered if, for example, they had earned a degree. Many of the leaders in administration availed themselves of this opportunity. Wayne Lerner earned a doctor's degree in public health, going to school on weekends for four years. Dr. H. A. Paul, already an M.D., earned a master's degree in public health. Linda Nolan, urology office manager and bladder cancer clinical coordinator, earned a master's degree in business administration. Lerner, Paul, and Nolan traveled to Ann Arbor to the University of Michigan each weekend to accomplish this. And there were countless examples of other individuals doing the same thing at other schools.

Oder was the perfect complement to Campbell. Many people, even some of the trustees, were somewhat intimidated by Campbell. He could be so relentless that he frightened people. As one trustee recalls, Jim Campbell was very serious; there were a few laughs, but not many and not for long. Oder, on the other hand, was easygoing and accessible. His knowledge of operations was very detailed. He knew how to get things done quietly and effectively, making minimal political waves. He was very direct and straightforward, but never mean. He was a great listener, sometimes a man of few words, but when he spoke, he always had something to say. He helped Jim in many ways without Jim's ever knowing it and, like Campbell, provided great stability in leadership as he served the medical center over so many years.

Oder characterized Campbell as an individual with whom you could be on good terms or, if the other way, you were out totally. And if you were on the outs with Campbell, it was too bad. You might as well move along and get out. On the other hand, tough as he could be, Campbell did not like to fire people. Nor does anybody else enjoy letting people go, particularly when you are working alongside them every day. So whom does Campbell delegate the job of firing people to? Don Oder, of course, one of the world's nicest people.

Oder continued to serve the medical center as its chief financial officer for many years after the Campbell era ended in 1983, and he also maintained a very active interest in the Near West Side community adjacent to the hospital. He and Roberta live at the attractive condominium complex on Harrison Street just east of the medical center which Trustee Charles Shaw developed in 1981. And in 1997, Don ran for state representative for the West Side 6th district.

Sheldon Garber, like Oder, was an important member of the Campbell team. He served as both secretary to the Board of Trustees and chairman of the Department of Philanthropy and Communications. In 1973, Garber had been recruited personally by Campbell to direct and oversee fundraising, when it became evident that while a hospital might grow and prosper with a modest endowment, an educational enterprise such as the revitalization of Rush needed to have a much stronger philanthropic base. Campbell was able to share with Garber what he had hoped to accomplish with Rush, and Garber in turn seemed to understand and relate this vision back to Campbell in a language that Campbell felt was highly effective in reaching Rush's many long-standing constituencies and the public at large. Before coming to Rush, Garber had been a consultant with the fundraising firm of Charles Feldstein and at one time had served as a reporter for the United Press.

Relating to the public was what Sheldon was all about. In this area, nothing was unimportant, nothing trivial. When Garber came on board the Rush team, he insisted on being a member of the management committee so he could more fully understand what was going on in the institution whose reputation he felt was his responsibility to guard.

Garber was able to relate the Campbell-Rush story to a public that had not grasped it well before. The marvelous Rush story was retold: the merger, the massive growth of the hospital following the merger, the resurrection of Rush Medical College, the development of the College of Nursing and Health Sciences, the graduate college, and the formal chartering of Rush University. And the story was related to Rush's many constituencies in language that was easily understood. Even some of the trustees who were among the elite leadership community of Chicago were not fully cognizant of how significant some of these events over which they presided had been.

Every statement bearing the institution's name was carefully formulated. The annual report was developed into a very effective communications tool. With just a glance, the report conveyed the sense that the institution was accountable to the broad public, an audience that was a thoughtful and deliberate one with decision-making powers that would be affecting the future. One could take a look at any fact in which there was a special need or interest and find a sober deliberative substantive statement in the report about what was going on at Rush.

Hand in hand with this effort, Garber and his associates developed a list of potential donors, and a solid basis for ongoing support of the medical school and many other medical center activities and programs that were being established. The Endowed Chairs Program began to grow rapidly. When the Campaign for Development under the leadership of Board Chairman Harold Byron Smith was undertaken in the late seventies, the effort was oversubscribed by $8 million in excess of the $75 million goal. The campaign was the envy of many throughout the country. In protégé Gail Warden's view, Campbell's ability to develop a strong fundraising program along with Garber was one of his most important accomplishments. Garber set up the elaborate infrastructure for fundraising, the contacts, the research, and the like, and often there was a trustee involved in the presentations. But Campbell was the salesman. Garber and Campbell believed that the Department of Philanthropy provided Rush with the "margin of excellence" to differentiate itself more completely from its competitors.

Garber, Don Oder, and Campbell as corporate secretary, treasurer, and president met with the Executive Committee of the Board of Trustees each month. The president of the medical staff also attended as the physicians' representative. At these conferences the inner workings of the organization were presented for discussion, review, and approval, and decisions on action were recommended to be presented to the full board. Several subcommittees of the Executive Committee met separately to deal with specific individual problems and issues.

As chairman of the Board of Trustees from 1956 to 1962, John Bent nurtured the conceptual idea of the merger of Presbyterian and St. Luke's Hospital and supported it in spite of very stiff opposition. Bent established sound financial management for the institution when he persuaded the retiring vice president of Commonwealth Edison, Mr. Herbert Sedgwick, to take over this responsibility.

George Young succeeded Bent as chairman of the board. He, too, encountered a good deal of opposition from many quarters because of his support for the merger. Young's instincts and interest in education provided essential support for Campbell's ideas and schemes for structuring and transforming the merged hospitals into an academic health center and, eventually, a health science university.

A. B. Dick III served as board chairman from 1966 to 1971, and Edward Blettner from 1971 to 1974. Board chairmen were selected from the elite of the Chicago business community. Blettner was vice chairman of the First National Bank. Dick owned and operated the firm of A. B. Dick and, in addition, was the great-grandson of Daniel Jones, the donor of the Jones Building, one of the original Presbyterian

Hospital structures. Both Dick and Blettner were astute businessmen and demanded strict financial accountability from Campbell. As Dick recalled, as chairmen, they hounded Jim. He had to recognize that this was a business and he had to run it like a business. Doctors would talk about the need for some expensive equipment. They would then be asked what would be the return on it. They didn't even understand the question. In time they did. One of the reasons Mr. Donald Oder was recruited as the chief financial officer for the corporation was to insure this approach and the discipline that was needed. Dick and Blettner insisted on a profitable financial operation. Failure to do so would invariably result in a downhill course, which had to be avoided. But at the same time, these influential financial leaders bought enthusiastically into Jim's overall vision for the institution.

Dick in particular was high on Campbell's ability as the great salesman. Jim had a manner of speaking that was totally disarming. Before you knew it, you were embracing his concept. You had to brace yourself and say, wait, aren't you forgetting something? In Dick's opinion, Campbell was the dominant medical delivery personage in the Chicago area of those times. He could be abrasive, and he had enemies. But he had more friends. Dick wondered if the institution shouldn't be renamed the Campbell Medical Center. Jim did it all. But at the same time, he was a modest person. Campbell never let you hold the door for him. He was the last through the door. Maybe this was a little thing, but it was symbolic. He always talked about the trustees: it was their hospital, it was what they had done, never what he'd done. This made him an even better salesman. He was extremely successful in raising money for the institution as well. Dick was astonished at the growth of the institution under Campbell's leadership.

Edward McCormick Blair of the investment firm of Wm. Blair and Co., served as chairman from 1974 to 1978. Blair also served on the board of the University of Chicago. He marveled at Jim's organizational genius in setting up the medical school so that both the school and hospital were under the same management, an arrangement unique and quite different from that of the University of

Chicago and Northwestern. Blair also oversaw the expansion of the Board of Trustees to include more members from the metropolitan area's growing constituencies of Catholic and Jewish communities. And under Blair's term of service, the institution continued to experience great growth, much of which Blair attributeed to Campbell's leadership skills. At the same time Blair recognized that Jim's great strengths could not help but result in resentments, jealousies, and animosities, such as the closing of Paulina Street. Jim could play rough when he had to, and when he had to, he moved forward without any hesitation.

During all the time that Campbell was working with the board, he was also interacting in their social world. The Blairs, the Youngs, the Dicks, and the Fields were close personal friends with Jim and Elda Campbell. The more outgoing, vivacious, and socially gifted Elda was a great salesman for Jim's programs and very well liked among this elite circle of friends. On the one hand, Elda could be very blunt, but at the same time she had a very good sense of humor, particularly if she knew you. Her close friends included Mary Young, Hope McCormick, and Claire Dedmon. Because the Campbells seldom socialized with people in the medical center, such as doctors and their wives, many never knew Elda Campbell very well.

The last board chairman that Campbell was to serve under was Mr. Harold Byron Smith, who held that position from 1978 to 1988. The Byron Smiths dated back to Prairie Avenue and the old St. Luke's Hospital. The Smith family had served both hospitals for several generations. Harold Smith, who was president of Illinois Tool Works, had been nurtured for a leadership position through his involvement in the associates group. This group was composed of younger prominent business people marked for future board responsibilities. This group included Jim DeYoung, John Dick, and future chairman Ned Jannotta. When Smith became chairman in 1978, the place was going full stride. Later on in the eighties, in the second half of his term, storm clouds began to appear on the horizon. But by that time, Campbell had passed on.

Smith's temperament was different from Campbell's, but his strengths included strong operational skills, so Campbell had to readjust. As Smith recalled, "the more you worked with Jim, the more you wondered, what's he up to?"[4] As he realized you were on to him, he increased his communication with you. Notwithstanding this, Jim came to Smith and the trustees with a vision, expressed in simple terms, and they enthusiastically embraced it. The trustees were very aware of Jim's insistence on a single standard of care for all patients, and the great personal relations that he enjoyed with the employees. Not all of his projects would work out as hoped, such as the hospital network program that Campbell had envisioned to protect 1.5 million people in the metropolitan Chicago area under the Rush health care umbrella.

Dr. Bob Glaser has emphasized that Campbell's ability to attract top quality people to the board of the institution was one of his greatest accomplishments. And to do this over an extended period of time was no accident. Campbell not only recruited these business leaders, but energetically engaged them in his mission. Prominent business leader Ralph Bard, Jr., who served the medical center in many capacities throughout his entire long and honorable career, never failed to be impressed with Jim's way of conducting Executive Committee meetings. One came away from these meetings anxious to do even more for the institution. As Edward Blair put it, the board tradition was such that many of Chicago's extremely able business entrepreneurs, such as Mr. Ben Heineman, Roger Anderson, Charles Shaw, David Grainger, and others, one way or another would be found working for Rush. And yet, in Blair's view, the board considered Campbell to be the consummate entrepreneur. He always seemed to have everything figured out and thus was very persuasive because he had already considered every eventuality and overlooked nothing. He was willing to take risks on tough issues in the real world. And at the same time, the balance sheets were consistently favorable.

4. Ibid.

15

The Last Chapter

In 1978, when the class of 1943B at Harvard Medical School met to celebrate their thirty-fifth reunion, Jim Campbell was sixty years old.[1] Sixteen of the class had died, and about half of the original 110 held appointments on medical school faculties. The paragraph-long autobiographical summaries submitted by members of the class were not all of a serious nature. Typical reunion-type comments with major emphasis on humor, hubris, and one-upmanship were more of the rule. "I'm glad I went to Harvard, especially then instead of now." "Growing old is not that great." "The hours spent fishing do not come off your lifetime." "Now all doctors are interchangeable parts." "My philosophic, religious, and social beliefs have survived the stormy adolescence of seven children, four nephews, liberal friends, and Richard Nixon." "My own view of medical practice is that we haven't done a spectacular job of preparing docs for the real world and I think the public has tumbled to it. So we push and nudge, but does the mountain move?" "The patient wants an easy way to enter the medical care system and then have the most expert care they can

1. Harvard Medical School, Class of 1943B, 1943–1978, *Thirty-Fifth Reunion Report*, edited by John C. Nemiah.

get. This is not the definition of family practice. The best is yet to come." "Haven't quite come up to the stage when I reach for *Medical Economics,* before the *New England Journal,* but almost." "I am still assiduously throwing in the wastebasket all communications from the American Association of Retired Persons and expect to be lowered into my grave preparing for tomorrow. I pray for a life after death so that I may hear my secretary on the phone telling the Dean, 'No, I'm sorry he can't take on that committee assignment. He's dead.' Requiescat in pacem." "A bridge away. I have little to say. The older I get the less I know. The harder I work the less to show."

Dr. Joseph Murray had not yet received his Nobel Prize for work on kidney transplantation, which had been carried out some twenty-four year before. The award was bestowed in 1990. Dr. Bob Glaser, then president and chief executive officer of the Henry J. Kaiser Family Foundation, described his recent work as doing business at the same stand as a philanthropoid, convinced it is more blessed to give than not to receive. Jim Campbell reported to his fellow classmates the following. "I have been interested in medical care and manpower to such an extent that I have been involved with opening a college of medicine, a college of nursing, a college of health sciences, and a graduate school; developing affiliations with about a dozen hospitals and affiliations with 14 colleges in five states. Everybody has to earn a living doing something." Stated another way, he might have been saying, "Here I am, one of the stars of the class. Look at me. Not bad for a poor boy from a humble parsonage in downstate Illinois."

This time was the pinnacle of his career. He managed to continue to find time for AOA, Knox College, the Crerar Library Board, the Sloane Commission for Higher Education and Government, the Donald C. Balfour Visiting Professorship at Mayo Clinic,[2] and was

2. The Donald C. Balfour Visiting Professorship, Mayo Clinic, 1975, Folder 7, Box 6, C97-052, James A. Campbell, M.D., Papers 1924–1983, Record Group 002000, Office of the President, Rush–Presbyterian–St. Luke's Medical Center/Rush University Medical Center Archives, Chicago, Ill.

nominated for the Center for Advanced Study in Behavioral Sciences in Palo Alto, California. But his focus remained intensely at his home base of Rush. The record of achievement of the medical center under Campbell as president was most impressive by any criteria: admissions, patient days, emergency room visits, operations, transfusions, medical staff, interns, residents, fellows, Rush University students, employees, endowed chairs, assets, total revenues, and endowments.

As a result of the successful $150 million campaign for development, plans were underway for construction of the new state-of-the-art Atrium Building, which alone would end up costing $75 million. The fundraising effort, which was oversubscribed by several million dollars, began at a kickoff dinner at which former President Gerald R. Ford presided. There were many hurdles to overcome to complete the Atrium project: the Paulina Street controversy; the staggering cost to construct the facility, which brought objections from various regulatory agencies; the difficult and time-consuming demolition of the Alden's building; and designing the structure within the limitations of the elevated CTA tracks.

When it was completed, the top floors of the Atrium Building commanded outstanding panoramic views of downtown Chicago and the redeveloping Near West Side. In the new structure, a number of rooms were designed to face an interior courtyard that contained twenty-foot trees in pots, a far different surrounding from the usual setting for hospital rooms. Campbell provided considerable input into the design of this facility. He was quite proud of the construction hard hat he wore. He seemed to know virtually every detail even to the point of where every sink would be located. The obstacles to completing the building were eventually overcome and it was opened on time over the Memorial Day weekend in 1982. A sense of accomplishment and an aura of success pervaded the entire Rush campus, and everyone looked to Campbell as the individual who made it all happen.

At groundbreaking ceremonies for the new building, the senior Mayor Daley's remarks from a previous ceremony for the Academic Facility which had occurred only six years before seemed again appropriate.[3] He commended Rush for providing more doctors to care for people of the city and the state, and thanked Rush for extending itself, time and time again, not only to the people of the West Side neighborhood, but to the people of the entire city. "All the people of Chicago are grateful. Now we have another great milestone in the record and in the achievements of Rush–Presbyterian–St. Luke's. We have a great city, and as Dr. Campbell said so well, you look to the east and see the fine financial buildings, great buildings of finance and commerce. You look to the west and you see the fine buildings which take care of humanity. Congratulations to all who played a part in giving us this wonderful building."

Not everything that was planned for worked out. Campbell and his staff had hoped to develop a network of affiliated hospitals, academic centers, nursing homes, mental health facilities, home care and primary care clinics, including health maintenance organizations and fee-for-service clinics that would provide for the care of some 1.5 million people in the metropolitan area. The Campbell Plan as formulated was considered quite visionary, well ahead of other comprehensive programs that were being offered or proposed at that time.[4] The system would be tied into the Rush University System for Health and would have two basic components: the academic component that would produce medical and administrative talent for the system and the other that would provide effective and efficient patient care.[5]

Rush itself would provide for complicated tertiary care in this arrangement. Affiliated hospitals would in turn develop training pro-

3. Academic Building Dedication, September 14, 1976, Folder 114, Box 6, C97-052, James A. Campbell, M.D., Papers 1924–1983, Record Group 002000, Office of the President, Rush–Presbyterian–St. Luke's Medical Center/Rush University Medical Center Archives, Chicago, Ill.

4. Montague Brown and Howard L. Lewis, "An Outside Appraisal of the Rush University Systems for Health," Aspen Systems Corporation for Hospital Management Systems: Multi-unit Organization and Delivery of Health Care, 1977.

5. Donald E. L. Johnson, "University Hospitals Will Anchor Vertical Systems," *Modern Health Care,* December 1979, pp. 50–54.

grams, and innovative health care delivery systems could be tested. Some components of these hospital affiliations did work out for training students and residents, but not very successfully in regard to the referral of complicated tertiary cases to the medical center. The affiliated hospitals were fearful of being dominated by Rush. And many of the affiliates were developing programs that were in themselves designed to handle advanced treatment programs such as state-of-the-art cardiac surgery facilities. And many of these were staffed by trainees from the Rush system.

Toward the end of the 1970s, storm clouds began to appear in the far distance that would not manifest themselves until well into the middle of the 1980s. Hospital occupancy rates began to fall. For Rush, in the beginning this would result only in a reduction of the waiting time for admission of patients, with no effect whatsoever in hospital activity, growth, and expansion. However, this trend would continue and, projected into the future, would have significant implications when occupancy eventually started to decline. A trend in the shift to an outpatient mode for many hospital services began to develop. The skyrocketing cost of health care was attributed to inpatient hospitalization costs, and an ever increasing pressure to reduce the length of stay eventually led to major government intervention for Medicare patients with the institution of the DRG system. Health insurance was drastically altered with the introduction of several prepaid systems, such as Anchor, which eventually eroded the income of the medical center and put pressure on many of the existing programs. Physician compensation for services also changed significantly.

Campbell was still working at his usual pace, still projecting a youthful appearance. As soon as he finished with one project, he was on to the next. Whatever he had accomplished was history, and he looked to the future for greater challenges. His struggle to remain serious-minded was exemplified in one of his personal reflections: "If the world were merely seductive, that would be easy. If it were merely challenging, that would be no problem. But I arise in the morning torn between a desire to improve or save the world, and a desire to enjoy and savor the world. This makes it hard to plan your day"[6]

He now was the unquestioned leader for developing health care systems in Chicago and was also recognized as a national authority in this field. He was featured in the September 1981 issue of the *Harvard Business Review*, in which he co-authored an article, "Outlook for Hospitals: Systems Are the Solution," with Dr. Thomas First.[7] Here the issue was debated of the not-for-profit hospital system versus the investor-owned management company. Who should dominate? Campbell was asked how he viewed the entry into the health care market of large national hospital management companies. He replied by saying,

> comparing these new entries with not-for-profit institutions like Rush was like comparing apples and oranges. Besides the fact that we both need to generate positive net incomes for our respective corporate purposes, I'm not sure we are in the same business. If we were in the health care business to make a profit, we wouldn't be engaging in the amount of research and training of health manpower that we are. Neither of these is a profitable undertaking. I am not sure that the hospital management companies are much more than holding companies operating a portfolio of properties. The extent to which they are interested in functioning as health care systems that stress access, continuity, coordination, and comprehensive services remains to be seen. The concept of proprietary, investor-owned hospitals worries me the same way the idea of proprietary trade schools worries me.

Symbolically, James A. Campbell, M.D., graduate of Harvard Medical School of 1943B, was appointed a professor in the

6. Index card quotations, James A. Campbell, M.D., Box 35, File 4, C97-052, James A. Campbell, M.D., Papers 1924–1983, Record Group 002000, Office of the President, Rush–Presbyterian–St. Luke's Medical Center/Rush University Medical Center Archives, Chicago, Ill.

7. Thomas J. First, M.D., and James A. Campbell, M.D., "Outlook for Hospitals: The Systems Are the Solution." *Harvard Business Review* 59 (September–October 1981): 130–41.

Department of Health Systems Management in the College of Health Sciences of Rush University by his son Dr. Bruce Campbell, dean of the College of Health Sciences in 1982.[8]

Campbell's concepts of health care for the betterment of all continued to attract many capable and talented administrators to work for him. Marie Sinoris had joined the medical center from college as a medical sociologist. She moved on to work under Gail Warden, and then after Campbell recruited her to be an assistant vice president, she became a major contributor in planning for the entire hospital operation, which was expanding very rapidly at that time. She helped create ArcVentures, a for-profit subsidiary for the corporation as regulations and market forces more directly influenced hospital operations. Marie would write several of Campbell's proposed plans for health care reform in the late seventies and early eighties. The Matrix for Organization and Reorganization that Campbell presented at many medical staff meetings was the creation of Sinoris. Even after the Campbell era had ended and for many years thereafter, the Campbell "club," which included Sinoris, Gale Warden, Wayne Lerner, and many others, would get together to reflect on the extraordinary Campbell years. Campbell's ability to surround himself with people of very different perspectives, to appreciate many diverse opinions, and to pick out the best among these ideas as he formulated programs was, in their view, perhaps Campbell's greatest strength.

Gail Warden was selected by Campbell to be Rush's chief administrative officer not long after he completed graduate school at the University of Michigan. Gail possessed an exceptionally fine eye for detail in his work, and he also became a major creative force in developing the College of Nursing and Allied Sciences of Rush University. Warden later was appointed to a high-level position at the American Hospital Association and also served as chief adminis-

8. "Appointments and Resignations," Folder 4, Box 1, C97-052, James A. Campbell, M.D., Papers 1924–1983, Record Group 002000, Office of the President, Rush–Presbyterian–St. Luke's Medical Center/Rush University Medical Center Archives, Chicago, Ill.

trative officer at the Henry Ford Medical Center in Detroit. But for Warden, in those times of the seventies, there was really nothing like Rush anywhere, then or since. Mark Lepper, Don Oder, and Gail really ran the place for Campbell, who knew everything. Gail still applies many of the things he learned from those days, one of the most important being that when adverse and unexpected events take place, the problems and issues that are involved should be addressed right away and confronted head on. Don't wait. Waiting always makes things worse.

One night a member of the operating room team brought his wife into the hospital to start induction of labor. As there were no beds available for admission, it was decided that it would probably be all right to wait until the next morning to induce. On the following morning after induction was carried out, the baby was born dead. The parents were grief-stricken. Within thirty-six hours, Campbell called the father and asked him and his wife to come to his office at a time when it would be convenient for them with his work schedule in the operating room and the like. Campbell sat down and spent a great deal of time expressing his concern and compassion. There had been no consideration of legal action by the parents. This would not bring the baby back. But the young couple never forgot how genuinely concerned Campbell was.

The father stayed on at Rush and became an important member of the anesthesia operating room team. Throughout the years as he would make his rounds late in the day or at odd hours, he would see Campbell there on the floors checking up on things. Campbell became a source of comfort to many who worked at Rush, a warm and caring person, which was what Rush, in their view, was all about. Amid the harsh reality of regulations, very hard work, tensions, stresses, occasional tragedies, and, yes, even the traditional Rush color, concrete gray, there was Campbell standing firm.

Changes were made in the admissions process to attempt to prevent this adverse event in the future. Perhaps Campbell might not have become so personally involved if the case had not concerned "hospital family." But the fact remains that Campbell acted quickly to do all he could. He didn't assign it to someone else. The man at the top spent a significant amount of his time with the grieving family. Countless stories of kindness and sensitive concern toward people who worked with and for Campbell have been related by many of the Rush family, all of which belie his insensitive tough-guy image. There was an insightful, sentimental, even shy element to Campbell's makeup. This sensitivity could not be completely covered over, not even with his innate acting ability, as he typically tried to project his image as one very tough individual.

All during the 20 years that Campbell was president, medical practices continued to grow, and graduate training programs for all of the medical and surgical specialties also grew accordingly. Top-level physicians were recruited from the outside as well as from Rush's own training programs. The explosions in technology were advanced into all of Rush's programs and for the most part in the traditional settings of private medical care. Many older established practices continued to grow, and newer practices came on board. Anxiety among physicians that the development of a medical school would result in the establishment of a salaried practice arrangement and the elimination of the traditional fee-for-service system was baseless. Using the criteria of number of operations, number of hospital admissions, and the like for hospitals always put Rush at the top or very near the top in both Chicago and the Midwest. Positions for internship, residency, and fellowship training programs were highly sought after well in excess of available appointments offered.

Nevertheless, Campbell's achievements were not universally recognized by a few of the physicians, particularly those who were his contemporaries. Campbell had not developed, perhaps could not ever develop, a sense of collegiality among many of his professional colleagues. He kept his distance from dealing with physicians on a personal basis. Because of the power and influence that he acquired through the authority of his office and his standing with the board, possibly this was necessary. Some expressed the opinion that, had he been a bit more outgoing, he might well have accomplished a good deal more. Some claimed that he had no personal friends. He projected himself to some as having no peers. One long-time colleague who had been recruited by Campbell and was a part of his team that built up the institution mentioned to Campbell one day that he had had an article published in the *New England Journal of Medicine*. Campbell sort of dismissed this and replied that he had an article published in the *Harvard Business Review*. That his interests changed from pure medicine to health systems management over the years as circumstances changed may not be a fair criticism, but his unkind and disparaging ways were another matter.

The three Campbell boys, Jamie, Bruce, and Douglas, all grew up in Lake Forest, before Elda and Jim moved back into the city. Jamie and Douglas attended Jim's alma mater, Knox College. Bruce attended Lake Forest College. Jamie, who described himself as a child of the sixties, then became a reporter for the *Sun-Times* and was on the scene at the time of the 1968 Democratic National Convention. Now a freelance writer, Jamie lives in California with his wife Linda. Bruce entered the field of hospital administration and served at Rush for many years but later moved on to become CEO for several major hospitals in Chicago. Douglas, an accomplished athlete, is in business in Chicago. The first Campbell grandchild, Molly, was born in 1978, an event Jim was very proud of.[9]

In addition to having an apartment on Lake Shore Drive in Chicago, Jim and Elda owned a summer home in Frankfort, Michigan, some three hundred miles north of Chicago. Elda spent her entire summer there, and Jim commuted back and forth on the weekends. In the winters, Elda spent a good deal of time at their home in Jupiter, Florida, while Jim again commuted back and forth as best he could. Since Campbell was ever present at the medical center, he could not have spent much time either in Michigan or Florida. That Campbell was married to his job, there was no doubt. It was his whole life. At work, he was the first to arrive and usually the last to leave.

In 1979, a small group of trustees who had been quite close to Jim over the years decided to honor him by arranging to have his portrait painted. They engaged the services of portrait artist Mr. Albert

---

9. Molly Campbell was subsequently awarded a master's degree in health systems management from Rush University in June 2000.

Murray, of New York, to do this. Murray's most famous portrait was of Admiral Chester Nimitz and General Douglas McArthur together at the signing of the Japanese Surrender on the aircraft carrier *Missouri*.[10] Murray's work, for the most part, dealt with World War II battle scenes and portraits of famous people and was featured in *American Heritage Magazine* in 1982. Campbell had to make several trips to New York to have this work completed. He complained to Don Oder that he didn't like doing this, but he did not protest too vigorously.

A dispute of sorts arose among the trustees about where and when this work should be installed at the medical center.[11] It is not clear whether this gesture on the part of the trustees would be tied into an anticipated retirement or not. For many of the trustees who led major companies, retirement age was mandatory. Mr. A. B. Dick, a close friend of Campbell's, later encouraged Jim to stay on as president after his sixty-fifth birthday. One trustee insisted that the Campbell portrait not be revealed and shown until after he retired, lest it offend his medical colleagues. A chair in his honor, called the James A. Campbell, M.D., Distinguished Service Chair, was subscribed for almost overnight. It was the only part of the massive Rush Campaign for Development that Campbell didn't know about or become involved in.

Campbell was asked to speak on behalf of the medical center to accept an award from the Union League Club on the occasion of the hundredth anniversary of the founding of Presbyterian Hospital.[12] Two physicians symbolic of the great success of the medical center who were presidents of the medical staff of the Campbell era were also

10. "A Painter at War: The World War II Combat Art of Albert K. Murray," *American Heritage* 33 (no. 2, February/March 1982): 30–39.

11. Portrait, 1979–1984, Box 2, Folder 5, C97-052, James A. Campbell, M.D., Papers 1924–1983, Record Group 002000, Office of the President, Rush–Presbyterian–St. Luke's Medical Center/Rush University Medical Center Archives, Chicago, Ill.

12. James Allan Campbell, M.D., Remarks on the Occasion of the Distinguished Service Award to Rush–Presbyterian–St. Luke's Medical Center on the occasion of Presbyterian Hospital's Centennial, April 13, 1983; Rush University Archives, folder 1, Box 12, C97-052, James A. Campbell, M.D., Papers 1924–1983, Record Group 002000, Office of the President, Rush–Presbyterian–St. Luke's Medical Center/Rush University Medical Center Archives, Chicago, Ill.

in attendance. Dr. Robert Jensik, the premier chest surgeon, had come from St. Luke's at the time of the merger and was a very positive unifying force in its success. Shortly after the merger had been completed, Board Chairman John Bent congratulated Jensik for his efforts on behalf of the trustees. Jensik and his associates had conducted a study of patients with lung cancer at the medical center that was the largest of its kind ever conducted in the country up to that time.

Medical staff past president Dr. Joseph Muenster was the first fellow recruited to train in cardiology under Campbell in the 1950s at Presbyterian Hospital. Called Uncle Joe, the talented Muenster was quite bright but with a very low-key temperament and a dry sense of humor. Although he was right in the middle of many scientific breakthroughs and a wizard in performing cardiac catheterizations, he downplayed his role in these activities, sort of passing off what he did as of no importance. He was the doctor for many of the families of the interns and residents. He was director of the section of adolescent medicine during the turmoil of the sixties and seventies. After one exasperating experience, he made the observation that all early adolescents should be placed in a jar and put on a shelf until the age of 18. Dr. Muenster was also Jim Campbell's personal physician.

Many of Chicago's civic leaders were in attendance at the Union League for Campbell's presentation, which was particularly effective. His forceful speech urged his audience to fight for the betterment of the city and its health care. He discussed the need for improved access to medical education and nursing education for blacks and Hispanics, the need for eligibility requirements for public insurance to be increased to permit broader coverage of the "near poor" and medically indigent, and the need for a reduction of excess hospital capacity in Chicago. His vision for the future was evident, as these problems have remained unsolved decades later.

When Campbell "invited" his audience to consider some of the points he was making, his presentations were exceptionally effective. He urged those civic leaders in attendance to consider the health of the community as one of the high priorities in planning for the future. He pointed out not only the problems but the opportunities that lay ahead in health care. Leadership such as that present in the room could meet the health challenge, he would say. He again invited the leaders and urged them to "fight for our city." He then wound up his presentation by restating one of his favorite aphorisms from John Buchan, "We can only pay our debt to the past, by putting the future in debt to ourselves."[13] Many present that evening felt Campbell's presentation was the finest he had ever made.

Just a few days after the Atrium Building opened in 1982, the medical center met to honor Dr. Mark Lepper on the occasion of his retirement.[14] A great leader would no longer be at Rush. So, too, although it wasn't evident at the time, Campbell's career would be ending within a year. And this event would mark the end of an era. Yet right at that point, there was no sign of any such thing happening. A few associates noted that Jim was becoming a morning person, and he would sneak off for a cat nap in the afternoon, something he hadn't done before. But otherwise, it seemed that all systems were go for Campbell.

Over the years, Campbell continued to keep in close touch with Knox College. Knox had been set up as one of the feeder schools when Rush was reopened in 1969. Knox students would spend their first year of medical school on the Galesburg campus during which time local Galesburg family practitioners participated in teaching by introducing students to clinical medicine.

Due to Campbell's influence with the Knox Board of Trustees, at least one of their quarterly board meetings was held in Chicago at Rush in Room 500 of the Professional Building. Knox President Inman Fox was counseled by Campbell in regard to many of the problems that arose there on the campus in Galesburg. On the one hand, he was the big boss, tough as nails, and connected

13. Index card quotations, James A. Campbell, M.D., Box 35, File 4, C97-052, James A. Campbell, M.D., Papers 1924–1983, Record Group 002000, Office of the President, Rush–Presbyterian–St. Luke's Medical Center/Rush University Medical Center Archives, Chicago, Ill.

14. A Celebration in Honor of Mark H. Lepper, M.D., Monday, June 14, 1982, Room 500, Rush–Presbyterian–St. Luke's Medical Center, Chicago, Illinois; File 9, Box 11, C97-052, James A. Campbell, M.D., Papers 1924–1983, Record Group 002000, Office of the President, Rush–Presbyterian–St. Luke's Medical Center/Rush University Medical Center Archives, Chicago, Ill.

with everyone important in business, Fox recalls, but on the other hand at the same time, he really cared. Campbell also became very close friends with Jarvis Cecil, a prominent Knox alumnus who also had gone to Harvard. It was rare for Campbell not to visit Galesburg at least three or four times each year. Campbell was one of Knox's proudest sons.

In 1981, Fox decided to accept an offer to move on to Northwestern University and a search committee was formed to find a successor. Campbell was appointed to the committee. Among other members of the committee was Mrs. Linda Kohler, also a Knox graduate. Linda's husband, Herbert Kohler, had attended Knox as well. At some point Campbell and Mrs. Kohler started seeing each other. It became evident to members of the Knox board that a serious relationship was developing between the two.

For Campbell, who had been married for over forty years and was facing a decision regarding retirement, everything started to become unraveled. He had tried to talk to his friend Bob Glaser a number of times about all of this but couldn't quite find the right setting or circumstances to do so. Glaser had sensed that something was changing. For those who knew Jim and Elda Campbell on a social basis, nothing appeared out of order. Elda and Jim had been very good parents. At the time of Elda's cancer surgery, Jim was most supportive. When Jim would play golf up in Michigan, Elda would become quite concerned about his climbing hills and the effect it might have on his heart. But in later years, they seem to have, for one reason or another, drifted apart.

Jim and Linda continued to see each other, and Jim realized that, if he decided to seek a divorce, his position at the medical center might be compromised. Divorce in certain circles simply was not acceptable. It was viewed as being disloyal. This might be even more so in Jim's case since he was the son of a Presbyterian minister and had projected a strong moral stance in his position as leader of the medical center. Jim didn't smoke or drink, and he often conveyed a strong sense of moral righteousness in dealing with his colleagues and associates. This pattern of behavior was, in fact, a major strength for Jim as he led the institution to its many great accomplishments.

His father's book, *Sermons of a Country Preacher,* represented Jim in the eyes of many.

Nothing was known of this relationship in the fall of 1982, when Campbell reached his sixty-fifth birthday. But another factor developed in the story that changed everything. Campbell's health began to deteriorate. He had been under the care of cardiologist and friend Dr. Joseph Muenster. Although his health in general had been satisfactory, he had been on medication for high blood pressure for several years and had sustained a blood clot in his leg while in Florida several years before but recovered uneventfully from that. He underwent annual checkups at the Cleveland Clinic in hopes of keeping knowledge of his health confidential, not an easy thing to do when you are president of a medical center.

Campbell began experiencing increasing fatigue, and early in 1983, in order to determine his heart status, a new state-of-the-art blood-pooled isotope study of his cardiac function was carried out in the Department of Nuclear Medicine at Rush. This study showed that his cardiac function was severely impaired. He had sustained at least one silent heart attack in the past. His heart disease was characterized by severe cardiomyopathy, and there was really no effective treatment for it. Medication would help very little. Transplantation in a later time might have been beneficial. Campbell was, of course, fully aware of what all this meant, and he related the knowledge of his dismal outlook to his old friend and former student, Dr. Janet Wolter, in August of 1983.

Jim asked Elda for a divorce in the spring of 1983, soon after Jim's heart condition was diagnosed. Elda apparently had been unaware of Jim's relationship with Linda and was most devastated. News of Jim and Linda's relationship then became public knowledge, and many were shocked when they learned of it. Campbell's actions were severely criticized by many. Campbell then announced his retirement as president in June to be effective in September, and the pomp and ceremony that this occasion would have otherwise warranted was very subdued indeed.

Speculations were advanced as to the reasons for the breakup of the marriage, such as long absences resulting from having homes

in Michigan and Florida and other plausible contributing factors, but
no one really knew just why it happened.

Jim continued as president through the summer, trying to
keep up the pace he had always maintained. Over the years, the busy
passageway from the Academic Facility Building to the Professional
Building on the fourth floor often could be negotiated by Campbell
several times a day walking at high speeds, whether going uphill or
downhill on the ramp. Now Campbell would have to walk very
slowly and stop halfway to catch his breath. At Jim's urging, Dr.
Bruce Campbell, Jim's son and administrator at Rush, had moved to
the University of Chicago. Jim visited Bruce there in September, and
Bruce recalls that his father that day could barely walk. Dr. Joe
Muenster made a number of visits to his office, trying new medicines
without success. Serious cardiac arrhythmias developed. Jim related
to one associate the observation that his blood pressure, which had
been chronically elevated over many years, was now low because his
dilated heart could not maintain its previous elevations. Campbell
was now a very sick man.

In October, Jim and Linda started out on a car trip to the West
Coast in hopes of starting a new life. Linda understood the serious-
ness of his health situation, and Jim had indicated to her that he was
not interested in heroic and extreme measures to prolong his life if
circumstances arose that might call for such actions. Campbell had
hoped to stay in medicine in one way or another and was working
on several leads. But with each passing week, he became weaker and
slept a great deal. He didn't like to take his heart medicine, which he
thought was slowing him down further. Jim promised to see a doctor in San Francisco as soon as they arrived, but Jim and Linda never
made it to California. They stopped to rest for a few days in Las
Vegas. And on Saturday night, November 19, 1983, Jim passed away.

On December 7, 1983, a memorial service was conducted out
of respect for Campbell at the Fourth Presbyterian Church in
Chicago. Among the overflowing crowd of those who attended were
Elda Campbell and her children, who entered by a side door and left
the same way. Those in attendance at the church were grateful for
her presence. Jim's Harvard classmates Drs. Bob Glaser and Herb

Scheinberg were among those present. Eulogies were delivered by Glaser, Don Oder, Board Chairman Harold Byron Smith, and President of the Medical Staff Dr. Andrew Thomson. Mark Lepper, Jim's old friend and colleague, expressed in summary what the other speakers communicated.

> Without reservation, I feel that under no other leadership would the resources available at the time Jim entered the presidency have produced anything remotely approximating the current medical center. . . . . Jim Campbell was a product of much of what has been right in our society in this century. From his family he brought a great humanism and love of knowledge both of the sciences and the humanities. In a real sense he lived at and acted upon the interface between the two great pools of human achievement. His high intelligence, nurtured in several of our best colleges and universities, gave him the skills that allowed him to study and master the intricacies of the management mission and policies of multiple institutions as he gained experience with each. At the time of his selection as president he accepted dreams not exclusively his. Although many were believed to be impossible by others, he did not concur. Rather his question was, "How are you going to make your dreams come true?" In a sense his answer was to bring together strengths in each dream and weave them into a comprehensive mission. But the greatest asset was his confidence in the abilities of the personnel and his ability to lead them as his friends and co-workers. He was a pragmatist as well as a dreamer. The history of his presidency almost exactly coincides with the idea expressed by Golda Mier, "Nothing in life just happens. It isn't enough to believe in something. You have to have the stamina to meet obstacles and overcome them, to struggle." Jim brought to his struggle his understanding of science and research, teaching and learning, care and its provisions, economics and management. His goals revolved around the primacy of the

patients whose needs included both comprehensive as well
as technically excellent care. Moreover the care should be
the same for all patients, and all socioeconomic and racial
groups should be represented in a "fair share" manner, that
is, representative of the entire Chicago metropolitan population. Teaching and learning should also be based upon
excellence with emphasis on the responsibilities to provide
humane and empathetic care in the context of scientific
excellence and high integrity.[15]

The proceedings of the memorial service were made a permanent
record of the Proceeding of the Board of Trustees out of respect and
appreciation for Dr. Campbell's enormous contribution to the community and, indeed, to the nation. On June 9, 1984, a Doctor of Humane Letters was posthumously awarded to Campbell at the Rush
graduation.

Many people up to the present time still are stunned by the
unexpected turn of events in the last year of Jim Campbell's life.
There had never been anyone else quite like Campbell. Yes, he was
flawed, but he still remained and remains today a figure larger than
life. Many people devote their entire lives to a cause and to their
work as Campbell did, but Campbell's strength of leadership was so
great that he motivated many others to be as committed and dedicated as he was. Campbell touched the lives of countless numbers of
people in the medical center in a very real way. Many people can and
still do devote their lives to the welfare of "the patient" as Campbell
would say. And many, many of these individuals attribute much of
the intensity of their professional ideals to the example set by Dr.
James Allan Campbell.

Campbell's decisions in the last months of his life understandably were criticized by many. And, as human nature would have it,

15. A Service of Remembrance, James A. Campbell, M.D., Fourth Presbyterian
Church, Chicago, Illinois, Wednesday, December 7, 1983, Rush–Presbyterian–St. Luke's
Medical Center.

those at the top often fall the hardest. But the passage of years has not diminished in any way his great record of achievement.

As the Rush success story became more widely known, the sensitive history of Rush and the University of Chicago needed to be confronted. The university had almost destroyed Rush in the process of developing its own medical school. Rush, however, was able to make a fresh start. Now it was Rush University for the Health Sciences. It was now a new kind of institution, an academic health center. And once it began, it developed to completion almost overnight. Those Rush people who had remained at the University of Chicago seemed genuinely gratified that Rush was back. They had lived the excitement of being the first and only completely full-time medical school in the United States. But they, too, recognized that nobody has all the answers.

In 1980, Dr. Walter Lincoln Palmer, the world-renowned gastroenterologist and a Rush graduate, spoke on the occasion of Rush's sixth commencement. Palmer's father had been a Rush graduate, and his son later would join the Rush faculty. Palmer, who had interned at Cook County Hospital, had decided to stay with the university at the time of the breakup of Rush Medical College and the University of Chicago. He related the following:

> In 1953, a brief few years ago but nevertheless in the fullness of time, a young man, a native of Illinois, a graduate of Knox College and of Harvard Medical School, returned to Rush as chairman of its Department of Medicine – a most felicitous choice, for he soon became dean, president of the Board of Trustees and the acknowledged leader. New incentives, new ideas, and a new spirit came to the school; money appeared miraculously – soon there was a college of nursing, a college of health sciences, with a basic science department and a graduate school with candidates for master's degrees and doctorates in philosophy. Relationships were established with superior colleges such as Knox in Galesburg and Grinnell in Iowa. This development would

have delighted William Rainey Harper for he had similar plans. New buildings were everywhere with plans for more. Rush College became Rush University. Rush has risen from the ashes as it were, shaken off the lethargy and is taking its proper place among the great educational institutions of our nation. As to the man himself, James Allan Campbell, his name will join those of Daniel Brainard, Frank Billings, William Rainey Harper, Robert M. Hutchins, and many other great educators and builders – men who in the fullness of time have built their own hall of fame. And so I salute the New Rush and the men who will keep its luster bright. They will carry it forward into the twenty-first century ever in the lengthening shadow of James Allan Campbell.[16]

In 1837, when Chicago's population was 3000 or so, Daniel Brainard established Rush Medical College to advance the highest ideals of professionalism and service to the community, which had been exemplified by the life of Benjamin Rush. The college grew in renown and flourished for over a century, only to be struck down, and almost destroyed through circumstances that were not of its own doing. But a renaissance man, James Campbell, as the second Daniel Brainard, reestablished Rush, and placed it once more in the forefront as one of Chicago's great institutions.

On June 11, 1904, President Theodore Roosevelt spoke at the dedication of the statue of Dr. Benjamin Rush in Washington. This beautiful bronze work of art, about eight feet tall, of a man standing on a marble pedestal gazes out from the top of a hill with a view of the Potomac River. It is near the Kennedy Center located on the grounds of the Bureau of Medicine and Surgery at 2300 E Street NW, in our nation's capital. The statue depicts Dr. Rush holding in his right hand a quill pen and in his left, a sheet of paper. It is con-

16. Walter Lincoln Palmer, M.D., Remarks, Commencement Banquet, the Alumni Association of Rush Medical College, *A Record*, pp. 13–15.

sidered one of the city of Washington's finest statues and a significant medical historical site.[17]

The bureau's curator, Jan K. Hermann, proudly boasts that the statue of the "Greatest Physician" belongs to the American people. The American Medical Association wished to honor Dr. Rush as other great statesmen, military heroes, naval heroes, painters, sculptors, and scientists had been. Over a period of several years the AMA gathered the funds necessary to complete this work.[18]

On the pedestal are inscriptions on each of the four sides above the base. On the front panel is inscribed "Benjamin Rush, Physician and Philanthropist, 1745–1813." On the left panel is inscribed "Signer of the Declaration of Independence." On the right panel is written *Studium Sine Calamo Somnium,* which can be translated "Study without Discipline is a Dream." And finally on the rear panel is inscribed "The first American Alienist [psychiatrist]." On the base in the front cut into the stone are the words, "Erected by the American Medical Association, 1904."

On behalf of a grateful nation, Roosevelt thanked the American Medical Association for a statue of a man who was foremost as a leader and pioneer in his profession, a great physician, and a great American. Roosevelt then went on to praise Rush for his work for the welfare of the general public and the state, duties that carried him beyond his own interests and concerns.[19]

Rush's posture in the statue appears to be forward looking. And, certainly, the accomplishments of the medical profession in the twentieth century would make Rush's gaze prophetic. Those of Rush

17. The statue was designed by Roland Hinton Perry, a sculptor of some note. Architect Louis R. Metcalf designed the pedestal and the statue was cast in the foundry of the Henry-Bonnard Bronze Company of New York. Courtesy, the American Medical Association Archives, Roberta Ann Ghidara, M.A., 30 January 2001.

18. Jan K. Hermann, *A Hilltop at Foggy Bottom* (Washington, D.C.: Bureau of Medicine and Surgery, Department of the Navy, 1996). No federal money was ever appropriated for the statue.

19. Remarks of President Theodore Roosevelt at the unveiling of the Statue of Benjamin Rush, Washington, D.C., June 11, 1904, Manuscript Division, Library of Congress. Washington, D.C.

Medical College and later Rush University would make very significant contributions to all of these advances. The achievements and
the benefits to society of the Campbell Plan, created some sixty-four
years later, might in and of itself have qualified Campbell well for
special recognition and commendation. He, too, went beyond his
own concerns for the benefit of the many. A master plan for health
education for the State of Illinois was formulated. A significant need,
a shortage of physicians and all other medical personnel for the State
of Illinois, one of the largest in the nation, was effectively addressed
and remedied. Campbell had also led the way in insisting on a single
standard of patient care for all people, a dream as yet to be fulfilled
for many in our country. The manner in which he communicated his
plea for this universal aspiration of the American people continues to
be inspirational. Keeping his approach to a high level, avoiding the
potentially politically divisive adversarial language of social justice
and citizen entitlements, and the professionally demeaning market
connotation of consumer protection and "getting your money's
worth," his concept is still something that everyone can identify with
and consider supporting.

The quill and paper in Rush's hand, symbolic of scholarship
and professional advancement, could be equally applied to Campbell.
Campbell had reestablished the great tradition of Rush Medical
College and then later Rush University. This heritage would then be
preserved for countless later generations of Americans, American
doctors, and health care professionals, as Campbell sought to upgrade
the professional status of all those committed to the care of the sick.

The twentieth century is often called the American Century.
And American medicine's contributions are enormous. Members of
Rush Medical College and later Rush University have been a signif-
icant part of all this as well. There have been so many: Herrick, Senn,
Hektoen, Bevan, Graham, Dick, Irons, Hass, Julian, Lepper, Galante,
and many others. But none stands taller or greater than James Allan
Campbell, M.D., truly a Rush Man for the Twentieth Century.

Harold Byron Smith, the Medical Center's chairman of the
Board of Trustees during many of the Campbell's years, reflected on
the meaning of Jim Campbell's life. Rush–Presbyterian–St. Luke's

Medical Center was his monument. He fashioned it as an instrument to deliver care, to offer education, to stimulate research, to express the comprehensiveness of his own mind, as the seed of a system.

He chose as one of his heroes, Dr. James B. Herrick, who believed that while a hospital must instruct the young and show the spirit of research, the central figure in the hospital is and should be the patient. That was the ideal he served. The establishment of the Mile Square Health Center and the elimination of hard-bench clinics expressed the guiding belief as much as did the acquisition of the most advanced diagnostic laboratory and the completion of a modern campus.

Teaching came with care. His grand rounds as chairman of medicine quickly became legend. The aisles and window ledges were crowded. In his view, to be a doctor was to be a teacher. Often he quoted from the Talmud, taking certain delight in doing so as the son of a Presbyterian minister: "From my teachers, I have learned a great deal, from my colleagues more, but from my students, the most."

Then followed the recommendations that continue to guide medical education in Illinois, the re-fusion of new life into Rush Medical College, and then into Rush University, with its four colleges. To him, research was not a tangential activity, but it is wedded to the patient priority. The motivation for research must be grounded in the mysteries of illness; its purpose and justification are to be found in healing.

Finally came the new and important concept of modern management. And Campbell was brilliant in this regard. His balance sheet was more than an expression of management. It reflected a quality of mind, the breadth of his character, and the largeness of his vision. It was an overview built upon day-to-day vigilance and vigor. Jim Campbell never became lost in the trees, for he saw the forest. He was a man of concepts. He gave us an understanding of the forces within and bearing upon the institution. He illuminated the way. He kept us on solid ground, and built solidly upon it.

Because of his leadership, patient care, teaching, research, and management would come together to express in a very significant way the highest aspirations of the medical center's celebrated motto, "To the Glory of God, and the Service of Man."

Curriculum Vitae

JAMES ALLAN CAMPBELL
November 29, 1917–November 19, 1983

Education

Rochelle Township High School, Rochelle, Illinois		1935
Knox College, Galesburg, Illinois	A.B.	1935–39
University of Chicago, Chicago, Illinois		1939–41
Harvard Medical School, Boston, Massachusetts	M.D.	1943
Knox College, Galesburg, Illinois	Sc.D. (Hon.)	1965
Lake Forest College, Lake Forest, Illinois	L.H.D. (Hon.)	1969

Hospital Appointments

Assistant Resident in Pathology, Billings Hospital, Chicago, Illinois	1941–42
Intern, Harvard Service, Boston City Hospital, Boston, Massachusetts	1943–44
Assistant Resident, Boston City Hospital, Boston, Massachusetts	1944–45
Resident, Boston City Hospital, Boston, Massachusetts	1945–46
Assistant Attending Physician, Presbyterian Hospital, Chicago, Illinois	1948–51
Associate Attending Physician, Presbyterian Hospital, Chicago, Illinois	1951
Attending Physician, Albany Hospital, Albany, New York	1952–53

Consulting Physician (Honorary), Child's Hospital, Albany, New York   1952–53
Consulting Physician, Veterans Administration Hospital,
    Albany, New York   1952–53
Consulting Physician, Veterans Administration Hospital, Hines, Illinois   1954–73
Attending Physician and Chairman, Department of Medicine,
    Presbyterian Hospital, Chicago, Illinois   1953–57
Attending Physician and Chairman, Department of Medicine,
    Presbyterian–St. Luke's Hospital, Chicago, Illinois   1957–64
Attending Physician and President, Presbyterian–St. Luke's Hospital,
    Chicago, Illinois   1964–69
Attending Physician and President, Rush–Presbyterian–St. Luke's
    Medical Center, Chicago, Illinois   1969–83
President, Rush University   1972–83
President Emeritus, Rush–Presbyterian–St. Luke's Medical
    Center, Chicago, Illinois   1983

Teaching Appointments and Fellowships
Assistant in Pathology, University of Chicago School of Medicine   1941–42
Teaching Fellow in Medicine, Harvard Medical School   1944–45
Assistant in Medicine, Harvard Medical School
    & Thorndike Memorial Laboratory   1945–46
Harvey Cushing Fellow Johns Hopkins Medical School &
    Johns Hopkins Hospital   1947–48
Assistant Professor of Medicine, University of Illinois
    College of Medicine   1948–51
Dean and Professor of Medicine, Union University,
    Albany Medical College   1951–53
Professor of Medicine, University of Illinois College of Medicine   1953–71
Professor of Medicine, Rush Medical College, Rush University   1971–83
Balfour Visiting Professor of Medicine, Mayo Foundation   1975
Professor, Department of Health Systems Management,
    College of Health Sciences   1982–83

Military Service
U.S. Army Medical Corps, Clinical Research Section & Executive
    Officer, Medical Division, Army Chemical Center,
    Edgewood Arsenal, Maryland   1946–47

Certification by Specialty Board
American Board of Internal Medicine (cert. #7365)   1950

Medican Licensure

National Board of Medical Examiners (cert. #13622)	1945
Massachusetts (cert. #20456)	1945
Illinois (cert. #02933)	1948
New York (cert. #71868)	1951
Virginia (cert. #35809)	1983

Membership in Scientific Societies

Alpha Omega Alpha Honor Medical Society
Central Society for Clinical Research
Central Clinical Research Club
New York Academy of Sciences
Fellow, American College of Physicians
American Heart Association
American Medical Association
Chicago Society of Internal Medicine
Chicago Heart Association
Lake County Medical Society
Illinois Medical Society
Sigma Xi
American Clinical and Climatological Association
Institute of Medicine–National Academy of Sciences

Appointments and Committees

Board of Trustees, Knox College, Galesburg, Illinois Alumni Trustee	1951–68
Trustee	1968–83
Internship Review Committee of the American Medical Association	1958–74
Board of Directors, National Resident Matching Program, Inc.	1959–83
Vice Chairman, 1959–68	
President, 1971–74	
Treasurer, 1974–76	
Vice President, 1968–70, 1976–80, and 1982	
Chairman, Association of American Medical Colleges	
Institute on Clinical Teaching	1959
Corporation Visiting Committee for the Joseph P. Kennedy, Jr.,	
Laboratories for Mental Retardation	1959–72
Board of Directors, Alpha Omega Alpha Honor Medical Society	1960
National Secretary-Treasurer	1960–78
National President	1978–80
Part III Committee, National Board of Medical Examiners	1960–65
Advisory Committee on Internships for the American Medical Association	1961–65

Task Force on Internships of the Council on Medical Education
    & Hospitals of the American Medical Association   1963–65
Curriculum Committee on Cardiovascular Disease, Council on
    Medical Education and Hospitals of the American
    Medical Association   1963–65
Chairman, Committee on Medical Education and Hospitals,
    Illinois State Medical Society   1963–64
Member, Board of Directors, Chicago Health Research Foundation   1963–79
Advisory Committee, Mount Sinai School of Medicine, New York   1963
Advisory Committee, Milton S. Hershey Medical Center
    of Pennsylvania State University   1963
Council on Mental Health of the American Medical Association   1963–71
Planning Director for Education in the Health Fields, State of Illinois
    Board of Higher Education   1965–68
Trustee, Board of Trustees, Presbyterian–St. Luke's Hospital,
    Chicago, Illinois   1965–69
Trustee and Member of the Executive Board, Rush–Presbyterian–
    St. Luke's Medical Center   1969–83
Member, Coordinating Committee of Medical Schools and Teaching
    Hospitals of Illinois, Illinois Regional Medical Programs   1965–68
Editorial Advisory Board, Hospital Practice Magazine   1967
Member, Alumni Council, Harvard Medical School   1968
Community Advisory Committee to the Junior League of Chicago, Inc.   1963
Member, Board of Directors, Illinois Regional Medical Programs   1968
Editorial Board, Medical Counterpoint Magazine   1969
Citizens Advisory Committee, Chicago City Colleges   1969
Member, Commercial Club of Chicago   1969
Environmental Advisory Council, Commonwealth Edison Company,
    Chicago   1970–72
Director, Board of Directors, the John Crerar Library   1973–79
Trustee, Board of Trustees, the Otho S. A. Sprague Memoral Institute   1973–83
Member, Comprehensive Health Policy Plan Committee,
    Comprehensive Health Planning, Inc., Metropolitan Chicago   1973–75
Member, Economic Club of Chicago   1975
Member, Chicago Commission for Health Planning and Resources
    Development   1976–80
Member, Advisory Council on Health Manpower   1975
Member, Advisory Council of Illinois 2000   1977–79
Director, Board of Directors, Morton Thiokol, Inc.   1977
Member, the Sloan Commission on Government and
    Higher Education   1978–80
Member, Chicago Bar Association Liaison Committee   1978–82

American Board of Internal Medicine, Ad Hoc Committee on
    Standards of Excellence   1978–79
National Board of Medical Examiners, Task Force on Policy
    Concerning Ethical Issues   1979
Hospital Research and Education Trust   1979
Joint Executive Operating Council for the Lane Medical Research
    Organization   1980
National Planning Association, Committee on New American Realities   1981–83
University Village Association, Advisory Committee   1981–83

BIBLIOGRAPHY

Scientific and Cardiovascular Studies

1. Hopps, H.C. and Campbell, J.A. Immunologic and Toxic Properties of Casein Digest as Prepared for Parenteral Administration. J. Lab & Clin. Med., 28:1203, 1943.

2. Campbell, J.A. and Tagnon, H. The Intravenous Glucose Tolerance Test in Liver Disease. New Eng. J. Med., 234:216, 1946

3. Handelman, J.C., Bing, R.J., Campbell, J.A., and Griswold, H.E. Physiologic Studies in Congenital Heart Disease: V. The Circulation in Patients with Isolated Septal Defects. Bull. Johns Hopkins Hosp., 82:615, 1948

4. Bing, R.J., Wandam, L.D., Handelman, J.C., Campbell, J.A., Spencer, R., and Griswold, H.E. Physiological Studies in Congenital Heart Disease: VI. Adaptations to Anoxia in Congenital Heart Disease with Cyanosis. Bull. Johns Hopkins Hosp., 83:439, 1948

5. Bing, R.J., Handelsman, J.C., Campbell, J.A., Griswold, H.E., and Bialock, A. The Surgical Treatment and Physiopathology of Coarctation of the Aorta. Ann. of Surg., 128:803, 1948

6. Bing, R.J., Handelsman, J.D., and Campbell, J.A. Physiologic Diagnostic Tests in Congenital Heart Disease. Mod. Concepts Cardiovasc.Dis. 17:3, 1948

7. Bing, R.J., Goodale, W.T., Eckenhoff, J., and Campbell, J.A. et al. Catheterization of the Coronary Veins and the Measurement of Coronary Blood Flow in Man. J.Clin. Invest., 27:525, 1948.

8. Griswold, H.E., Bing, R.G., Handelsman, J.C., Campbell, J.A., and LeBrun, E. Physiological Studies in Congenital Heart Disease: VII. Pulmonary Arterial Hypertension in Congenital Heart Disease. Bull. Johns Hopkins Hospital., 84:76, 1949.

9. Campbell, J.A., Bing, R.J., Handelsman, J.C., Griswold, H.E., and Hammond, M. Physiological Studies in Congenital Heart Disease: VIII. The Physiological Findings in Two Patients with Complete Transposition of the Great Vessels. Bull. Johns Hopkins Hosp., 84:269, 1949.

10. Campbell, J.A. and Selverstone, L.A. the Effect of Exercise on Circulatory Dynamics as a Criterion for Cardiac Competence. J. Lab. & Clin. Med. 36:807, 1950.

11. Fisher, D.L., Campbell, J.A., Baker, L., and Vawter, G. Hemodynamic Studies in a Case of Primary Amyloidosis. J. Lab. & Clin. Med., 36:821, 1950

12. Griwwom, R.L., Campbell, J.A., Sleverstone, L.A., Fisher, D.L., and Donova, D.L. Clinical Physiologic Studies of Patients with Pulmonic Stenosis and Auricular Septal Defect. J. Lab. & Clin. Med., 36:831, 1950.

13. Selverstone, L.A., Paul, O., Donovan, D.L., and Vawter, G. The Effect of Ouabain Upon the Circulatory Dynamics of a Patient with Nonspecific Myocarditis. J. Lab. & Clin. Med., 36:988, 1950.

14. Selverstone, L.A., Fisher, D.L., Donovan, D.L., and Campbell, J.A. Recognition of Asymptomatic Arrhythmias During Cardiac Catheterization by Means of a Cathode Ray Oscilloscope; with Report of Four Cases. J. Lab. & Clin. Med., 36:989, 1950.

15. Paul, O., Meyers, G., and Campbell, J.A. Electrocardiograms in Congenital Heart Disease. Circ., 3:564, 1951.

16. Grisson, R.L., Campbell, J.A., Selverstone, L.A., Fisher, D.L., and Donovan, D.L. The Diagnosis of Congenital Stenosis of the Pulmonic Valve with Associated Auricular Septal Defect. In Studies in Medicine, Keeton Anniversary Volume, Charles C. Thomas, Springfield, Illinois, p.151, 1951.

17. Campbell, J.A., Selverstone, L.A., and Donovan, D.L. Studies in the High Output Cardiac Failure of Occidental Beriberi. J. Clin. Invest., 30:632, 1951.

18. Fell, E.H., Paul, O., Campbell, J.A., Davis, C.B., Selverstone, L.A., and Grissom, R.L. Mitral Stenosis: Physiological Studies, Diagnosis and Treatment. Arch. Of Surg., 65:128, 1952.

19. Campbell, J.A., and Graettinger, J.S. Application of Cardiac Function Tests. The Med. Clinics of N. Amer., 39:31, 1955.

20. Campbell, JA., Graettinger, J.S., Muenster, J.J., and Checchia, C.S. High Output Cardiac Failure: Preoperative and Postoperative Studies of Patients with Peripheral Arteriovenous Fistulas. J. Lab. And Clin. Med., 46:801, 1955.

21. Graettinger, J.S., Muenster, J.J., Checchia,C.S., and Campbell, J.A. Correlation of Clinical and Hemodynamic Studies in Patients with Thyroid Disease. Clin. Res. Proc., 4:120, 1956.

22. Campbell, J.A., Graettinger, J.S., Muenster, J.J., and Checchia, C.S. Hemodynamics of Congestive Failure Associated with Peripheral Arteriovenous Fistulae. J. Clin. Invest., 35:695, 1956.

23. Campbell, J.A., Graettinger, J.S., Muenster, J.J., Checchia, C.S., and Grissom, R.L. A Correlation of Clinical and Hemodynamic Studies in Patients with Hypothyroidism. J. Clin. Invest., 37:502, 1958.

24. Campbell, J.A., Graettinger, J.S., Muenster, J.J., Cheechia, C.S., and Grissom, R.L. A Correlation of Clinical and Hemodynamic Studies in Patients with Hypothyroidism. In Year Book of Endocrinology, Year Book Publishers, Inc., Chicago, Illinois, p.45, 1958–1959.

25. Graettinger, J.S., and Campbell, J.A.   The Hemodynamic Common Denominators of the Syndrome of Chronic Congestive Heart Failure. J. Lab. &Clin. Med., 54:819, 1959.

26. Graettinger, J.S., Muenster, J.J., Selverstone, L.S., and Campbell, J.A.   A Correlation of Clinical Hemodynamic Studies in Patients with Hyper thyroidsim with and without Congestive Heart Failure. J. Clin. Invest., 38:1316, 1959.

27. Campbell, J.A., Muenster, J.J., and Graettinger, J.S.   Correlation of Clinical and Hemodynamic Findings in Patients with Systemic Arteriovenous Fistulas.   Circ., 20:1079, 1959.

28. Campbell, J.A. et al. Joint Institute on Biochemistry and Internal Medicine. Fed. Bull., 47:86, 1960.

29. Campbell, J.A. et al. Clinicopathologic Conference: Heart Failure, Pulsatile Liver and Ascites. Postgraduate Medicine, 30:604, 1961.

30. Graettinger, J.S., Parsons, R.L., and Campbell, J.A. A Correlation of Clinical and Hemodynamic Studies in Patients with Mild and Severe Anemia with and without Congestive Failure. Ann. of Int. Med., 58:617, 1963.

Military Papers

1. Campbell, J.A. First Aid and Field Treatment of Chemical Casualties. Medical Division Reports (Chemical Corps), 1947.

2. Campbell, J.A. et al.   Methods of Prevention of "Nerve" Gas Casualties. Medical Division Reports (Chemical Corps), 1947.

3. Campbell, J.A. et al. Physiological Effects of "Nerve" Gases: First Aid and Treatment. (War Department Circular), 1948.

Medical Education Papers

1. Campbell, J.A. The Library's Impact on Medical Education. Bull. Med. Library Assn., 41:7, 1953.

2. Campbell, J.A.   The Rose of Research in Graduate Medical Educations. JAMA, 170:439, 1959.

3. Campbell, J.A. Five Smooth Stones. The Pharos, 24:135, 1960.

4. Campbell, J.A. A Critical Look at the Unfilled Internship, Fifth Annual Conf. On Graduate Medical Education, Beverly Hospital, (Oct.) 1962.

5. Campbell, J.A., The Internship and Graduate Training. Invitational Conf., National Board of Medical Examiners, Philadelphia, Pa., (March) p. 30, 1964.

6. Campbell, J.A. The Internship: Origins, Evolution, and Confusion, JAMA 189:273, 1964.

7. Campbell, J.A. The Organization of Medical Education. In Medical Education and Practice: Relationships and Responsibilities in a Changing Society. Association of Amer. Medical Colleges, Chapter 4, 1965.

8. Campbell, J.A.   Teaching of Postgraduate Clinical Medicine.   J. Medical Education, Part 2, 40:116, 1965.

9. Campbell, J.A.   Medical Education–Adaptation to Change.   Albany Medical College Alumni Bull. 29:7, 1966.

10. Campbell, J.A., The Future of the Internship.   In, The Medical Staff in the Modern Hospital, Ed. C. Wesley Eisele, McGraw-Hill, Inc., p. 423, 1967.

11. Campbell, J.A., Tucker, W. R., and Turner, I.R.   Report on Education in the Health Fields.   Volume I and II.   State of Illinois Board of Higher Education, Springfield, Illinois, June, 1968.

12. Campbell, J.A.   The Role of a Medical School in Rational Health Care Systems.   In, Getting It All Together II: Summary Proceedings of an Institute on Local Health Care Systems; December, 1971, Chicago, Illinois, Ed. Roger Meyer, M.D.

Health Care Delivery Papers
1. Campbell, J.A., and Sinioris, M.D.   Shoulder to Shoulder.   A Role of a University Teaching Hospital in a Multihospital System: A Case Study of the Rush System for Health.   Proceedings from Multihospital Systems/University Teaching Hospitals Conference, AHA, AAMC, RPSLMC; August, 1978, Chicago, Illinois.

2. Campbell, J.A.; Cabot, L.W.   A Program for Renewed Partnership: The Report of the Sloan Commission on Government and Higher Education.   Cambridge, Massachusetts, Ballinger Publishing Company, 1980.

3. Campbell, J.A., Lepper, M.H., and Sinioris, M.E.   Rationalizing the Health Care System in Chicago, a Report to the Mayor.   Chicago, Rush–Presbyterian–St. Luke's Medical Center, March 21, 1980.

4. Faber, S.J., Campbell, J.A. et al.   Report of the Ad Hoc Advisory Committee on Standards of Excellence.   American Board of Internal Medicine, Portland, Oregon, June, 1980.

5. Campbell, J.A.   Hospitals, Clinics, Physicians: Networks for Resource Utilization.   Proceedings of the Annual Meeting of the Association of Academic Health Centers, p. 11, 1981.

6. Campbell, J.A. et al.   The Role of the University Teaching Hospital: An International Perspective.   Report of a Conference Sponsored Jointly by Duke University Medical Center and the Josiah Macy, Jr., Foundation, p. 121, and 236, 1981.

7. Campbell, J.A., First, Thomas J. Jr., and Goldsmith, Jeff. C.   Outlook for Hospital Systems are the Solution.   Harvard Business Review, 59:130, 1981.

8. Sinioris, M.E., and Campbell, J.A.   The Rush System: A Model for Vertical Integration.   Ambulatory Care and Regionalization in Multi-Institutional Health Systems, p. 51, 1982.

List of Interviews

The following sources are from the notes by Mr. Jim Bowman in preparation for *Good Medicine: The First 150 Years of Rush–Presbyterian–St. Luke's Medical Center* (1987).

Bard, Mr. Ralph, July 15, 1986

Barton, Dr. Evan, June 2, 1986

Bent, Mr. John, June 23, 1986

Blair, Mr. Edward McCormick, June 16, 1986

Campbell, Mrs. Elda, June 23, 1986

Carton, Dr. Robert, June 25, 1986

Christman, Dr. Luther, June 13, 1986

Combined Staff Meeting and Trustee Meeting, September 3, 1969

DePeyster, Dr. Frederick, June 24, 1986, September 30, 1986

DeYoung, Mrs. Virginia, and Mrs. Caroline Chappell, June 11, 1986

Dick, Mr. A. B., III, June 16, 1986

Excerpts of tape recording of Rush Alumni Meeting, June 18, 1963, June 10,1986

Faber, Dr. L. Penfield, July 7, 1986

Friedberg, Dr. Stanton, June 2, 1986

Geittmann, Dr. William, July 8, 1986

Gilchrist, Dr. R. Kennedy, July 14, 1986

Graettinger, Dr. John, June 123, 1986

Hegyvary, Dr. Sue, June 12, 1986

Hejna, Dr. William, June 26, 1986

Henikoff, Dr. Leo, June 20, 1986

Johnson, Ms. Ruth, R.N., May 29, 1986

Jones, Dr. Philip, June 9, 1986

Kinney, Dr. Janet, June 6, 1986

Kittle, Dr. Frederick, June 3, 1986

Lerner, Dr. Wayne, June 18, 1986

Muenster, Dr. Joseph, June 10, 1986

Oder, Mr. Don, June 16, 1986

Pomerantz, Dr. Rhoda, July 8, 1986
Proposed outline for book composed
   of 22 chapters, undated

Russe, Dr. Henry, June 19, 1986

Scheaf, Dr. Charles, June 7, 1986
Schmidt, Dr. Ruth, June 11, 1986
Shorey, Dr. William, June 12, 1986
Smith, Mr. Harold Byron, July 18,
   1986
Summary of Interviews and Editorial
   Advisory Board, June 21, 1986

Trufant, Dr. Jack, June 17, 1986
Turner, Ms. Irene, June 6, 1986

Young, Mr. George, June 25, 1986

Author's Interviews
Abelmann, Dr. Walter, October 3,
   2001
Adams, Mr. Reginald (Hats), April 23,
   1998
Addington, Dr. Whitney, May 15, 2002
Anderson, Mrs. Linda, February 2,
   1999, December 16, 1998
Anderson, Mr. Roger, September 22,
   1998
Anderson, Dr. Truman, May 12, 1999

Baldwin, Dr. David, March 15, 1998
Bard, Mr. Ralph, August 26, 1998
Beattie, Dr. Edward J., February 14,
   1998
Beebe, Dr. Richard, June 23, 1998
Bing, Dr. Richard, July 5, 2000
Blaauw, Dr. Bernard, June 11, 1998
Black, Dr. Harrison, Marcy 25, 1999

Blair, Mr. Edward McCormick,
   August 28, 1998
Bogdonoff, Dr. Maurice, March 3,
   1999
Bowers, Mrs. Frances, June 23, 1998
Bradley, Dr. Craig, September 14,
   2000
Brown, Dr. Arnold, October 19, 1999
Brown, Mrs. Rhoda, February 15,
   1999
Buenger, Dr. Richard, May 19, 1998,
   September 1, 1998
Bulmash, Dr. Jack, December 19,
   2001

Caldarelli, Dr. David, February 28,
   2000
Campbell, Dr. Bruce, October 27,
   1998
Campbell, Dr. Stuart, October 19,
   1999
Campbell, Mr. Jamie, December 27,
   1998, January 22, 1999
Campbell, Mr. John, September 1,
   1998
Campbell, Mr. Thomas, May 13, 2000
Carleton, Dr. Richard, October 23,
   1998
Carton, Dr. Robert, February 12,
   1998, October 26, 1999
Cecil, Jarvis, October 20, 1998
Ceithaml, Dr. Joseph, January 29,
   1999
Christman, Dr. Luther, June 14, 2002
Clark, Dr. James, October 6, 1998
Clasen, Dr. Raymond, February 10,
   1998
Coogan, Dr. Philip, May 7, 1999
Corbett, Mrs. Sydney, June 27, 1998
Crocker, Dr. Diane, October 29, 2000,
   September 14, 2001

Hobart, Mrs. Nancy, March 16, 1999

Holmes, Dr. William, December 13, 1999

Hovde, Rev. Dr. Chris, August 26, 1999 , July 6, 1999

Hubbard, Mrs. Evelyn Coogan, May 15, 1998

Huckman, Dr. Micheal, May 14, 1999, July 19, 1999

Huckman, Mrs. Gloria, January 23, 2001

Irons, Mrs. Mary, 5 December 1999

Irving, Mr. Leroy, July 2, 1998

Jamieson. Dr. Rodney, May 13, 1998

Javid, Dr. Hushang, February 16, 1998

Jensik, Dr. Robert, October 21, 1998

Johnston, Dr. Louis, June 1, 1999

Jones, Dr. Phil, January 13, 1999, January 5, 2000

Kapsalis, Mr. Thomas, April 20, 1999

Katz, Mr. Gary, October 27, 1998

Kelly, Dr. Frank, Jr., September 12, 1999

King, Dr. Lowell, June 25, 1998

Kirsner, Dr. Joseph, June 4, 1998

Kittle, Dr. Fred, October 26, 1999

Knight, Mr. Rusty, April 12, 1999

Kramer, Mr. Ferd, June 27, 1998

Kuettner, Dr. Klaus, January 28, 2001

Lopota, Ms. Jean, February 28, 2000

Lashof, Dr. Joyce, November 2, 1999

Lichter, Dr. Edward, May 4, 2000

Lerner, Dr. Wayne, July 4, 1998

Levin, Dr. Stuart, April 5, 1998

Lyne, Sister Sheila, May 24, 2001

Long, Dr. John, May 2, 1998

Logan, Dr. Archibald, September 11, 2001

Landau, Dr. Richard, February 28, 2000

Maikler, Mrs. Virginia, June 22, 2000

Malkinson, Dr. Frank, December 12, 1998, May 12, 1999

Markovin, Dr. Vera, October 1, 2001

Matthews, Dr. Guy, February 24, 1999

McCarter, Mr. John, September 17, 2001

McCleod, Dr. Bruce, June 15, 1998

McKiel, Dr. Charles, March 4, 2001

McNally, Dr. Randall, August 8, 2000

Megan, Mr. Thomas, October 12, 2001

Merricks, Dr. James, July 28, 1999

Michael, Dr. Isaac, October 1, 2001

Milloy, Dr. Frank, March 15, 1998

Minks, Mr. Merrill, January 13, 1999

Murray, Dr. Joseph, February 8, 1999

Najafi, Dr. Hassan, February 1, 2001

Narboni, Mr. Raymond, November 14, 2000

Nemiah, Dr. John, February 9, 1999

Oder, Mr. Donald, November 4, 1997, May 24, 2000

Oder, Mrs. Roberta, July 24, 1999

Palmer, Dr. Henry, August 10, 1998

Paul, Dr. H. A., May 24, 1999

Peden, Dr. Joseph, January 19, 1999

Phelan, Dr. William, May 14, 1998

Ramsey, Dr. Michael, March 8, 1998

Ramsey, Dr. Ruth, March 8, 1998

Ratko, Mrs. Arthur, April 30, 1999

Richmond, Dr. Julius, December 22, 1999

Roseman, Dr. David, June 1, July 6, 1999

Rothstein, Dr. Ruth, May 29, 2001

Russe, Mrs. Pastora, April 30, 2001

Sanders, Mr. Herbert, March 6, 1998

Sassetti, Dr. Richard, February 10, 1998, July 6, 2001

Saunders, Mr. Werner, November 22, 1999

Saxena, Dr. V. R., March 6, 2001

Scheinberg, Dr. Herbert, June 29, 1998, July 20, 2000

Schenk, Dr. Robert, April 2, 1998

Schlaretski, Mrs. Eleanor Campbell, December 19, 1998

Schnur, Mrs. Doris Burkhead, September 14, 2001

Schoenberger, Dr. James, May 19, 2000

Schwartz, Dr. Theodore, June 28, 1998

Seery, Dr. Cyrus, May 21, 1999

Seim, Ms. Sandy, September 24, 2001

Selverstone, Dr. Louis, March 21, 2001, June 20, 2000

Sessions, Mr. Robert, October 15, 1998

Shallot, Dr. Charles, May 19, 2000

Shinekopf, Dr. Mitchell, June 27, 1998

Sinoris, Ms. Marie, October 8, 1998

Smith, Mr. Harold Byron, September 14, 1998

Stefoski, Dr. Dusan, May 10, 2002

Steele, Commissioner Bobby, May 29, 2001

Straus, Dr. Albert, October 6, 1998, September 17, 2000

Taylor, Ms. Margaret, March 25, 1998

Theil, Mr. Jack, July 12, 1999

Thomas, Ms. Loy, January 26, 1998

Thomson, Dr. Andrew, January 15, 1998

Tobin, Dr. John, March 7, 2001

Trobaugh, Mrs. Marjorie, October 1, 1998

Trufant, Dr. Jack, October 27, 1998

Tucker, Mrs. Alice, February 7, 2001

Tucker, Dr. Randy, November 25, 1998

Waggoner, Dr. Norma, January 26, 1999

Warden, Dr. Gail, January 11, 1999

Weinberg, Dr. Milton, June 23, 1998

Whisler Mrs. Jeanette, January 21, 2001

Whisler, Mr. Ken, June 12, 1999

Whisler, Dr. Walter, November 19, 1998

Widen, Dr. Arnie, May 15, 2002

Wien, Mrs. Luan, April 11, 1999

Williams, Mrs. Ruth, March 7, 2001

Wilson, Mrs. Ruby, May 14, 1999

Wissler, Dr. Robert W., June 25, 1998, January 19, 1999

Wolfe, Dr. Charles K. Wolfe, April 2, 1998

Wolter, Dr. Janet, April 29, 1998

Yon, Dr. Kimel, March 23, 1998

Young, Dr. James Harvey, June 25, 1998

Young, Mrs. Mary, May 15, 1998

Index

Cope, Oliver, 72
Cornell, 242
coronary thrombosis, 27
Cotsonas, Nickolas, 219n5
Cournond, Andre, 89
Crerar Library Board, 300
Crichton, Elda. *See* Campbell, Elda
Crichton, Kyle, 84
Cugell, David, 84
Curley, James Michael, 80
Cushing, Harvey, 87–88, 96
Cyrus, Adams, 92

Daley, Richard J., 154, 155–56, 301–2
Daley, Richard M., 156
D'Angelo, Oscar, 191, 285
Darley, Ward, 225–26, 227n17, 233n24
Daughaday, William, 76, 77
David, Vernon, 29, 94, 105, 119
Davidson, Carter, 10, 62, 111–12
Davis, Danny, 197–98
Davis, Floyd, 156
Davis, Jefferson, 1
Dedmon, Claire, 296
Deinhardt, Frederick, 223, 289
Deinhardt, Jean, 223
Democratic National Convention of 1968, 196
dePeyster, Frederick, 223
DeTakats, Geza, 162
Deutsch, Emil, 102n4
Deutsch, Thomas, 102n4
Deutsch, William, 102, 102n4
DeYoung, Jim, 296
DeYoung, Virginia, 152, 159
Dick, A. B. III, 170; Academic Committee, 233n24; as Board Chairman from 1966 to 1971, 294, 295; Board of Trustees, 207; search committee for president of Rush, 208n7

Dick, A. B. Sr., 94, 171, 204, 288, 309
Dick, Albert Jr., 147
Dick, George, 30, 64
Dick, Gladys, 30
Dick, John, 296
Dickinson, Richards, 89
Directions for Preserving Health of Soldiers, 17
Directory of Medical Specialists of 1939, 55
Diseases of the Mind (Rush), 19
doctors, national shortage of, 222–23
Dodson, John Milton, 35
Donald C. Balfour Visiting Professorship, Mayo Clinic, 300
Donnelley, Elliot, 233n24
Donovan, Daniel, 104, 110
Douglas, Stephen A., 21n19
Douglas, William Angus, 124, 152
Dowling, Gertrude. *See* Campbell, Gertrude
Dowling, Harry, 217, 234
Dragstedt, Lester, 64
DRG system, 303
Durovic, Marko, 119–20, 121
Durovic, Stevan, 119–20, 121
Dye, Sam, 162, 163

Ebert, Michael Higgins, 250
Ebert, Robert, 63, 233n24, 250
Eckhardt, Dick, 92
Economou, Steven G., 100
Edgewood Arsenal, Maryland, 85
Edsell, David, 48
"Education in the Health Fields for the State of Illinois," 229–30
electrocardiography (EKG), 27
Emery, Edward, 29
Enders, John, 72
endowed chairs, establishment of, 231
Engel, Frank, 124

fessional component necessary for
the development of the medical
school, 225; report of outside management consultant, 207–8; search
committee for leader, 208–10; "St.
Luke's section," 158; support by
Daley family, 155–56; vision of mission, 206; volunteer service, 153.
See also Rush University Medical
Center
Preventive Medicine, specialty of, 219
Professional Buildings, 278–80, 283
proprietary institutions: hospitals, 32;
medical schools, 20
Pullman, George, 145

radio-immunoassay, 99–100
Rafelson, Max, 244
rehabilitation programs, 282
Remington, Jack, 219n5
"Report on Education in the Health
Fields for the State of Illinois"
(Campbell), 182–83
Richmond, Julius, 29, 225, 227n17,
233n24, 243–44
Richter, Richard, 29–30, 64
Ricketts, Henry, 64
Ricketts, Howard Taylor, 30
Ripon College, 242
Roberg, Norman, 83
Robert and Terri Cohn Research
Building, 100, 156
Rochelle, Illinois, 1, 2
The Rochelle Messenger, 4
Rockefeller, John D., 21, 22–23,
24–26, 33
Rockefeller Foundation, 34
Rockefeller General Education Board,
34, 42
Roosevelt, Franklin, 47
Roosevelt, Theodore, 318, 319

Root, William, 176, 177
Rosengard, Major, 69
Rothstein, Ruth, 196
Rummel, Beardsley, 47
Rush, Benjamin, 17–19, 318–19
Rush Anchor System, 221, 259,
260–61, 270, 303
Rush McCormick Institute for
Infectious Diseases, 30
Rush Medical College, 12; affiliation
with University of Chicago, 21, 23,
25, 27; Amphitheater, 20; Central
Free Dispensary, 19, 31, 46, 130,
195; closing to undergraduate medical education, 55; declining class
size in later 1930s, 44–45; destruc-
tion by Chicago Fire, 19; deteriorating relationship with University
of Chicago, 13–14, 37–38, 49; educational and professional environment, 21; end of affiliation with
University of Chicago, 13, 41, 44,
50–52, 53, 54; faculty disagreement
with University of Chicago model,
45; faculty sense of betrayal over
University of Chicago's cutting of
ties, 50–51; football team, 21n19;
founding, 15–16, 318; funding for
reestablishment of, 231; organizational configuration, 244–45; original investigational programs,
31–32; Rawson Building, 37;
reopening, 54; Rush Library, 108;
surrender of 1837 Charter to
Presbyterian–St. Luke's Hospital,
232; tension with Hutchins, 49;
99th commencement, 247, 249–50;
transferees from feeder schools, 31;
transformation to Rush University
for the Health Sciences, 242;
tuition-dependence, 45